A Lark Ascending

A story of love and hope

Harry Moore

First published by Longhirst in 2007

Longhirst Publishing
Hanover house
Hanover Street
Liverpool
L1 3DZ

Tel: 0845 803 5818 Fax: 0151 285 3939

Printed and bound by Antony Rowe Ltd
Bumper's Farm, Chippenham, Wiltshire, SN14 6LH

Cover Design by Redpath
ISBN: 978-0-9555465-0-1

Dedicated to Laura

and

all children that have been touched by
Cancer or Leukaemia

Also to Gail, her mother who fought for her throughout with
tenacity, courage and a mother's love; for her twin brother Kit
who gave everything he could for the love of Laura; for Adam,
the baby brother she loved and for Georgina her dear sister.

There is always hope
In life, in death
Love never dies

Foreword by Esther Rantzen

I first met Harry Moore at a charity luncheon on behalf of the Rainbows Children's Hospice. The hospice was founded by Harry and his wife Gail and provides support and respite to families facing the tragedy of a child's death. I was deeply inspired by the courage of all those I met there. I felt honoured to accept an invitation to be patron for their latest appeal to build a young adults centre. It was at the luncheon that Harry told me about his book.

Most parents have times of stress when their children are ill. Thousands of parents every year become aware that their child has a life threatening or life limiting disease. Many of these illnesses are rare and virtually untreatable. The families move into a different world; the sort of world they have only read about or seen on TV Incredibly they cope. They become carers as well as parents.

Harry wrote this deeply moving book as a therapeutic exercise to help him try to understand what had happened to his daughter and family. It is about completion and hope. It is set as an autobiographical novel and is an exploration into the purpose of life as seen through a young girl with leukaemia and her father.

Death is one of the great taboos in life. We are naturally afraid or reluctant to talk about it. The risk of death in children is beyond our comprehension. Children should not die before their parents. It is not the natural order of things, yet some do. This book is a journey, nothing more. It contains no answers save one; that in all things there is hope and that throughout life and death love never dies.

The Lark

The lark rose from its nest in a flutter and a flurry. It had been disturbed by noises rumbling across the meadow. After ascending a few yards it began to sing. As its song lifted so did the lark rise higher and higher in steps and hops until it commanded a view over its nesting area close to a red brick farmhouse building known as The Children's Hospice. The hospice is situated in meadowland overlooking the Shardwood Forest close to the University town of Bramford. Locally the area is known as the Backwoods. It is an area of greenery and woodland steeped in the history of England and was one of the forests referred to by Sir Walter Scott in his epoch of English medieval history, 'Ivanhoe'. At one time it was a place for hunting. The deer still roam and game is abundant but now the forest has been handed over to the local populace as a place for walking, bird watching and other more gentle pursuits.

From a distance the forest interior looks bleak and black. If you walk through it on one of its many winding paths you are aware of a prevailing musty scent of oak, beech and sweet chestnut. However, hundreds of its oak trees were felled during the Second World War to make rifle butts and gun carriage. Their vacated ground is now covered in varieties of fungi and wild flower. Trails of ivy cluster around the twisted roots of the remaining five hundred year old oak trees. Within the bounds of the forest there are also small stretches of deep green meadow, broken fences and ancient hedgerow. Upon these islands of green the sun shines creating pools of light that contrast with the dark forest.

The most attractive way to approach the Hospice and, indeed, the town is to take the road through the forest. It follows an ancient Anglo-Saxon route which meanders according to the lie of the land. As you ascend the rise you can just see the building in the valley below through a tiny window of a clearing in the woodland. The descent opens up a view of the town, its university and environs.

This particular day was a special day in the town.

As the lark reached the plateau of its musical ascent and floated, hovered and sang it overlooked a scene of activity around the hospice. A crocodile formation of children was the centre point of this activity as it wended its way down the small road to the hospice car park. The children were happy. They were singing to the accompaniment of teachers with guitars and older pupils with tambourines. They had the morning off school and they were off to meet a Prince. What could be more exciting on a spring morning?

The blades of the helicopter spun through the air, and, as this big bird approached, the lark fell to the earth in quiet descent to sit with its own children. The helicopter touched the ground and there was the silence of expectation. Eventually the Prince stepped from the machine to cheers and applause.

His latest controversies meant nothing to the crowds of people who were there to greet him. He was met by the Lord Lieutenant of the County, a genial man and kind man, who with his wife took his position seriously and also seriously cared about the people of his community. The Lord Lieutenant escorted the Prince toward the hospice. The Prince had his own agenda and was keen to speak to the children from the local school. Conscious of the timetable that he had carefully worked out with the founders of the hospice the Lord Lieutenant guided the Prince away from the children.

"What! More dignitaries?" uttered the Prince

"No! These people are the founders. No doubt you have been briefed on them your highness."

The Prince duly met the husband and wife who were the founders. They stood by the actor who was a trustee of their charity and a social friend of the Prince. The Prince recognised him and recalled some social occasion from the past. They smiled together. The founders guided the Prince through the hospice. The place was created to provide care for dying children and to support their families. The founders explained its different services. They walked with an entourage and introduced him to the many people who were involved in the project. Eventually they arrived in a room known as the "special bedroom". This was the last resting place for the children, a place of cool tranquillity. In this room in a few quiet moments alone with the founders the Prince aired his views on life and death.

"I believe there must be something after death. There must be some purpose in our lives. I really believe that"

He went on.

"It must have been tremendously hard work for you both to create this place."

"Yes, but we had a lot of supporters'" replied the husband.

"What was the inspiration behind it? How did it all start?"

The husband became quiet. He glanced around the room, at the bed, the pictures on the wall and a cluster of children's toys neatly stacked in a corner.

"I suppose it started with a game of soldiers," he said.

The Prince looked at him inquisitively.

The wife smiled at her husband and then began to tell the Prince of how they researched the need for a children's hospice and how they ran the campaign to raise the money and build it. As his wife talked the husband's mind wandered. He looked out the window and saw the lark begin to rise in song again. He saw the field and the forest and thought of a time some years back when a father was walking across the meadow with his daughter and son. Twins. They were happy, having enjoyed a walk across the fields to the stream down by the mill, and were looking forward to tea.

"Let's play soldiers before tea Daddy'" cried the little boy. The little girl agreed.

"Good idea," said their father. "We will."

So it began.

A Game Of Soldiers

The children and their father dashed up to the little boy's bedroom where the soldiers were already laid out on the single bed under the window.

The little boy played with a Scots soldier. The little girl held a Red Indian on horseback. The soldiers became real people with names and personalities. Their father encouraged their make believe game. He played with them using an old soldier with a bent gun he had kept from his own childhood. Unimaginatively, he called it 'Bent Gun'. He also gave names to all the places in their pretend world.

The game went like this.

The Red Indian on horseback had been captured by the Phantom and lay imprisoned on Pillow Hill. The Scots soldier bravely fought his way across Eiderdown Plain toward her assisted by Bent Gun. He knew the way was perilous but his goal was a honourable one, to save a brave Red Indian who was also his dearest friend and his sister.

The guardians of the castle saw him coming and attacked the little Scots soldier with ferocity, but he pursued his task to rescue the brave young warrior who was his friend and soul mate. Relentlessly he pursued his goal. The way up Pillow Hill seemed daunting. The ripples and furrows of the incline hindered his progress but he staggered forward until he could see the place of her imprisonment.

The Red Indian rode a white stallion and had the looks of an Apache Indian in full battle flight. Unfortunately she was now in the grip of an unknown Phantom of Evil who was devious, sharp and deceitful. She had not expected him to attack her, as she was distracted with thoughts of this bewildering and beautiful world in which she found herself; but he did, and did it with such surprise and speed that she gasped and trembled with the surprise of it. She quickly and easily fell into his awesome power where she lay awaiting an uncertain future.

She loved the little Scots soldier. She loved him with all her heart. He was dearer to her than anyone. He was capable of the most daring deeds and when he joined forces with his ally 'Bent Gun' they became an unstoppable duo, fighting every opponent and overcoming the most difficult of odds.

As she lay captive in the garrison on Pillow Hill she saw the Scots soldier and his ally relentlessly fighting their way through the gun smoke and hail of arrows. In the background, by Bookcase Mountain, someone, who had just come into view, was directing the course of the battle with a subtlety that disguised the wisdom and fortitude of her position. The children's mother could see the whole picture and probable course of events. She smiled as she implored Bent Gun and the Scots soldier to take the safest course through the battlefield. She could see the hazards ahead.

Eventually, and with many scars, the two ascended Pillow Hill to meet the brave young captive. When they arrived they found that the Red Indian on horseback had managed to fight off the unknown phantom, but was afraid that he might return before she could be rescued. She therefore implored her allies to hasten her escape. As they tumbled down Pillow Hill on the way to freedom, life and joy they looked anxiously over their shoulders to see if the Phantom was following.

He was nowhere in sight.

However, standing by the door, their mother called to them. "Watch out! I can't see him, but I'm sure he's following you"

They hurried their descent and collapsed in a heap of relief and excitement at the bottom of Eiderdown Plain close to Bedside Fall.

Their Mother said it was time for tea. They left the toy soldiers at the bottom of the bed and walked to the door. Something made them pause. When they looked back they could see the threatening orifice of the little golden brass cannon of the Phantom. It was pointing towards them and it was loaded.

A Bubble Bursts

The first blast started with a muffled overture. Within a second it broke into a screaming roar like a thousand wild and piercing gales whistling through the forests of the world on a stormy night. It was an explosion of steam, the like of which humankind had neither seen nor heard before. Not seen in such a confined space. It was the explosion that had been expected and feared but had not really been prepared for. The panic button had been pressed twenty seconds earlier, not enough for mental preparation let alone real preventative action. The pressure was so great it lifted the upper plate of the reactor. The upper plate weighed 1,000 tonnes. It floated like a shuttlecock. Fragments from the core of the explosion scattered everywhere. They illuminated the way for the second great bang. This came only two or three seconds later when the hydrogen exploded.

According to observers outside unit 4, burning lumps of material shot into the air above the reactor. Some of them fell back down again starting fires throughout the building. The graphite blocks of the reactor vomited out into the main hall and spread themselves in abundance. The emergency cooling system collapsed. The damage to the roof caused an inflow of air. The air ignited the hot graphite and the biggest graphite fire of the world began.

This was the worst ever nuclear disaster. It was twenty-four minutes past one o'clock in the morning. Most people in the neighbouring towns and villages were asleep, or at least indoors. They had no idea of the inheritance coming to them, or indeed, to those hundreds of miles away.

The heat came through the walls and it seemed as if the whole place would melt. Pieces of flaming metal continued to soar into the air and crash through the roof. Those near the reactor stood little chance. If the heat did not get them then the immediate radiation burned their skins and brains to oblivion.

After the explosion of flaming granite came the smoke. It rose slowly at first. It lingered above the reactor. The sun's rays filtered through it casting fragments of distorted light on the shattered dome like an obscene rainbow. The roaring of the central reactor started again and a great fireball made its way upward through the lingering smoke. Everyone who saw it and lived said it was spectacular and awesome. The fire fighters who came to put out this great torch were overcome by the spectacle. They stood and gaped as the radiation penetrated their inadequate respirators and clothing and filtered into their blood streams and bones. As they gasped in awe and for breath they gasped their last. They would, within hours, as they were shrouded in the wards of bewildered hospitals, become posthumous heroes of the Soviet Union. The Scientists stood by in white gowns and masks recording the details of the explosion.

A cloud slowly began to rise from this doomed building like some terrible balloon full of light and flame. It slowly began to drift away from the dome. It hung momentarily in mid air. Early morning children in the nearby fields stopped helping parents bring in the crops to watch this great spectacle. They stood and gaped at this beautiful white cloud as it drifted over them, unaware of its sinister and threatening nature. As it left their sight they saw in the distance the still-burning dome. They were to see it burn for many days and were to see many more clouds rise and float away.

The cloud floated gracefully toward the setting sun. It drifted slowly and aimlessly, scattering its dust over the lands of northern Ukraine and Belarus before it finally settled in the lakes, mountains and streams of Southern Sweden.

Chapter 1

Breathing

The lack of daylight through the kitchen window suggested approaching rain. It had been a terrible summer. It was already August and so far they had only had weather fit enough for three barbecues in the garden.

The twins sat at the kitchen table and played. Their mother and father stood by the sink under the window and discussed holiday arrangements. He had just come home from work, his tie half undone and jacket thrown over the back of one of the pine kitchen chairs as if he had made an attempt to change but lost interest partway through the process. The twins' mother was keen to go to Sweden for a week. In fact she had already booked it. Their father was still undecided, but she knew he was easily persuaded by a fait accompli.

Their main holiday was planned for September with his parents. They planned to take them to Germany. Mum decided they needed a few days on their own. She knew that if he went on his main holiday after a long stint of hard work he would be restless and unsettled for a number of days. By the time he had settled down it would be time to return. True to her style she had booked the holiday first then told him afterwards that they were going to Sweden.

When they looked back, Mum and Dad always said that it started in Sweden. They were convinced of it, but others said it was coincidence and that they should not look into these things too deeply.

Laura was never quite sure what they meant. She did not see life as a journey. It was a state of being and on the dim edge of the world there was a future. In her mind was also a reflection of her fore-life. It was blurred but warm.

Fading into the darkness of her memory were her misty feelings of that time. Although her Mum's body had been comfortable she had felt compressed and confined for - she didn't know how long - (she could not measure time in the womb). She had left it early she was told afterwards. It should have been the twenty-third day of the month but she had appeared on the seventh day at seven o'clock.

It was a deep dark place in which to grow, a time when she was aware of senses and sounds and, in particular, her own body and its rapid change in shape and feeling. Her journey through the womb was graceful yet perplexing. Its momentum was relentless.

She knew she was not alone. Apart from the deep pulse and throbs of life around her there was another one like her nearby.

She knew that part of her pain was due to her brother Kit who was waiting in the same space. Of course, she knew it was her brother, because his body felt like it was the other half of hers. Yet, she could not reach or touch him. She could hear and feel the vibrations of his coming into life, the pulsation of heart and the rhythms of his soul. His sustenance came from the same tissues, the same liquid and the same food given by the keeper of this dark warm world of theirs. In fact, not only could she feel his presence, she could hear his breathing and movements. Sometimes she heard his pain and cries of anguish about where he was and where he was going. She felt his fear of the future like he felt and understood hers. Sometimes he called to her in the silent language that was to be forever theirs.

As they grew Kit began to feel the bodily pressure of his sister who appeared to lie so close to him that he could feel her kicking and moving and pushing him out of his own little piece of their world. When she did not kick he became anxious. Then he would move his body toward her to reassure her that he was here, sharing their space. They would touch, the touch of fluid and impulse that spun through their growing forms. Some day they would understand the meaning of this liquid half world, he thought, as only embryos can think, and then they would probably want to keep it to themselves and perhaps return to it in the perpetuity of the great life.

Laura became anxious. The pain on her head increased. She blamed Kit for pushing her in a continual upward direction She could feel her head begin to contract and distort in shape. Kit was also anxious. He felt that his body had grown as much as it could do. If this was the case it was time to move on to another place. He did not want to, but it was an urge of nature so strong that he was only a passenger to its desire.

For Laura, perhaps the greatest pain came closer to her birth day as her brother's growth forced her into the ever smaller cavity that pressed upon and around her little head moulding it into the shape of a pear. Increasingly the place became uncomfortable and she felt that things must change. She felt a screaming in her head. She felt Kit kicking and kicking. They span round. They felt volcanic vibrations and heard the cries of SHE who carried them. This time the cries were sustained and filled with wanting and urgency. SHE was frightened. Was this the end of their life or the beginning of a new one? Her last memory of this place was of noise and movement and pain. Oh yes! Pain and even more pain! The heaving, stretching, pulling and twisting she felt going on around her were confusing and painful. Her mind screamed and cried yet made no sound. There was no one to hear the silent sound of her silent screams.

Suddenly the pain ended and she catapulted into a sea of blaring lights and strange shapes. She did not expect the light, such light that she never imagined existed; such light that she could not even open her eyes to see it, only feel it penetrating her eyelids and piercing her brain. She entered the light of the world; a light that she never knew existed.

Images and physical contacts flitted by until she finally descended into the arms of a face and eyes that were to be known to her as Dad. Opposite her in her Dad's other arm was another whose presence she sensed and was familiar with. It was Kit! So he had arrived here as well. So all was well. At least we are together, she thought. Now we start a new adventure.

She closed her eyes to the new brightness. She was to keep them closed for many days until the light no longer hurt her.

After the trauma of being thrown into the world everything seemed steady, slow and natural. The faces that were her Mum and Dad appeared to be in control of everything she did or did not do. On occasions faint and distant voices within her would ask. Why am I here? Why? Where am I going? But they were not questions that lingered. In the main she was happy to be swept along the stream of living into which she and Kit had leaped.

It was a bright, sunny and cheerful Friday afternoon when they crossed the marshes, water and wide horizon of the Fenlands toward the eastern coast and the still waters of Harwich where their ship lay.

They drove in a state of euphoric optimism. High spirits filled the car. The flat countryside of Huntingdon, Cambridge and then Essex lay mellow in the autumnal sun with the colours that only an English Autumn can display; colours that carried the memories of ancient invaders of this landscape from across the sea. Sprays of orange sunshine falling between billowing white clouds accompanied them. An array of berried hedgerow, woodland, cottage and village pub glanced by the windows of the car as they glided over fields and fens. Every village they drove through seemed to be a holiday destination of its own despite the fact that they were not far from home. The occasional flotilla of geese would fly over their path in formation, crying to each other and to those below that they were on their way to weir and water.

After two hours of cruising through the countryside they slipped into a roadside restaurant for a late lunch. Heads turned to smile at this family's obvious happiness and preoccupation with itself.

The parents, of course, felt proud for they knew they were not the focus of interest, that it was the children; the twins. The past two years had been full of the experiences of other people's curiosity. Perhaps it was the fact that they were a boy and girl that attracted such interest in such twins. Without doubt they were an attractive pair, an opinion of many, not only their proud parents. Perhaps it was the novelty of seeing two heads in a traditional Silver Cross pram, of seeing the interaction between two small humans and of their delight in each other and their world. When shopping, the children's parents would always take two trolleys around the supermarket with one child in each, legs dangling and heads whirling to see the array of shelved colours. The twins would communicate with each other by sound and vision and other shoppers would be amused by their correspondence even though they perhaps felt glad that they themselves did not have such a responsibility to manage.

They arrived at Harwich a little early so decided to spend a few minutes on the beach before boarding the North Sea ferry. The twins stood on the sand throwing pebbles into the sea. Dad showed them the technique of skimming flat stones across the surface of the water, something he had developed as a child on the waters and lakes of Cheshire in northern England. As he looked at the cold expanse of water chillingly named the North Sea, he realised that these waters and what lay beyond were unknown to him. His business had taken him to most parts of Europe, east and west but never to Scandinavia. As he gazed across the sunlit waters an excitement and anticipation of going to a new land rose within him along with a tinge of unease of what he might expect and hope to encounter.

Mum looked at Dad sympathetically, his hands thrust deep into his pockets, looking out over the North Sea in a contemplative mood.

"Isn't it about time we drove down to the port?" she asked gently.

"Plenty of time," said Dad, casually looking over his shoulder, "there's no point in rushing to queue up. It doesn't make any difference whether you arrive late or early. You still get on the ship at the same time."

Dad was a much-seasoned traveller and accordingly was relaxed about the procedures and etiquette of travel. Inevitably they ended up rushing to the Ferry Port and arrived just as the last cars were boarding. The Marshall was standing by the entrance to the boarding area to collect tickets. He was not pleased and told them off for being late. Dad complained that the ship was leaving too early but this made little difference to a man whose day was determined by schedules and timetables concerning many hundreds of travellers not just a few late but loquacious individuals. As Dad manoeuvred the car into the line of the last remaining vehicles the twins could see their ship berthed alongside. It looked enormous to Laura; almost like a travelling world, full of light and subdued activity. The sight of it made them excited and everyone realised that the voyage was imminent.

At last they were on board. After they had found their cabins and explored the ship a little, the family made their way onto the deck ready for departure from England. They leaned over, and in the case of the twins, through, the rail, and looked toward the country they were about to leave. The ship slipped away from its berth and glided down the estuary of the harbour. The sun tumbled down onto the western horizon and cast long shadows of the harbour buildings across the eastern waters. Mum and Dad felt like a couple of characters out of Charles

Kingsley's Westward Ho on their way to a great adventure across unknown seas. They watched the houses and buildings on the shoreline drift away from them. The water was calm and the ship moved like a swan through the tranquil waters leaving only a small wake.

"Where is our car, Dad? " piped up Laura, standing by Mum's side, "Why can't we drive all the way to Sweden?"

"Because Sweden and England are separated by the sea," she replied, knowing the next question would be "Why?" and it was, to which she had no immediate or intelligent answer.

After the children's curiosity had been partly and inadequately satisfied they all began to explore the ship further and eventually returned, feeling rather tired, to their cabins. The thought of sleeping on bunk beds delighted the children and they giggled with excitement when they saw them. However before sleep came dinner.

The ship lights skipped along the dark water, hopping over crest and foam. The distant flat plane of the sea carried the stars and early rising moon. They stood as a group in the small bar near the dining room where Mum and Dad had a gin and tonic each and the children iced coca cola and looked out to sea in silence.

Nearby some elderly Americans on a trip across Europe and Scandinavia were discussing the nuclear disaster at Chernobyl.

"It'll be all right honey!" said the plump man in the check trousers and Hawaiian shirt. "It'll all be gone by now."

Mum and Dad looked at each other in silence.

They entered the dining room and met white clothed tables, potted plants and a tinkling grand piano. In the centre was the Scandinavian Smorgasbord, full of colourful invitation. It was romantic and a great thrill for Mum and Dad to consume herring, eel, caviar and a bottle of Chablis to the sound of a piano and the sight of the ship's lights on the water. Mum had overcome her initial trepidation about seasickness and Dad could tell from the sparkle in her eyes that she was happy. Everything was fine until Kit's unstable stomach decided it did not like the motion of the ship and he dejectedly presented the family with breakfast, lunch and dinner. Unfortunately this display must have upset the other passengers as one by one a number of white-faced diners rather sheepishly sloped off in the direction of the toilets.

The children were excited when they went down to their cabin after dinner. They had never slept on board a ship before. The cabin was small. Mum and Dad found it quite claustrophobic. Laura and Kit got undressed with enthusiasm. Laura climbed into her favourite pink pyjamas. This was much better than sleeping in a bedroom in a house. The cabin was done out in a blue decor. The walls were blue. The blankets and the beds were blue. To match the sea Dad said. The beds were actually bunk beds and despite their cries of dismay Mum and Dad decided to put the twins on the bottom bunks because they were afraid they might fall out. As soon as the children's heads touched the pillows they fell asleep. Mum and Dad held each other close that night. They felt the sway of the ship and the ripple of the water, which gently rocked them to sleep. They could not see the sea and the sky as their cabin was in the bowels of the ship but they could imagine the sight they might see could they afford the luxury of a cabin with a view. This was enough for their immediate happiness.

The next day they awoke to the bustle of the ship. Dad got up first and went to find the shower. Although they had a toilet in their cabin there was no shower. He came back to report that the facilities were quite acceptable although there were a lot of unwashed people wandering around looking for the showers. Kit and Laura gradually came to understand the importance of toilet facilities to their Dad, especially in a morning. Eventually and slowly everyone got ready and they went up on deck to look at the North Sea. The sky was a pale blue. The moon and the stars had gone and now the morning sun rested on the bobbing waves. It cast long early morning shadows on the silver surface of the decks of the ship, which had either been washed during the night or suffered from some rainy storm. The children were intrigued by the fact that all they could see was water.

"Where are we going Dad?" said Laura, with a note of concern in her voice.

"We are going to Sweden. Soon this water will come to an end and we will see land. When you see it I want you to shout 'Land Ahoy!' That land will be Sweden".

From then on Laura kept her eyes wide open expecting the land to appear suddenly and without warning. She was not sure whether it would suddenly replace the sea or whether she would see it sailing across the sea until it arrived by the side of her ship. Whichever way it came, it was certain that she needed to keep her eyes peeled otherwise it would come and go. They sailed gracefully through the cold waters of the Skaggerak and although Denmark was supposedly visible they did not see it until they tipped Skagens and sailed into the Kattegat to approach Goteborg. The land of Sweden actually appeared when Laura was asleep and she never forgave it.

They arrived in Goteborg in the evening as the Scandinavian sky turned black. After leaving the ship the Ford Sierra moved cautiously through a small network of industrial buildings then almost without notice began it's way up a small incline towards the most beautiful span bridge they had seen. Everyone hoped they would pass over this bridge and with great delight they did. The night-lights of Gotenborg shone below them, illuminating the water with an orange tint. They came down on the other side and drove alongside the estuary with the city on their right hand side and the water on their left. The twins, although tired, were excited with being up so late and at the sight of the city lights. Dad continued to peer with intensity through the windscreen until he finally relaxed exclaiming that they were now on the main route to the holiday home. After they left the city and the last set of traffic lights they cruised down a perpetual stream of forest, lake and village under a clear starlit sky.

The children drifted in and out of twilight sleep secure and captured in their car seats. The sound of Clannad playing "Lady Marian" drifted over them from the car stereo as they sped through woodland and village, a sound that was to stay in Laura's memory. When she heard this music again she thought of deep dark forests and the night sky. It brought back feelings of mysterious anticipation and sleepy excitement along with visions of impenetrable woodland and sleeping towns and villages. They were reflective and nostalgic feelings of contentment.

It was in the very early hours of the morning that they arrived at their destination. Mum had rented a log cabin at a camping site in a forest clearing on the side of a mountain. After finding the keys to the cabin in an envelope hanging outside the closed reception office and identifying which was their cabin everyone soon settled in. Dad made a fire in the hearth with some kindling wood and a couple of logs he had found outside the cabin door. He and Mum then sat on the small porch with a glass of red wine and breathed in the clean crisp Swedish night air. The twins were abed and hopefully sleeping like the other residents on the site. The stars overhead twinkled and sparkled as if demonstrating their satisfaction with all they observed below. It was well past midnight, not the usual time for the first drink of the evening. The Dad relished the first sip of his wine with an "amah! This is the life!" As the last syllables departed his lips he had a sense of foreboding or, rather, despair. It was at this point that he heard the door "click" shut. He looked at Mum and smiled in a sheepish sort of way.

"What's wrong dear? " she asked in a nonchalant fashion, expecting him to make a declaration of love or at least express some form of tenderness.

Triggered by the soft night breeze, the front door had slowly closed behind them. Dad had a sinking despondent feeling.

"I think we may have locked ourselves out, and the twins in," he said, looking apologetically at Mum.

"Oh no! Didn't you take the latch off before you came out?"

"Well, you know these stupid foreign locks, I thought it was off, but there doesn't actually seem to be a latch. Why they can't have the same sort of locks as in the UK beats me! "

"That's not the point is it? The point is we are locked out. What are you going to do about it?"

Dad decided to try the keys of the other residents who hadn't arrived which meant opening all the envelopes that hung outside the reception door. "They're not going to be pleased about that!" said Mum. None fitted. He then tried to break a small window but the glass was so tough it wouldn't break and as Mum pointed out it was so small that no one could get through it anyway, save a very small animal.

Some teenage boys were sitting on a nearby terrace watching the nocturnal antics of Dad with amusement and delight. Dad noticed they were speaking German.

"Those boys are speaking German. I can speak the lingo so I'll go and ask if they have any ideas or see if I can borrow their key" he said to Mum who was becoming increasingly concerned about the welfare of the twins, despite the fact that they were securely locked in the cabin and unaware of their imprisonment.

Dad's German was so good that the boys, who were Swedish, replied in English.

At that point many lights came on throughout the site and it seemed that everyone on the campsite circled their log cabin, poking the woodwork, stretching to see inside, tapping windows and scratching heads in a quest for the solution to family's predicament. One of the boys showed Dad a window that was very slightly open and said that if someone inside could remove one of the pins used in the mechanism they would be able to get in. The only people inside, of course, were the twins. As they were so young, the window so high and mechanism so complicated everyone fell into dismay. Nevertheless it was agreed to give it a try.

Mum and Dad tapped on the window of Laura's bedroom first but she wouldn't wake up. They tried Kit's and his sleepy little face lifted from the pillow in wonderment at this intrusion. Kit thought it was strange that Mum and Dad were talking to him from outside the cabin. What are they doing there, he thought, but children easily accept the most bizarre situations without question. They implored him to get up and walk through to the living room, which he dutifully did. The only way for Kit to get to the window was to put a chair on the dining table and climb on it. Dad guided him through the motions with a lot of help from everyone else. The Swedish teenagers were now getting quite excited by the adventure and treated it like a round of "It's a Knockout", offering encouragement when it was needed and exuding disappointment when there was a setback. Other residents were speculating on the success of the operation.

Eventually little Kit got to the window and in triumph took the pin out. With great speed and agility one of the teenagers clambered through the window and in seconds appeared at the door with a big grin, the key in his right hand and Kit's hand in his left. Mum and Dad sighed with relief and thanked Kit rapturously for being such a hero and saving the day, or night. Little were they to know that this was only a sequel. Kit would be a hero once again, but this time in a real adventure when he would truly save a day and a life.

The family spent the next morning walking through the surrounding forests, investigating the local plant life, jumping over streams and generally exploring. The pathways of the forest encapsulated them in an aura and aroma of pine and freshwater stream. They followed one stream that tumbled over each dip and curve as it made its way to one of the many lakes. Dad could not resist reaching his hand into the meandering waters as they fell over a small group of rocks and to take a drink. Laura did the same. So did Kit. The water was crisp and sharp and took their breath away like the fire of life consuming itself.

In the afternoon a rowing boat was hired on the nearby lake.

The lakes near the cabin were large and devoid of other vessels. They took a picnic basket with them and spent the whole afternoon gently floating across the series of connecting lakes. They came to the innermost lake. It was bridled with small sandy beaches. The water shone. It was clear. It reflected the small houses and pine trees clung around the banks of the rippling water. It was world within world. Laura became drowsy. The water was magnetically bright and very reflective. It drew her toward it. She leaned over the edge of the boat to look for her own reflection. Instead she saw a myriad of images, of the sky, of clouds, rolling across the plains of a distant land, the smoke rising and of white shapes around a crux of erupting noise and light. She saw billowed clouds of incense and a glaring whiteness that dazzled her. She leaned over the side of the boat and let her fingers run through the water. The images were not there. The boat slowly made its way across the lake.

Eventually the twins became tired and Mum and Dad lay them down in the bottom of the boat, allowing the gentle water to caress the boat and lap them to sleep.

> Falling on this glassy place
> From fields of fire in distant space
> Little child in innocence
> Breathing in the air cadenced
> Humanity's incense.
>
> Peaceful waters turn the sky
> Upon itself; the mirror flies
> To showers of deathly dust
> Reflecting souls lie crushed
> Unearthly hush.
>
> Quietly singing in the breeze
> Of lifting leaves and stirring trees
> While she floats and like Shalot

In solitude accepts the plot.

The water was tranquil. A ribbon of deep green surrounded the icy glass. Dad never before felt such solitude and peace. They floated and floated as if an invisible current carried them from shore to shore. It was as if they sailed the universe toward infinity and hope, traversing peace and solitude. It was so quiet even the birds hung in the air in silence and isolation. They had drifted into a different world that was a surreal image of everything to be desired from landscape and geology.

Specks of rain appeared on the water. Strange, thought Dad, it's not raining. It wasn't. He knew it must be a dream.

Laura drifted and dozed. Her sleepiness had made red spots around the circumference of her eye. Her vision was blurred by the red of oxygen, of energy, and of life. The drops of rain were pure white. She felt them as well as saw them. Their clarity was powerful. It dazzled her. She saw the white spots growing and multiplying, strange small embryos of life like hers in the womb that just grew and grew and grew until they exploded in a glaring blaze of whiteness that blinded her. The red in her vision died and the light bright white was all there was. It must be due to waking up suddenly to the brightness of water, she thought. She awoke from her tranquil afternoon doze and half dream into confusion.

Everyone returned to the cabin that evening rather exhausted. Mum had brought lots of food and wine so that they did not have to worry about eating out or shopping. They dined on homemade Lasagne and salad washed down with a bottle of Cote de Roussillon. Afterwards they sat round the stove breathing the aromatic fumes of ancient pinewood fuelling the flickering flames and recounted the events of the day. After tumbling into their nightclothes the twins went to bed unwashed and fell asleep immediately. On going to bed themselves Mum and Dad looked in to see the children. They looked contented and tired. However, one of Laura's eyes appeared slightly swollen. Mum and Dad assumed it must be from the bites of insects from the lake but mentally noted that they must check it again in the morning.

The next morning the bad weather had arrived so they explored the surrounding area in the car. Laura's eye seemed a little better. The weather stayed dull all day. They travelled a little north to a place called Jonkoping set on the southern shore of the Vattern Lake. The lake was beautiful and so huge that from the south shore they could not see the northern shore, only the horizon. Laura wondered if she was looking at the sea again. Having no real sense of geography the fact that it might be the sea did not perturb her. To her and Kit there was, after all, only one sea and that could appear in any place at any moment. When Dad talked of the North Sea and the Mediterranean Sea he only caused confusion in their minds. The sea was the sea and the land the land. That is all that mattered. Kit was mystified by the size and bleakness of the Vattern Lake. This mystery was further enhanced by a grey rainy mist clinging to the centre of the lake like a spectre.

Later, as they wandered through clinical streets of this small town they found a MacDonald's restaurant much to the delight of Kit and Laura. This helped make what was a rather bleak day a more colourful one. On their way back to the cabin Dad pulled the car in at an obscure and strange place.

A large wooden house lay off the road. The reason they noticed the house was that from a distance they could see a very large wooden model of a very large pirate protruding from behind its eaves. Dad turned the Sierra off the road and parked outside the house that was set behind a tall fence, broken only by an open gate. Inside the garden were several enormous and grotesque caricatures of animals and characters from a child's world. Perhaps it was a Swedish fairy story or legend. No other visitors and no caretaker confronted them. Laura did not like this place. The characters were too large and too lonely. After a few minutes they left. Laura kept the images in her head.

On the way back to their cabin Mum noticed that Laura's face was beginning to swell up beneath her left eye. It became quite acute when they eventually arrived back at the cabin so they quickly drove off at great speed down the Varnamo road to the nearest hospital. The hospital was really a medical centre and was absolutely empty apart from a receptionist and a middle aged blonde haired nurse with a pristine clean uniform and pristine clean face. The whole centre looked as if it had been deserted. After a long wait a doctor came to see them. Blonde, young and cool, he had a distracted look as if he had just left a life or death situation. Perhaps he had. He examined Laura thoroughly but could not diagnose the problem. He believed it to be some form of infection that, typically, could have been caused by a bite from an insect. Mum and Dad thought of the time on the lake and the children's sleep in the boat. Could there have been an insect on the bottom of the boat?

They collected their medication and returned to the log cabin after spending a few moments walking around this small town. The next day they packed up and drove back to Gutenberg to meet their ship home to England. The journey back was overcrowded and not as pleasant. Laura was admitted onto the bridge where she was given an eye patch to protect her swollen eye from the cold air. She was quite proud of her eye patch when the family arrived home but Mum and Dad took it off as soon as possible.

The swelling on the eye soon went down, but Laura never seemed to quite recover her energy. She was lethargic. Three weeks later the whole family set off on holiday again, this time with Grandma and Grandad to the Mosel district of Germany and the next stage of their great adventure.

Chapter 2

Gymnopodie

Their journey to Germany included a one night stop-over in France to allow Grandad to see some First World War sites. The party pampered to his nostalgia knowing he would be so disappointed if he had to miss the opportunity of seeing the places where his father had fought and where his father's friends had died. The result was a delay in the itinerary and Dad, who was driving, had to hasten the journey in order to find somewhere to stay the night. Nevertheless the hastened journey was tinged with certain sadness. The flat lands of Picardy had a bleakness and sobriety that lent itself to minds indulging in the grey distance of the Great War and it's lost youth.

Grandma and Grandad had only left the British Isles once before and had never been to Germany so were quite excited about the trip. Grandad was very specific about which sites he wanted to see and many detours were made to accommodate his interest. Dad had driven many times through France and wanted to arrive in Germany as soon as possible. Grandma was totally fascinated by everything she saw and did not complain about the long journey. Laura sat on Mum's knee in the back and, like Mum, did not enjoy long journeys.

The journey southeast was fascinating to Grandma and Grandad but tiring due to the many diversions to find treasured pieces of First World War history for Grandad. On the rise of a small hill on the main road south they saw the entrance to a British cemetery and stopped. They left the car to walk through a small archway into an unending sea of white crosses in rows that touched a distant horizon. They walked through memorials of young dead in silence and sadness.

Everyone was relieved to find a suitable looking cafe just south of Cambrai for a break in the journey. Grandad remembered his schoolboy French and held a full discussion with some men at the bar in an attempt to find a decent hotel in the area. It was decided to push on toward Mezieres and the border with Luxembourg. After Coffee for adults and Cokes for twins they drove on.

They found the small provincial town of Mezieres in Picardy slightly off the main road nestling amongst the woods. It looked a promising sort of town, warm, inviting and comforting. The sort of town that welcomed travellers as if it was solely created to cater for such people. The car was parked and everyone stumbled out with stiff legs and aching backs. Coats were distributed, bags sought and pockets checked for money. The party of six then set off to find a hotel. Darkness was descending. Concerns ranged between finding somewhere economical to being happy that it was clean and comfortable.

They chose a small and friendly family hotel overlooking the railway station and main road. It was filled with Dutch and Scandinavian guests. As Mum and Dad unpacked some things in the small bedroom they noticed that Kit had a high temperature and fever. He was stripped, doused in tepid water and kept cool, but not cold. It was decided to let the fever run its course.

Laura felt the day was never going to end and only wanted to be in her own bed. She felt tired and her head felt hot. Whilst Mum and Dad got changed she momentarily slept. However the excitement of the occasion and the proximity of Grandma and Grandad overtook her need to sleep and she tumbled off the bed to visit Grandma's room. The bedrooms faced each other across the corridor so the children could move backwards and forwards between parent and grandparent.

They took a short walk to a small restaurant that Dad liked the look of. Dad had been to France many times and it was taken for granted that he knew the cuisine and could guide Grandma and Grandad through it. Although he knew it, he was always troubled by it, having spent his younger days amongst the Paris restaurants and bistros under the guidance of an expert leaving him uncertain of his own navigation through the menu. Sitting round a window table covered with a white cloth they enjoyed a quiet meal of local fish for the women and children and something with Beef for the men. Grandad's eyes frequently strayed to the view through the window of the street and its bustle. His eyes sparkled and he was pleased he had had an opportunity to speak French in France and was proud of his accomplishment. The French are a proud people, he said to Dad. They drank the wine and beer with much enthusiasm and clatter of conversation and felt better for it when they walked back to the hotel.

24

Kit's temperature kept peaked through the night, subsiding a little in the early hours of the morning. As they sat in the breakfast room watching, through lace curtains, the comings and goings of the little Picardian town, Kit seemed to be in brighter spirits. As usual the twins pulled their faces at French coffee but made an attempt at the croissant, butter and jam. Grandad managed to get some rather weak tea and wondered about a boiled egg. The twins were always very good at table. The previous evening they had sat quietly throughout the meal and Kit had endured his high temperature in relative silence apart from the odd trip to the toilet. Grandma and Grandad were not used to children being out so late but Mum and Dad took them everywhere it was possible for two children to go. This morning Kit was feeling excited, having slept in a new bed. To awake and find Grandma and Grandad still here was an additional joy. The twins had dashed into their grandparent's bedroom as soon as Mum had allowed, just like they did when they stayed at Grandma's house. Mum joked that Grandma was a little tiddly at dinner the night before and told Laura of some of the funny things she had said and how she fell over, but Grandma was always falling. This made Laura laugh her deep throaty laugh, a laugh that was so infectious it made Dad laugh with her.

Outside, autumn prevailed. The morning air was thick with it, in the smell and dampness as well as the colour and mustiness. The sky was copper. The French were about their business and school very early leaving the streets hushed and quiet when the travellers greeted it. Opposite the Hotel the old Railway Station dominated the view from the hotel windows. In front of the station was a spinney of trees, mainly horse chestnut. Most of the leaves had turned to gold or brown. There was a steady and graceful shower of these leaves floating to the ground to form a carpet of bronze. This carpet was pinpricked with shiny brown horse chestnuts.

Dad and Grandad took the twins into the Spinney to collect the horse chestnuts or "conkers" as they knew them, whilst Grandma and Mum did some window-shopping in the town. Laura particularly enjoyed collecting the horse chestnuts even though she knew that she was unlikely to play "conkers" with them when they got back home to England. It was not her sort of game. Nevertheless it was good to collect them and see who could find the biggest, or even the smallest, conker.

The trees continued to shed their golden brown mantle in spiralling traces that made the leaves flutter and glide gently onto the soft bed that swished beneath the feet of the children as they gathered the fruit of the giants towering above them. The noise of the morning traffic, as it made it's way to various places in town, left them behind and could no longer be heard. Laura was back in the countryside, the countryside she loved so dearly. Here beneath the horse chestnuts she felt joy and pleasure. Amidst autumn's decay of summer's crown she picked the fruits that would give birth to spring's emerging life. The mould of decay that marred some of the fruit she found deep beneath the leaves tarnished her pleasure. She continued under Dad's watchful eye to gather until the little pockets in her little red coat were bursting.

As Dad watched her he realised how fragile was this thing called child. How dependant it was upon him for care and comfort, yet how independent of him for it's own life. He was there in the making and in the direction but he could not steer its ultimate course; only smooth and advise the way.

He knelt beside her and helped count the fruit of her morning's exercise. The little brown spheres lay softly in her small hand, glistening like newly polished shoes. Each was it's own little world. Some would spring to life after winter had covered them. Others would crack, open, and begin to grow, but finding no sustenance, die.

As Dad stood in the spinney observing both Kit and Laura at play, he was filled with those autumnal feelings that are a mixture of nostalgia and optimism. Laura felt those same feelings but in a different way. She liked the crunchy feeling of the leaves under her feet and felt cosseted and comforted by the ambience of leaf and bark. This place took her back to a life before, a feeling she had never ever really or fully known. It was a time of long dark clothes, of elegance and dignity as well as beauty and refinement. She had not yet learned the name for her feelings, but she knew what they meant, what they conveyed to her. She felt that she only had to reach out, to grasp and all would become clear. She would be taken up into this world where she felt she belonged, a world with which she now felt at one and a world she had never really left. Surely her soul was in this very place, in front of this railway station sheltered by these trees of the past. She spread her arms as if to float and moved her feet in dance, gently stirring up the leaves from their premature slumber and their total absorption into the welcoming earth.

What is this feeling? She asked herself but there came no answer. Why had Dad brought her here? Was he a part of this thing from the past, her past, or was it, in fact, a small part of his past she had come to know.

As she looked from the ground to the sky a single leaf began its descent from the tallest of the trees. Its spiral path downward totally absorbed her attention. Her eyes followed every detail of its descent. At times she thought it would never arrive on the ground, its journey was so erratic, floating hither and thither. At first she became anxious because she wanted to collect this particular leaf in her hand, but as it meandered she became glad that it had made its journey in its own successful way. It landed directly at her feet. In fact it landed on her bright little shoe that shone like the wet black nose of a nocturnal creature in the dense undergrowth of leaves. She picked the leaf up and put it in her pocket. Dad found it several days later and wondered how it got there.

As they left the town Laura looked through the car window with a tinge of sadness and a feeling of apprehension. Her head still felt muzzy from yesterday and it made her tired. She slept throughout the drive across the small but beautiful principality of Luxembourg still dreaming of France and her dance of Gymnopodie beneath the horse chestnuts.

They drove into Trier in Germany in the sunshine. Grandad still thought of Germany in terms of the two world wars. Grandma thought about the time that Dad came to Germany when he was very young, staying at the Jugendenbergen and falling in love with the rivers, inns and people. Because he liked Germany she knew that she would like it as well.

Laura felt better after her sleep in the car. She had missed the beautiful countryside of Luxembourg but was pleased to be in Trier where there were shops. She was hungry. After parking the car they stopped at a small cafe.

"Bitte, zwei Rhurei fur unsere kinder," ordered Dad when the young waitress appeared.

The twins had not tasted scrambled eggs with ham before and were delighted with it.

"Fur mich, bitte, ein Bitburger Pils," Dad shouted to the departing waitress and then ordered the same for Mum and Grandad. Grandma wanted tea. The grown ups spent a considerable time over the menu and Laura could not understand why it took them such a long time when they very quickly decided what the children would eat. Laura was pleased when she saw that Dad had ordered Ruhrei the same as her whilst the other grownups had grown up sandwiches. It was almost as if his choice had endorsed hers.

"You've got the same as me," she said with a fetching little grin on her face.

"No! You've got the same as me," responded Dad

"But I got mine first!" she exclaimed, the pitch of her voice rising on the last syllable.

"All right! I confess! I only ordered Ruhrei because yours looked so good. You are not going to take it off me are you?"

Laura looked at him mischievously and with a great big giggle pinched some food from his plate with her fork and popped it into her mouth with obvious relish and enjoyment over her victory.

She looked across at Grandad and said, "I've pinched Dad's dinner!"

"Laura's pinched Dad's dinner," echoed Kit hoping someone would pinch his as he had seen something more interesting on another table in the form of a young boy of similar age tucking into a rather large piece of Schokolade Kuchen mit Schlagsahne.

After lunch they walked into the town to see the Roman gate, mainly because of Grandad's avid interest in Roman history. Why has he never ever been to Rome, thought Dad as the clambered and panted up the steep stairs of the gatehouse? The twins came but Dad carried Laura all the way up because she liked to be carried and totally disliked walking when there was a convenient Dad available. Dad always said that his right arm was specially shaped to carry Laura but that it would have been more convenient if God had attached a little chair to his hip. At the top they looked over the balcony down toward the cafe and Grandma and Mum sipping their coffee. Mum took a photograph, which Dad could not find when they got home. It would have only shown their little heads peering above a high parapet like enquiring souls looking for heaven.

"Can I have a drink, please Dad? " asked Laura.

She was always thirsty, more so on this holiday. Her favourite drink was her Dad's tea when it had cooled a little.

"We'll go and see Mum and Grandma and have a drink with them. What would you like?"

"Tea!"

"Of course. You will like the tea in Germany."

Dad said this knowing that the tea would come as a Pickwick tea bag in a cup with separate hot water enabling Laura to pour the water on the tea bag, add the milk and sugar and, in other words, make it herself. Laura, of course was not aware of this as they traversed the square toward the place where Mum and Grandma sat. She reflected on the times at home when Dad made her tea. Then it came served in her little yellow mug. A little yellow plastic mug that came free with a meal at Happy Eater with a picture of a black cat on its side. But, it was more than a mug, for Laura associated it with those warm cosy times in the kitchen at home when she would drink tea with her Dad.

She particularly remembered the mornings at home. Her room was at the front of the house, and it was her own room. She didn't have to share it with Kit. Originally she did; for her room was the nursery comprising first one cot for two, then, as they grew, two cots for two babies. Those days of two cots for two were glorious. They used to make such a noise, such a racket, such laughter and much giggling. They both used to stand at the rail of their respective cots and jump up and down in unison, knowing that Mum or Dad would soon appear to mildly chastise them.

"Oh, you are naughty," Mum would say, and Laura would look at Kit and giggle. If Dad came up he would inevitably play with them and probably take them out of the cot. During those pre-walking stages this meant that someone had to supervise their roving.

Because her room was at the front and facing south, the sun at the break of day did not visit the window. However, the small close in which they lived was bright and receptive to light. Some of the houses on the other side of the close were painted white and accordingly reflected the morning sun back into the close illuminating Laura's house. Her curtains were light blue with a degree of transparency. So it was that each morning her room slowly filled with light.

They travelled alongside the River Mosel with some leisure. Halfway to Cochem an accident occurred and they were held up. Dad was annoyed. Laura did not like it when Dad was angry, although now he was only annoyed and not angry and she could tell the difference. The car slowed down and eventually stopped.

"What's that?" she exclaimed from her place on Grandma's knee. She pointed to the sky. The noise came first. It was a helicopter. It landed, quickly, scooped up the accident victim and rose again up to the sky and away from the River.

"Toward Bitburg," Dad said. "He'll be drinking Bitburger Pils tonight."

"That comment is in poor taste," said Mum

"Yes, it is!" said Grandma

"It might be a woman," said Grandad

Silence overcame them and the car moved on its way. The road declined into the depth and warmth of the Mosel and its vineyards. They saw the grape vines in the early evening. There was a bronze blue hue in the sky that put the vineyards in long shadow. Row upon row they rose like soldiers and ascended the valley side.

Laura saw this picture of peace and felt comfortable. Her body still felt tired. She did not know why, only that it was tired. In fact her body felt like a secondary part of her at the moment. Perhaps it would feel better soon.

It was early evening when they arrived at Cochem, their destination in the Eifel district of Germany. It was a place that Dad knew well. It was a place where he had drifted through his youth. It was here that he abandoned his youth in England to pick grapes before the October Fest. As a result it was here he got drunk for the first time and made German friends. Here he came to a fondness of the German people that was stimulated by his reading of the country's history, both good and bad, and consolidated by his experience of their depths of sentimentality and their romantic view of life. Enough that visiting the place in the late 1960's only confirmed his emotions about the country. He particularly took an interest in the period of the Weimar Republic, this mixing bowl of every extreme political views in which the future of Europe was prepared. Dad always said he was a socialist at heart. He was sad at the way it had all gone. He felt he understood the German soul. This feeling was so powerful that he wrote a novel. He never tried to get it published, but then he never really finished it. It still sits on a shelf in the kitchen. Laura sees Dad take it down on occasions and browse through it. 'Damned good!' he mutters, then drifts off into the living room to lose himself in a world of Remarque, Isherwood, Brecht and Kurt Weill.

One day everyone went sightseeing to Burg Eltz, just off the Mosel valley. Laura had lost so much energy that she had to be pushed all the way in a buggy. With twins it is easy to see when one or the other is not too well by making a contrast. Kit was bubbly and lively. Laura walked slowly and continually sucked her thumb. That night her temperature soared once again. The next morning Mum bought some medication from the pharmacists assuming that she had the flu or a very bad cold. She perked up a little that day and it was assumed, wrongly, that she was on the mend. Mum and Dad were to learn later that this pattern was quite normal. In the evening she soon became tired and fell asleep at the dining table. This was unusual for Laura, a girl who loved her food. Their meal of Jager Schnitzel and noodles with the local house wine lost its attraction for everyone and they went to bed fairly early after deciding to wend their way to the coast the next day in order to take Laura home.

The hotel overlooked the Mosel. Although the sky was bright and sunny the water was covered with a morning mist that floated damp and eerie and crept to land in cool grey fingers. Mum had telephoned the port to tell them of the family's impending arrival and they hoped to be home before midnight. Laura maintained her temperature all day so the stops were kept to a minimum, as they were anxious to be home to put Laura in the hands of the family doctor. The car sped across the motorways and highways of northern Europe with ease. They seemed to pass every vehicle on the road and encountered no delays. The Townsend Thoreson car ferry was crowded when they arrived at Calais and there was some difficulty getting on board.

"We have a sick child here, and have driven all the way from Germany. If you don't let us on we'll drive on," insisted Grandad grimly.

Eventually they boarded and the ship set sail just as the sun had gone down. Mum nursed Laura all the way back. Her temperature was still high.

"She's going to be all right you know, " said Grandma, looking at Mum's and Dad's anxious faces, " She's not going to die, you know"

Those last words seemed rather excessive to Dad. Later Grandma was to tell Dad that she thought Laura might have had pneumonia.

Dad broke the speed limit on the M25 and M1 and they landed home just before 11 o'clock. Laura's temperature had not subsided and she was even more lethargic so Mum decided to call out the local doctor right away. She had the symptoms of tonsillitis so he prescribed accordingly, including Calpol to get her temperature down.

The next few days she improved and seemed to lose a lot of her lethargy. About a week later, however, she spiked with a temperature in the middle of the night. Dad brought her into his bed. She lay in his arms perspiring and breathing very heavily, something Mum and Dad had not witnessed before. Dad often put Laura into bed beside him if she could not sleep. It was an indulgence. The feeling of her small warm body nestled beside him gave him the greatest comfort. He had waited a long time to have children. His dear young wife had rewarded him with a boy and girl at one go. To hold your own child close in physical comfort is one of the greatest pleasures of parenthood.

That night Laura felt very hot and her breathing began to get heavier so that she was almost gasping for breath. Mum and Dad remained undecided about calling out the doctor who was not always pleased to be called out and demonstrated this in his curt manner. Just as they had made the decision and were about to call him, the temperature subsided and Laura began to sleep peacefully.

However Laura still seemed lethargic and Mum was not happy. After a couple of days she took her back to the surgery. This time her symptoms had developed into what looked like glandular fever and more medication was given. Mum was asked to come back if things did not improve.

They say mother knows best. Mum began to feel that Laura's illness was becoming serious. She made a return visit. The general practitioner in the village examined her all over, felt her spleen and made some notes. Mum asked about the possibility of a blood test and it was agreed that she would take Laura into the Belgrave Royal Infirmary casualty department with a doctor's note. Mum wondered what was in the note as she sped down the A50 to Belgrave with the twins in her Sierra. She wondered what she was going into and tried to work out the possibilities as she drove. She stopped the car, stopped wondering and opened the letter. From amongst the untidy scribble of black ink across the page one word stood out - Leukaemia. Leukaemia. Leukaemia! The word screamed in Mum's head.

The general practitioner had actually written 'test for possible Leukaemia'. Wasn't this cancer? Was this not terminal? From her understanding of children's diseases, this was the one she had always dreaded and here she was taking her dear Laura to hospital faced with the possibility of taking on a very serious disease. She was now charged with the responsibility of introducing her into a world she knew little of, where she had little control. She took some comfort in the fact that Laura was only to be tested for Leukaemia. It was not confirmed. Nevertheless as she looked out of the car window at the rolling hills and green meadow, at the birds skipping along the hedgerow, the cattle in the field and newly ploughed soil waiting for winter barley seeds she felt they belonged to a different world, a world she was now leaving. She was overwhelmed with a sense of unreality.

Chapter 3

Tell me it's not true

Dad was in a meeting with one of his clients when the telephone rang. Laura did not know very much about his work. She knew that once he was working with computers. He used to come home with a big computer that made funny beeping noises. When it made those noises Laura would hear Dad shout and become very annoyed. She assumed the Computer was being very naughty. It seemed to do things of it's own accord.

"I'm taking Laura into hospital for a blood test, " Mum said in a frightened voice. "I saw the doctor this morning and was not happy that we were getting to the bottom of the problem. He advised going to the Royal Infirmary with a doctor's note to get a blood test. At least this way we'll find out what is really wrong with her. We'll probably have to stay in overnight."

"I'll come home", he responded.

"No, no, it's all right," she replied in a voice that said it was not all right.

"I'll come home now, you are obviously upset."

"I may be at the hospital, so see me there."

"Hope everything is okay", everyone cried as he left. He drove at a brisk pace from the client's to his Birmingham office, where he collected a parking ticket from a frosty faced traffic warden. Once he had informed every one of his whereabouts and rearranged a few things, he was on his way down the Aston Expressway to the M6. The SRi responded well to his demands for speed and they seemed to sail down the M6 to Lappenworth.

The house was empty when he arrived home, so he turned about and made for Belgrave and the Royal Infirmary. The place appeared austere, oppressive and imposing, when he turned into the car park. As he asked the warden for a parking place he was little to realise that this place would become as familiar as his own home.

Mum sat with Kit and Laura in the Casualty department of the Belgrave Royal Infirmary with growing impatience. Did these people not realise the urgency of their situation? Next to her a rather unkempt mother and child distracted her thoughts by insisting on an outpouring of their problems. The little child had pneumonia. What was she doing in Casualty, Mum thought, as she edged away from them, afraid of another threat to Laura? She thought of the letter and the one phrase screamed at her. 'Test for possible Leukaemia'. She kept saying to herself that it's only a precaution.

Eventually Mum was seen and she was told to go to one of the children's wards. She made sure a message was left for Dad so that he knew where to find them. She dearly hoped that he would come to them, and soon.

Mum was actually on a different ward when Dad arrived. There was apparently no room for them on the main one. They were in a private cubicle. It all seemed rather cosy. Laura was quiet when Dad came in, although Kit was cheerful and a little excited. Both Mum and Dad anticipated Laura staying overnight and as consequence discussed who should stay with her. A blood test had been carried out but the results had not, as yet, been returned. Eventually they were interviewed by a young house Officer who wanted to know the full story of how Laura had eventually ended up with a visit to hospital. This included an account of the family's trips to Sweden and Germany and the journey of Laura's illness. After a good half an hour the house Officer went away without even indicating what might be wrong.

The hours passed. It had to be glandular fever or some blood related disease they said.

Mum knew what they meant. Dad didn't. People like us don't get problems like this, he thought. He could not come to terms with being here.

Mum was determined to get to the bottom of the problem as quickly as possible and was becoming a little impatient with the response so far. Eventually, after pestering different doctors she managed to get an interview. A consultant invited them into an office. It was late in the day. The light had disappeared from the sky and streetlights intruded through the window. The consultant projected a confidence that only comes with several years in a profession. The consultant was calm and wanted to tell Mum and Dad as much as possible but they could see there was some nervousness in the face, a nervousness that said, "How will they take it? Will there be repercussions on me?"

Mum and Dad sat down and waited.

"What would you like to know?" the consultant said in a tone that betrayed some concern.

"The truth! " said Mum.

"What do you mean by the truth?"

"We mean what is the matter with Laura. We are not stupid you know. I have some idea of what might be wrong."

"But sometimes our conclusions are based on assumptions that can prove to be totally wrong. Our conclusions can take us down the wrong path if they are based on assumption and a little knowledge of medical matters."

"The Truth is what you want to tell us," said Dad.

"Truth is Truth."

"I've read the letter!" Mum interrupted with a confidence and power that instilled a temporary silence in the rather warm and stuffy room. Dad looked at her with surprise that betrayed an unhappy feeling that perhaps he did not know her as well as he should.

"What! You mean the doctor's letter of referral?"

"Yes, of course. Why not? It's about my daughter for goodness sake!"

Dad was overcome with admiration. Surely here was a woman in control. The doctor also looked at her with some surprise that quickly changed into relief. At least we can now talk about realities and not the vagaries of consultant speak, she thought.

"So, what would you like to know"?"

"Does she have Leukaemia?"

"We have tested for a number of things so nothing is conclusive. However, it looks likely that she has some form of Leukaemia."

The answer stunned Dad. He died. He sank into his chair with dismay, but it was a momentary shock. Mum seemed better prepared. She came back with determination.

"So, where do we go from here?"

"Well, first have to carry out more tests and find out which type of Leukaemia it is as the diagnosis will affect her chances. The best one is known as Acute Lymphoblastic Leukaemia or A.L.L. or children's Leukaemia. If she has this then we have a good chance."

The words were cold, clinical and said with care. The doctor knew what the impact would be. She had been here many times before; this same room; the same message. The parents looking at her helplessly as if they expected her to say "Sorry. I have made a mistake. Your child is perfectly well. This is just a dream.'

Mum looked at the wall. There was a chart of the human body with the names and graphical illustrations of various organs. Next to it was a notice announcing a talk in the clinical Sciences building on Palliative Care. She tried to read them. She saw the potted plant by the window. It's leaves, which had accumulated dust, looked sharp and clear. She concentrated on it. Then her gaze came back to the wall. There was another chart. It listed a number of drugs whose names meant nothing to her. It was next to a board containing a variety of pamphlets on childhood diseases. Cystic Fibrosis, Asthma, Cancer, Leukaemia and names she had never seen before. But she saw it. Leukaemia. Cancer. Leukaemia. Cancer in a child. Children don't have cancer, she thought, but they get Leukaemia. Alma Cogan died of Leukaemia she remembered Dad saying once a long time ago. Who was Alma Cogan anyway?

She heard Dad talking, trying to ask intelligent questions as if he might be able to resolve this problem as if it were one of his management problems. He thinks it's another challenge, another exercise. Then she saw he was quiet. He looked lost, beaten, but yet, he still seemed to grasp at every opportunity that arose in the conversation as if he could solve the problem by dialogue.

He wants her to say it's going to be all right, she thought, but it's not. It can't be all right. Oh, what are we doing here? It can't be true that this is happening to us, to me, to Laura. As she said it she felt herself descending into a pool of acceptance. She pleaded to a higher authority, which she could not or would not comprehend. Tell me it's not true! Tell me; tell me please, it's not true, please, please tell me it's not true. It's not true. It cannot possibly be true. It's a dream. It's a documentary on TV It's someone else's life. It's a book I've read. It's a film. It's not true!

Mum and Dad came out of that meeting realising that they had suddenly transferred from a normal healthy family life into the unknown. Things could not be the same in the future. As they walked out of the doctor's office Dad met a business colleague, whose child was under observation. He smiled and wanted to make conversation but Dad brushed straight past him as if he was an intrusion into a very delicate and intimate part of his life. Dad telephoned his parents and asked them to come down straight away. Mum spoke to her parents. They were distraught.

They decided to go home that night to be on their own and, hopefully, overcome the grief they felt so that they could help Laura over the coming, what? Weeks? Months? They were to learn from here on in that every decision they were to make would be crucial in their management of the situation and their ability to cope. This ability to cope would probably be the biggest thing in their lives from now on. They would have to learn to manage their time with precision, to arrange their lives so that they could serve Laura and control their emotions even though they were going into an unpredictable course of events. For every living, and sometimes sleeping, minute of their lives the problem would dominate. They were now different, one of that group of people whom you read about or see on some TV documentary. It was horrible, it was foreboding, but it was to be the most honourable thing they were to ever do in their whole lives.

Chapter 4

The most honourable thing

Dad, Mum and Kit arrived home to an empty and inhospitable house. This was the first time they had been separated from Laura. It had always been the four of them - Mum, Dad, Kit and Laura, and in particular, Kit and Laura, the inseparable. They were the two that were actually one. It was inconceivable that they could be kept away from each other, even for a short time.

When they arrived home Mum went to talk to a neighbour whilst they were waiting for Grandma and Grandad. Dad got Kit into bed and then sat with a cup of tea. The phone rang. It was one of Mum's sisters.

"Hello, yes, I'm sorry, you've telephoned at a bad time. We have just come back from the hospital. It looks like Laura has Leukaemia."

There was silence on the other end, then....

"I'm so sorry. What can I say?"

She asked about the diagnosis, but what could he tell her? Mum returned and spoke to her sister.

Grandma and Grandad eventually arrived and were a source of comfort to Mum and Dad as were the other relatives and friends they had spoken to on the telephone. Grandma said she urged and willed the car down the motorway. Grandad had gritted his teeth at the steering wheel and drove at his best speed, determined to fulfil his role in this great event.

Mum and Dad hardly slept that night. They both dreamed the same dreams. Black cars and funerals featured. It was the ultimate nightmare. Your healthy happy child, your world, is suddenly turned into horror, into the termination of everything you knew.

Dad's mind swam with visions of death. All he wanted was for Laura to be in his arms, for her to snuggle up next to him with her head on his shoulder as she frequently used to when she crept into this bed in the middle of the night. He became obsessed with the thought and wanted nothing else. He could even feel her physical presence next to him. He could not come to terms with the reality that this small child whom he loved so much should now be threatened with the taking of her life. He reflected on her innocence and naivety. She was so happy with life, so free with it, but, most importantly, so innocent. She must have expected a future, such a wonderful future with Mum and Dad. How could she comprehend the absurdities of medical care, the absurdity that in attempting to make her better they would make her sick, oh so sick.

Morning arrived. Dawn breaks. Realisation wakes. Those first few seconds of wakefulness are the worst. You open your eyes and your mind slowly comes to life, to receive the creeping vines of yesterday's events crawling over you in a cold damp mist, making you shiver with the awful reality with which you are now confronted. Did those things really happen? Was it not just an awful nightmare? You know it was not and you begin to perspire in panic, fear and nausea as the awesome truth penetrates your mind and overwhelms you. You don't want to get out of bed but know that you must. We all have these feelings. They might be due to be the shame of too much exuberance at last night's dinner party or that yesterday was the day you were told you no longer had a job. Worse, your daughter might die.

Mum and Dad awoke early that morning, before the light had begun to filter through the chinks between curtain and wall. They showered and stumbled downstairs to a Muesli and coffee breakfast prepared by Grandma. They felt they had not slept, although they had slept a little as morning came and their physical tiredness overtook their mental vibrancy. They thought they had only dreamed and their dreams were still with them. They could not stomach the thought of breakfast. They had to get to Laura. Grandma insisted that they ate before they left. You will need your strength, she said, for Laura.

They left the house at 7.30.am. The early morning radio intruded into their silence and grief as they drove through the villages of Belgraveshire. The signposts flashed up the village names. Names they had hardly noticed before. Arneham, Sharsby and Moston appeared in the headlights of the car as they sped on their way. The sun was making it's first halting advances into a watery sky and it's orange beams skimmed across the treetops illuminating the early morning scavenging crows as they flitted from field to field and tree to tree. The air was damp and clinging but had a freshness which only morning time brings. Dad normally enjoyed driving early in the morning, listening to the car radio, calling in at a Little Chef for breakfast, but this morning the music was intrusive. He switched channels to Radio Belgrave. The theme from the Snowman was playing and seemed to convey a message of hope in a day of hopelessness.

Dawn also broke for Laura. She had slept fairly well out of sheer tiredness rather than relaxation. As she slept she heard noises that would momentarily awaken her consciousness, her eyes would blink a little, then she would fall back into a deep slumber. When she finally awoke she felt disorientated. She assumed she was in her own bed at home but as the realisation swept over her she became frightened and felt lonely and deserted. A nurse came in and asked her if she was all right. She said she was, more to make the nurse go away than anything else. She wondered where Mum and Dad were and as she did they walked through the door, with a look of slight disappointment on their faces that she had awoke before they arrived. They regretted this forever. Strange are the things that we feel guilty for.

Laura's waking song

Dawn breaks and realisation wakes.
I am alone
You were not there to greet my waking.
You were without me.

Day breaks and tomorrow is today
I am awake
You were not there to hear me say
Where are you?

I am in this place for all it takes
Dawn breaks and realisation wakes.
Your eyes show you care
But you were not there.

Laura was quiet but looked reasonably well Dad thought. She was not allowed breakfast as a general anaesthetic was planned for a particular test. Dad picked her up from her bed. They clung to each other and as Dad carried her up and down the ward, looking at the mobiles, pictures and nurses it seemed that the next few hours stretched in front of them like some awesome and horrible marathon which had to be endured. His brain screamed to know what was going on yet he knew the most important thing was to comfort and support his daughter. They waited patiently for the doctors to arrive. Dad held her in his arms all the time. Eventually they swept in on their morning rounds, led by a consultant like some invading General. The consultant examined Laura very thoroughly.

"You understand the implications, " The consultant said.

" Yes," Mum and Dad both nodded.

They left and a nurse came in to say that they were to be transferred to the ward that dealt with childhood cancer. Dad complained, as they were quite comfortable here. His words made little difference. They picked Laura up and carried her across to the ward.

When they arrived on the ward the strangest and bizarre sight met them. It was as if they had stepped into some unreal and macabre world. They stood and momentarily gazed upon what lay before them. There were children with no hair, some with hair half falling out, others with bloated white faces, children vomiting, children attached to drips with tubes coming out of their arms and chest and, worst of all, children screaming. As the three of them stood and looked at this terrifying sight the nurses fought amongst themselves over whether there was a bed for the new arrival.

Eventually a red-haired State Enrolled nurse approached them and directed them to a bed in the open ward.

"I want a private cubicle," Dad said with firmness, "my girl is very ill."

"All the children are very ill on this ward," she said, "anyway, there aren't any private cubicles available."

Dad became annoyed with her. She was probably one of the best paediatric nurses at the Infirmary and he was later to regret his attitude to her and learn to appreciate her technical competence, ability and caring attitude. Like many of the staff on this the busiest ward in the hospital she was under intense pressure. Remarkably it never showed.

They settled Laura into her bed, which was near the window in a bay of six beds. There were two open wards on ward 12 plus a number of isolation cubicles. The State Enrolled nurse came across with two mugs of hot sweet tea, a gesture that was strictly against the rules, but was typical of this nurse's attitude to her patients and parents.

"Here you are," she said. "You'll need this. You've got a lot to go through. But we're all in the same boat in here. You'll also be surprised at what we can do."

She dashed off to attend to a little baby making strange noises.

The time came for Laura's test. She had been quiet all morning, spending most of her time observing. Mum and Dad agreed that Dad should take her in for the test. They were taken into a room known as The Treatment Room. Thankfully the State Enrolled nurse was there. She seemed to know what she was doing and was directing some of the other staff and keeping an eye on the doctors. Laura had two tests. They were both to become very familiar. The first one was to check if there was any disease in her nervous system. This was known as a lumber puncture. The second was a bone marrow aspiration to extract some marrow for analysis. In addition, they wanted to fit a cannula to her arm to take intravenous drugs. Because they had not obtained the full results of the blood tests they were now reluctant to use a general ananaesthetic. A local one would have to suffice. The senior house officer prepared himself. In his white coat and protective glasses he reminded Dad of the pictures he had seen from Chernobyl of the scientists running around attempting to control the disaster.

Laura was laid out on the treatment couch.

The doctors clinically stripped her to expose her buttocks. She cried. They told Dad to hold her still. They laid her on her side on the treatment couch, which was covered in a red plastic slab covered in a clinically clean white sheet with the name of the hospital around the edges. He looked at the name and wondered why it was there. Were they concerned it might be stolen?

Dad and Laura fell out of control.

"Bend her knees please. Push her knees into her chin, then hold her so tight that she cannot move"

Several pairs of arms pinned her down, principally Dad's. She lost her dignity. She looked helpless, imprisoned and Dad didn't like that. He laid his face next to hers. Their cheeks touched. He gripped her tight to hold down her fighting body, his arms around her and one hand cupping the back of her head.

"Tighter, tighter."

He gripped her so tight he was frightened of bruising her. He looked up and could not believe the size of needle they were using. As they put on their gloves and checked the needle he clung to Laura. She cried. They seemed to poise for minutes with the needle projected upward, but it must have only been seconds. The needle hit her. Quickly and deeply into her back they drove it. Having done this they paused and slowly and leisurely turned the screws to draw out the marrow in painful drops.

" Daddy, Daddy, Daddy..." Her voice, weak and helpless, faded away in a sea of pain.

Laura and Dad clung to each other. The tears flowed from each of them and were fused, binding them together forever, like Red Indian blood brothers sealing a lifelong partnership, although his pain was only emotional. It was borrowed and unreal and could never match hers.

She thought. "Why have they taken me from my home of peace and calm to this madhouse of noise and pain? Surely I don't deserve this pain, or is it perhaps that all children undergo the torments of adults. If so, why me alone and not Kit?"

This was the worst nightmare. It was a real daytime nightmare from which she could not escape by waking up.

The junior doctors stood by in their white gowns and masks and recorded the events meticulously for clinical and public record.

Laura and Dad had a breathing space when the whole world around them seemed to relax. Dad even remembered some doctor making an amusing observation about one of the ward clerks. Minutes later the medical team were on them again. Another needle was driven deep into her body involving more pain and tears. She cried. How she cried, and Dad, unashamedly, cried with her. As soon as he had recovered from this pain they attacked her arm to fit an intravenous drip. It was another needle into her hand. With the treatment of Leukaemia you learn that there is no rest, but a continual bombardment with needles and drugs. What they were going through now was to become a regular occurrence. The drip, the needles were to become common threats.

The doctors placed the results on little glass plates. They seemed pleased with the work they had done, but beneath the pleasure was a discomfort that betrayed their humanity. Dad asked how the marrow looked. The smiled at his naivety and patronised him with an answer that would suit his intelligence.

Laura's memory of this was different. Her confused senses saw what Dad had failed to see. She looked in the mirror on the wall and saw no reflection. She saw a face. It was a man's face. It was the same man Mum and Dad had told her about. They had been to London to see a show in which there was a phantom in a mask who had danced and sang and enticed and bewitched a young girl. Laura remembered the story vividly and thought of it often. He sounded just like the Phantom that she and Kit used to battle against with their toy soldiers at home. She often heard her Mum play the music the Phantom made. His face was half covered in a mask, but the part of his face she could see was white. His clothes appeared white. He beckoned her and began to move out of the mirror. He sang. His song was powerful and swept over her. He took her in his arms and they began to dance. It was a strange swirling kind of dance. As they danced he continued to sing, although his song contained no words only music. She danced in a flowing red dress and he in a white suit. As they swept around the room she looked down with horror to see her red frock become tainted by the whiteness of his clothes. He span her around and around until she became dizzier and dizzier. The music became louder and more intense and the redness of her dress faded into the whiteness of his suit save a few unblemished spots. At this point he unmasked his face to reflect the white glare from her dress. She screamed. That was when the last needle hit her and she sank into a sea of pain.

"It's all right now Laura. It's all over," said Dad, wheeling her out of The Treatment Room.

Dad took Laura back to her bed where Mum was anxiously waiting. She had been quite busy in his absence; having made contact with other parents and had gained a

45

greater insight into the nature of the treatment and the role of the parent. Already she had embarked upon her future role in the treatment of Laura, which was that of Guide. She was to learn and understand the nature and treatment of Leukaemia to such a degree that she left many members of the medical team standing. This knowledge was a determining factor in ensuring that Laura had the best possible treatment. Although medical practitioners will disagree, there is still a tendency amongst many of them to act on the patient's and parent's behalf under a "your life in our hands" philosophy. Mum and Dad would never allow that to happen regarding Laura and would question everything that was done to her. On occasions this led to changes in the way things were done. It sometimes led to arguments with nurses and doctors. However, in the main Mum and Dad got on well with the medical staff and only wished to worked alongside them.

This was not true of some parents. Some would never ask questions and would be completely submissive. Others would react to the pressure of the situation in a negative manner by continually falling out with those closest at hand - the nurses. There is still this mystique about doctors. Many people seem afraid to question what they are doing and why.

Dad did ask questions. He quite often fired the bullets but it was Mum who supplied the ammunition.

Laura sat on her bed sucking her thumb whilst her body and mind absorbed the pain. She stared out of the window as if in a trance. She did not look around the ward or acknowledge the presence of others, except when she heard a child cry out. It was almost as if she had decided to switch off and withdraw inward into her own little world. In reality this is what she did to draw on her own quiet inner strength. She, at less than three years of age, must have known she was embarking upon a journey with a very uncertain destination.

Next followed a period of waiting. It was only midday and Mum and Dad were told that the results would come out that evening or the next morning

One of the mothers came to see them. Her little boy was under treatment for Common Cell Acute Lymphoblastic Leukaemia. This was the one known as the children's leukaemia and was considered to be the most treatable. It was the "best" one to have. Mum and Dad hoped that this would be the one that Laura had. They read some of the booklets supplied by the Leukaemia Research Fund given to them by the health visitor. These confirmed that the only form of leukaemia with a reasonable prognosis was Common Cell A.L.L.

Laura's temperature was taken every hour and her parents were told that as she was very anaemic she would probably have a blood transfusion tomorrow. The treatment itself would be in the form of chemotherapy and radiotherapy but would not start until the type of Leukaemia had been properly diagnosed.

Laura's bed was on the right hand side, by the window, of the "Cancer bay" on The ward. It was nice to have a window to look out of and these prime bed positions became real prizes in the allocation of beds. Not only did you have the joy of looking outside, but also, you had more privacy as you only had another bed on one side. You also had the added advantage of a low window-ledge for use as an additional seat or surface. The view itself was not terrific, rows of terraced houses, the odd church and factory and the Hazel Street Football Ground. However the view was towards the south and they knew that in that direction was their village, the countryside and home.

In the bed directly opposite to Laura was a young boy named Edward. He had been admitted some months ago with a very serious form of cancer that seemed to consume him completely. He had lost his hair and although he looked unwell he seemed to keep fairly cheerful. His mother sat quietly by his bed. To his right was a young girl just into her teens. Her name was Arlain. Her hair was half falling out. She had tumours in one of her legs and was very poorly. She looked very pale and was sitting up most of that afternoon vomiting into a sick bowl - the after affects of chemotherapy. Between spasms of her nausea she looked across at Dad and smiled. This smile was a great inspiration to him and from that day he had a special affection for Arlain and always admired her bravery. Again, her parents sat quietly by her bedside, gently tending to her needs. Immediately next to Laura, in a cot, was a little baby boy, not unlike Kit in his looks. He had a tumour in the kidneys and had recently been operated on. The tumour was about 2lbs weight. His total body weight was only 9lbs. He had a stitch that went completely across his tummy. He was also fitted with a nasal gastric tube, as he would not eat. Otherwise he seemed quite a lively little chap.

The ward was continually busy with people coming and going all day. There was always something to watch, not all of it pleasant. The cry of children under some form of discomfort or pain was continually there. Eventually little Laura would get used to it. Just now it was a startling and bewildering world. Her whole family had been transferred to this strange place. Why could they not stay at home? Why had she got to lie here all day waiting for who knows what. All Laura wanted to do was to sleep, to shut out the noise of this place and fall into a deep sleep in her own bed. If she tried really hard she could sometimes pretend she was at home. Why did Mum and Dad not take her home? Why did they allow those doctors to hurt her?

She had never seen Mum and Dad like this before. Dad's face was red because he had been crying. She had never seen him cry before. It unsettled her. Was it because he felt her pain too? Mum was also very upset and was asking other parents many questions about their children who were in hospital. Dad sat quietly by Laura's side. The afternoon passed peaceably, although every hour one of the nurses would place a thermometer under Laura's arm and write her temperature down on a chart. Laura dozed most of the afternoon. The pain of the morning had made her tired. She looked out of the window to see the sun leave the sky and wondered what Kit was doing. The early evening shadows crept over the city and street and house lights began to flicker. Eventually darkness covered the sky.

The consultant came onto the ward and asked Mum and Dad to come to the office. A nurse came and sat with Laura. About half an hour later they returned sounding quite excited and looking pleased despite Laura's predicament.

" We have a fighting chance little girl, " said Dad, "we're going to get you better!

"We've still got a long way to go!" piped up Mum, "although she has Children's Leukaemia it's not going to be easy."

So Laura was diagnosed with Common Cell Acute Lymphoblastic Leukaemia; the children's leukaemia. As the doctor said, "If you are going to get Leukaemia, this is the best one."

To Laura these words meant nothing. She only felt tired and wanted to go home to sleep in her own bed. Perhaps she would never get home. Perhaps all these children live here all their days.

Dad made a camp bed next to her bed that evening. There was little space, but Dad managed to find room. Her bed was much higher than his and as Laura looked down on him she felt somewhat isolated. She was on a special bed, which only sick children slept in. She felt exposed to the excesses of doctors and nurses who wanted to hurt her. After today her body felt, and was, battered and bruised. How long was this to be kept up?

The ward began its demise into slumber as first one then another child began to sleep. In the corner of the ward the little baby was making irritating gurgling noises. Eventually Laura got used to his sounds and the noise of the Nurses trying to relieve his suffering. Dad sat on his camp bed holding Laura's hand as she settled her head on the pillow. As she snuggled down she felt secure, lost in a new little world. Bed always seems a secure place. Surely they cannot harm me now. I am here with my Dad. All is well.

She dreamed that night. The dreams were deep and complex. A tapestry of images and faces unfurled in her young mind. Pain was mixed with pleasure and she felt the confusion of mixing those she loved with those who inflicted the pain. The White Phantom that she had seen in the Treatment Room rose up from within her. His bloody smile revealed his pleasure in dominating her body. He consumed her energy like a jealous lover. He accepted no compromise save complete submission. His only gifts in return were lethargy and vulnerability. Her shield against the ailments of the world had been cruelly cast aside. She lay exposed on a tablet of cold white stone with hounds of infection and disease baying all around. Only Mum and Dad kept them away, but it seemed like a never-ending conflict. She awoke feeling hot and frightened to see Dad leaning over her with a glass of orange juice and a white tablet, saying:

"Take this sweetheart, it will take your temperature down and let you sleep more easily. " He leaned over and popped the tablet in her mouth. She drank the juice and swallowed the tablet automatically. As she settled down on her pillow once again, she could see a nurse standing in the background smiling. She must have asked Dad to give me that tablet, she thought. I hope it doesn't hurt me. However she was too tired to pursue this thought much further. She fell asleep to the sound of Dad settling into his camp bed, the little baby gurgling and the night nurses holding a whispered conversation.

Chapter 5

Radella dreaming

Two beds away from Laura lay a young girl of less than two years of age. She had only just appeared on the ward. Although Laura had been here for a few days now, she had only ever seen this little girl being carried past the end of the ward down the long corridor that went to the Playroom and ultimately, home. Her Mum always carried her on her hip almost as if she was fixed there. She had mousy hair that was tied up in a little parcel on the top of her head and an impish face that said, "Play with me!" The little girl's name was Radella. She had spent the last few days confined to an isolation cubicle, hence Laura not seeing her.

Laura could not understand why this little girl had been locked away from everyone else. Mum explained. The doctors make the children very poorly by destroying their ability to fight coughs and colds. Mum told Laura that this happens because they need to make her strong again and the only way to do it is to clean out all her blood. Because the children are in danger of becoming very poorly through coughs and colds they have to be put in special isolation cubicles. Laura's turn to go in the special cubicle would come very soon. Laura was not sure this was a good idea. There were lots more children on the ward and she felt less alone here. She remembered her first night in hospital when Mum and Dad had left her to go home because they were upset. She felt very lonely and isolated. She hoped that Mum and Dad would not leave her this time.

Little Radella was pleased to be on the ward again. Her Mum was not. She had enjoyed the privacy of a private cubicle where she could sleep in relative comfort next to her daughter. Radella had a Non-Hodgkins Lymphoma, but her treatment was just the same as Laura's. Her face was translucent white and the hair on the sides of her head was beginning to fall out giving her a ghostly transparent look. She seemed unreal, like a beautiful white doll. Laura had brought a beautiful white pot doll back from Germany. Radella reminded her of it and she suddenly wanted her dolly again.

"Where's my dolly? " she piped up, her voice penetrating the silence of the ward.

"Which dolly, Laura? " Mum asked

"My dolly!" she stressed, frustrated that Mum did not know that she wanted her dolly. There was only one dolly in her mind. Why could grownups not understand what she wanted? They always had to ask questions. Laura knew what she wanted.

"I want my dolly, that dolly you brought me from my holiday home," she said with a tremble in her voice suggestive of impending tears.

"I'll bring lots of your dollies tomorrow," Mum said, with a disarming smile that relaxed Laura and enabled her to drift into the anticipation of having her dolls around her, a further link with home. Perhaps if she could forge a bridge of toys and personal artefacts she might travel across it and eventually reach the peace of home.

Laura sat on her bed sucking the thumb on her right hand that she held cupped in her left hand. She looked across at Radella with sideways glances showing a reluctant interest in the only child near her age. Radella glanced back with a smile. A bond was forged whereby each identified with the other's situation. Radella was in a cot. She sat curled up like a tiger cub, purring at the children, nurses and parents who surrounded her. She was defended by an abundance of toys and games in which she displayed little interest. In her hand she clasped a child's cup containing her favourite drink that changed on a weekly basis. She sipped it infrequently in between glances across to Laura.

The ward became quiet. The amber night lights cast an unearthly glow over the sleeping children and their paraphernalia of bleeping infusion pumps, medical charts, pictures, books and toys. The hushed whispers of the night nurses rippled across the floor like the sound of the evening tide on a pebble beach. Laura and Radella sat up and looked at each other. They knew the game. You had no choice but to take on the challenge, uncomplaining and resourceful. Those who complained lost the battle. An image crossed Laura's mind of a picture she had once seen on the wall of a place that was dedicated to the display of paintings. It had stuck in her mind because it was powerful and real. It was of Jesus standing outside a doorway with a lamp in his hand. The light shone on his face. She felt as if she could walk into it and be there with him so real was the image.

She remembered the images she saw each time she went to church. Jesus was always on his cross. He did not carry a light. She remembered one of the times that Dad stood on the chancel steps reading from the bible. He talked about the things that Jesus had said. They were all written in the book he held. Laura vividly remembered the words. Jesus had said that he was the Way, the Truth and the Light. She could not understand how even someone like Jesus could be those things. How could someone be the truth?

Dad sat by her side, silently smiling. His hand was warm and clasped hers with a gentle pressure. She loved him and he loved her. There was contentment and hope. With that she slept.

It was a deep sleep and when she awoke Dad was there again smelling of soap and toothpaste. His face was bright and his hair damp. He wore a dressing gown and pyjamas, something he never wore at home. He clutched a cup of tea in one hand. In the other was a small plastic cup containing a number of coloured tablets and a syringe full of a yellow substance

"The nurse said you slept very well. Dad had to sleep in the playroom last night. I couldn't play with the toys because the nurse made me switch off the light."

Laura smiled faintly at Dad's attempted humour

"When can I have my bebbets? " she asked. The twins had a pet name for breakfast, which was "bebbets". Although they had progressed beyond baby talk this one word had persisted.

"What would you like? Radella is having cornflakes. "

Young Radella was already tackling breakfast, perhaps with less enthusiasm than her mother would have liked, but she was putting on a brave face. Laura looked across and her glance was returned. Cornflakes did not seem very appealing this morning.

It was 7:30 in the morning and the ward was getting into swing. The breakfast trolley had appeared and parents and nurses were preparing meals for the children. Some children who were labelled "Nil by Mouth" looked sullenly on. Breakfast time on the ward became a time of conflict for many parents and children. Some children would face it with enthusiasm, having slept well and being reasonably hungry. Others, who were perhaps undergoing more intensive chemotherapy, would nauseate at the idea of food in the morning. Laura was still at the stage where the idea of breakfast in bed was a novelty, although she had not got the appetite of the days when she was well. The hospital provided cereals in individual servings, which interested the well children. In addition a trolley was sent up from the Canteen containing bacon, eggs, sausage and soggy toast. Very few children took an interest in this menu. Perhaps the most favourite food in a morning was toast, but it had to be fresh. Dad became an expert in making good toast. When Laura eventually moved into a cubicle Dad would make a plate full of fresh toast and jam every morning. On the open ward he would pick up the fresh loaf contained in the trolley and make toast for everyone.

The parents always encouraged their children to eat breakfast as they knew that, in many cases, the day ahead was going to be hard and little appetites would diminish. It was always felt that if the child ate a hearty breakfast it would sustain them throughout the day. In addition the children were more susceptible and vulnerable in the mornings and it was the opportunity for parents to force the issue.

Seeing Radella eating cornflakes, Laura piquantly asked:

"Can I have cornflakes too?"

"Of course you can, " Dad replied, and wandered off to the trolley. He opened a small packet of cornflakes and emptied them in to a bowl. The milk was in a fading grey plastic jug. He poured it over the cornflakes. The sugar, sprinkled with the brown spots of numerous teaspoons lay in an even greyer and more fading plastic bowl. Dad took out a spoonful and sprinkled it over Laura's breakfast. The nurses always prepared orange juice for the children. In actual fact Laura preferred tea in the morning. As a consequence Dad had to dash off to the kitchen to make fresh tea as well. He was not too displeased at this because it gave him the opportunity to make himself a cup of tea. In actual fact Dad used to share Laura's breakfast by always making sure he made too much toast. This was frowned on by some of the Medical Staff who tried to insist that parents used the drinks machine in the lift lobby. Dad would always blatantly ignore this rule on the basis that he always ate breakfast at home with Laura and did not see why he had to change now that he was in hospital. In reality most of the doctors and Nurses tended to sympathise with this view. Once Dad had breakfasted with Laura he would wander off and change into his suit for work.

Radella was always one step in front of Laura in her treatment because she had been diagnosed that much earlier. She was the only child of two wonderful people who were in the teaching profession. Their lifestyle contrasted superficially with that of Mum and Dad. However, on close analysis it was apparent that their degree of commonality was greater than their difference. As a consequence they got on very well and Mum and Dad grew to be very fond of them. They could talk to each other in common terms about the treatment and the social implications of a child with cancer. Their encounters on the ward were brief but the impact of their dialogue was impressive. Their minds were sharp to the realities of a life or death situation and, accordingly, senses were acute. It took little to inflame a situation and prompt a reaction from them.

There was a Social worker on the ward. Unfortunately much of her role had been relegated to that of allocating financial assistance. However, as a matter of course all parents were directed to her a few days after diagnosis. For most of them it was an opportunity to vocalise their fears and anxieties. For many it was an opportunity to exploit the opportunity for financial assistance regarding transport and associated expenses. Dad went to see this lady and was quite happy to talk about his feelings, which helped crystallise the situation in his own mind. Mum and Dad found, throughout this problem, that the best people to talk to were those involved in the problem. The worst people to talk to were relatives, who were less patient to listen and more inclined to offer clichéd pieces of advice, like:

"I'm sure that our little girl will be all right, she's too tough. She's too brave to give in. Don't worry she'll show them what she's made of!"

Mum and Dad learned that it is all too often the brave who die young.

Radella's Dad also went to see the Social worker. She asked him how he was coping with the situation.

" Listen," he said, " It's not me that has the problem. It's Radella. You tell me what you can do to make her better. That's all that I am interested in at the moment."

Dad and Mum were often to recall these words as they really summed up the reality of the situation. It is not the parents who have a problem, although quite often it is the parents who display the emotions. The children complain very little. They just seem to get on with coping. But it is they who have the problem. Accordingly Mum and Dad have to forget their own grief, because when a child is diagnosed with Leukaemia or Cancer the parents go through the symptoms of grief, and concentrate on what is best for the welfare of the child patient. This can be difficult. It means taking a completely selfless attitude and putting aside one's own sadness and grief for the welfare of the child. Once that step has been taken things become that much easier.

Dad was walking back onto the ward one day after visiting the WRVS shop on the ground floor to buy some sweets for Laura. He pushed open the double doors and walked down the long corridor toward the depth of the ward. It consisted of two open bays of 6 beds surrounded by a number of small rooms known as isolation cubicles for children with infections, those particularly vulnerable to infection and the terminally ill. There were 8 such cubicles. Total accommodation on the ward therefore was 20 beds. Integrated into the ward was also a High Dependency unit for children requiring close observation. This unit was just being built when Laura first went into The ward.

As well as beds for patients The ward had a Treatment room where children were given bone marrow aspirations, lumbar punctures, fitted with cannulae etc. There was also an office for the nurses and the usual sluices and toilets. It was, too all intents and purposes, an integral unit. There was also a playroom. However this playroom was the smallest of all the paediatric Wards in the hospital despite it being the busiest.

As Dad walked down the corridor he heard a commotion.

"Peter! Will you get back in your bed right away! " Screamed a nurse with the sort of conviction that said - I'm wasting my time.

"Will you please stop running up and down the ward, and can I have my thermometer back!"

As Dad approached the Bay where Laura was a young boy of 11 years of age collided into him. He looked a healthy individual apart from the fact that he had no hair whatsoever. Dad recognised this individual from their first day on the ward. He recalled that he was in trouble with the nurses at that time also.

"Hello," said Dad. " Where are you going?"

" I'm escaping from the nurses. They want me to stay in bed. I have to go for a bone marrow test today. I can't stand them bone marrow tests. I hate it when they put you to sleep. All they ever want to do here is give you loads of tests. I hate it."

All the words came tumbling out one after the other. He had a fairly broad County accent. His face was brown like that of a village boy, and due to his entire lack of hair, his head was brown also. Dad believed he had met the real William Brown!

"I've seen you on here before," the boy piped up. "Are you Laura's Dad. I've just been talking to her Mum. Don't worry. I'll look after Laura. She'll be all right. I've been here a load of times."

Strangely Dad felt comforted by the helping hand of this small boy.

"What's the matter with you?" he said." Why are you in here?"

"Oh me? I've got Leukaemia. That's cancer you know. Lots of them kids in here have cancer."

"I see you've had chemotherapy. You've lost all your hair. How do you feel about that?"

"I like it. I don't have to wash me hair no more, " he chuckled with great enthusiasm.

"What about the children at school? Don't they call you names?"

"Not likely! They used to call me baldy, but now I bash 'em so they don't call me names no more"

At this point a nurse distracted the boy with a needle who wanted to take a blood test.

"I had one of them yesterday," he declared. "I don't want any more"

With that he dashed off down the ward toward the playroom. The nurse pursued him at a swift walking pace with a wry smile on her face. She knew that he was displaying this rebellion as a means of retaining some control over the situation and his own destiny.

Life on the ward was not as difficult for Mum and Dad as they had first imagined. Their exposure to other parents enabled them to communicate more easily with others in a similar situation and as a consequence they gained many new friends. For Laura it was strange to sleep in such a large room but she gained comfort from the fact that other children were in the same situation. To her it seemed a normal thing to do because she was not aware it was abnormal. It was the noise that perhaps made the biggest impression on her. Throughout the day things were continually happening, doctors and nurses in clusters discussing patients, children being fitted with drips, drips bleeping demanding to be adjusted, parents persuading their children to eat or drink, the television and children screaming, crying, laughing or, sometimes, just dying.

At night the ward stayed alive. There was invariably some child who had a problem or who simply could not sleep. The treatment continued unabated throughout the night and quite often it was the time when blood transfusions and platelets were administered. At these times the child felt alone and afraid. It took a long time for them to build up their trust in the nurses. Dad slept with Laura each night but some parents had to leave their children. If these parents knew how much some of these children cried at night for their Mum perhaps they would not leave them. Often other parents would go across to the lonely child and offer some comfort. The nurses could not always afford the time to sooth these children, especially if there was an urgent case on the ward. Dad was also surprised at the number of children on the ward who received few visits from parents, but he did realise that it was not always possible for many, especially if they were single parent families, who could not afford the time off work or lived a long way from the hospital. The joy on the faces of these children when their Mum or Dad came to see them was illuminating. However, some of those who had undergone some pain in the absence of their parents would become sullen for a little while, as if to send a message to Mum and Dad that things were not easy for them.

Laura had treatment every day, including blood tests, which were taken through a needle in the back of the hand. The children got used to the routine of blood tests but hated them. They say you can tell the chemotherapy children by the way they automatically hold up a limp hand and turn away when a doctor approaches with a needle. Eventually Laura's veins began to clog up and the blood tests became more difficult. This meant that the doctors had to try several times to get some blood. Some doctors, especially those who had been trained on the Neonatal ward were particularly good, but it was not always possible to use them, as they might not be available.

There were many junior doctors on the ward. Their attempts at blood tests left many children in a despicable condition. One young doctor whose ambition was to be a mortician tried eight times with one child and ended up putting a drip in her foot, which meant she was immobile for several days. He tried to fit a cannula to Laura's arm. After trying several veins in her arm he went for the main one in the wrist, a safe bet. He failed leaving her in despair.

"We'll have to try the ankle," he said.

"If you do that," said Dad, "then Laura will not be able to walk. How much experience do you have?"

"We all have to learn."

"So how did they teach you at medical college?"

He laughed. "Oh, we practised on oranges!'

"Go back to college," Mum said, "Practise on oranges, not on my daughter. I want the senior registrar. He is competent in Neonatal. Go and get him."

Dad leaned over. "Henceforth you can have three goes. After that you must get someone else. Three goes!"

The registrar from Neonatal came over and swiftly found a vein in Laura's arm. She would be able to walk about the ward. But he was not pleased.

The other parents on the ward heard this story. After this all the parents stipulated "Three goes and no more!"

The following day Dad was called into the office on the ward. The consultant was sat behind a desk and looked sombre. The ward sister sat adjacent. Although the consultant had a serious expression there was a twinkle in the eyes.

"I heard about yesterday and your comments to the doctors. Parents do not dictate the regime on this ward. We work in the best interests of the patients. Making judgemental and arbitrary decisions about the way we deliver that care is not helpful. It is my role to determine how treatment should be delivered, not the parents."

"I hear what you are saying. I will not have my daughter as a training ground."

The consultant stood up, walked to the window and paused, then turned to him.

"Do you really think that we know all the answers? Your daughter is on a clinical trial. We are all trying to find the answer, the solution, the cure. We are all on the same journey. The key to that journey is learning. The only we can learn is by treating real people. The answers are out there on the ward, not in a book or a laboratory."

The consultant sat down.

Dad paused and looked into eyes of sincerity.

"In which case, we need to know everything. We need to be involved."

"You will be, henceforth. You have started something. But I have a problem about only three goes at putting up a drip."

"It's not the number of goes. It's that we don't want drips in the foot."

The consultant stood up. The meeting finished.

In her first few days Laura also had an X-Ray. For this she had to go down stairs. The trip down to the X-ray unit became an adventure and a real opportunity to get off the ward, which at times felt like a prison. She enjoyed these trips. The porter who pushed her trolley was usually quite jolly and made silly jokes. He would pretend he was her chauffeur and called her "Miss". She liked that. She felt important.

Mum and Dad talked to lots of parents on the ward. Sometimes Laura listened.

"How long have you been in?" asked Mum

"A few weeks, a few weeks too long," said the lady, looking to her husband who looked as if his mind was elsewhere.

"We are getting used to this place. Too used to it! "He said with a smile.

"What has your boy got?" asked Mum, acknowledging his smile but wanting to know more in her never ending quest to fully understand their predicament. It was perhaps a strange question for a parent to ask another parent. It was abrupt, curt and straight to the point, but parents of children with cancer had little time for normal courtesies. His parents recognised that.

"A.M.L" she replied, "What about you?"

"A.L.L"

"How are you doing?"

"Very well. We should go in isolation soon. They say she has a 95% chance of achieving remission. We'll be glad to go home"

"You'll be back. They all come back," said the lady with irony and a hint of bitterness.

"Have you come back?" asked Dad, alarmed at what the lady said.

"Yes!" said the lady looking again at her husband. "We can't escape this place."

The husband leaned over almost secretively.

"Tell me? What do you think of this place? What do you think of the consultants? Do you think they tell you the truth?"

Dad responded, " I think they're quite good, but I have nothing to compare them with. We were thinking of going to Great Ormond Street but they said we would receive the same treatment, only in more cramped conditions. As to whether they tell the truth, I don't know."

"They don't tell the truth. Take it from me. They don't tell the truth because they don't know. They are fighting a losing battle but won't admit to it, and they tell you nothing."

"Have you asked?" enquired Dad.

"These people talk a different language. It might be all right for you to talk to them. Perhaps you understand them. Perhaps you know the questions to ask."

"But they are nothing special. Just people doing a job like you or I."

"You try talking to the consultant. You only get bad news if you ask questions."

Mum and Dad left the conversation and returned to Laura's bedside. Dad was quite despondent.

"That doesn't sound very hopeful for US!"

"Their boy has A.M.L, Acute Myeloid Leukaemia. It's normally found in adults. It's more difficult to cure without a transplant. Their situation is different. We have the best form of cancer."

The best form of cancer indeed! Should they be happy? Perhaps they should. Their cancer was curable. They had hope.

Arlain had less hope. The cancer in her young pubescent body continued to grow despite an avalanche and bombardment of chemotherapy and radiation therapy. She took it all but it slowly eroded her teenage frame. Nevertheless, her female beauty shone through. It radiated from her eyes. She was still beautiful. Her face was translucent like a porcelain doll. No hair, ulcered and deathly pale, she was serene and beautiful. Dad looked at her and thought that she was the loveliest thing he had seen. Unfortunately the treatment was not destroying the tumours, which stayed and grew. More severe action was needed. One morning they took her to the operating Theatre on the ground floor. Silence, like ice, chilled the ward. Even the children were quiet. People spoke in hushed tones and thought of what was happening below in the operating theatre. Her parents sat by her empty bedside waiting for her return. They stared into a distance that was not there and held each other's hands.

Eventually they were called into the office. A gasp echoed through the door and down the ward. The cancer was rampant. They had amputated both her legs. Her parents came back onto the ward, sat quietly and waited for their daughter's return. The whole ward cried for them, and for Arlain. She was 14.

Blood is actually produced in the bone marrow. The nature of the Chemotherapy is to destroy the bone marrow or at least suppress the production of blood cells. This is done on the basis that if the marrow is completely wiped clean it can make a fresh start and, hopefully, will only produce good healthy cells. Leukaemia occurs when the marrow over produces young, immature white cells and these take over the blood stream. Some children are not diagnosed as having Leukaemia in the marrow. Some have it in the central nervous system. All have to undergo similar chemotherapy to destroy the marrow. Because the chemotherapy suppresses the marrow it also stops the generation of all white cells into the bloodstream. The white cells fight infection. Hence the child's immune system is effectively destroyed. The blood tests enable the medical staff to monitor the suppression of the marrow by analyzing the blood. Eventually the white cells become very difficult to detect in the bloodstream and the doctors know the marrow has now been destroyed. At this point the child becomes very vulnerable to cross infection from other children. Laura had now reached this stage.

Mum and Dad looked upon this stage as a step forward as there was visible evidence that the chemotherapy was working. For Laura, it meant she was beginning to feel very nauseous and tired. She had now been in hospital for ten days. It was beginning to take its toll.

The little sister came up to Mum.

"You are going into isolation tomorrow if a cubicle comes free."

"What happens if it doesn't come free?"

"Well, you'll just have to stay here a little while longer."

"Well, what happens if it never comes free? Do we have to stay in the ward all the time?"

"There are some people who believe that it is not necessary to use the cubicles for isolation. We can keep the children free from infection here on the ward. And, anyway, it is quite impossible to stop all the coughs and colds from coming on the ward with so many visitors."

Mum was somewhat confused by the logic of this argument but at this stage did not have sufficient knowledge of the treatment to pursue it further. She was later convinced that the medical practitioners had got it horrendously wrong and Laura suffered as a consequence.

She told Laura that they would be going into a cubicle like some of the other children

"Will you stay with me?" Laura asked, "and can I have a television like Peter?"

"Yes of course you can. Dad will stay with you at night and Mum during the day as we always do. It will be our own little room."

At that point the consultant appeared and asked rather shyly. "You've been told you will be going into isolation soon?"

"Yes, the sister just told me. How long will we be in there?

"Oh, about ten to fifteen days at the most I should think. It all depends how we progress. Laura's count is coming down quite nicely. Her white cell count is less than 2. It should be 1.5 or less tomorrow. She is now becoming Neutropaenic and will be less able to fight infections. We can keep a better eye on her in the cubicle.

With that the consultant picked up one of Laura's toys and commented on how nice it was, but it was a cold clinical attempt at friendliness. The words came across correctly but coldly. The smile looked like an attempt to cheer the soul of the speaker rather than others. There were a lot of children on the ward at the moment and as a consequence the demands on the consultant were immense. One had to remember that here we were not dealing with children suffering from broken limbs or tonsillitis but children whose very lives were threatened. The consultant could not be completely aloof from the harshness of that fact. The pain of all this suffering did not leave even a clinical heart untouched. But the parents would not know that. They assumed that to the consultant it was just a job. They did not know that the soul of the consultant had been scarred, and the wounds were deepened with every new family entering the ward. Perhaps this child could be given the hope that others could not. Perhaps these parents would understand better when things started to go wrong and would not blame their clinical adviser. The consultant did not bring this disease to these children. So why did the parents look so accusingly when they were told the bad news "Your child has cancer!" Did the consultant not feel as guilty as the Greek messenger waiting to be killed for bringing the message?

Although the chances of long-term remission were improving all the time, the pain did not diminish. Hope and expectation increased and the pain grew because parents became less accepting of failure. The treatment became extended to gain more successes and the pain grew further. With all this attention and all this time surely somebody must be lucky? But cancer does not play to the rules of the clinicians. It makes it's own as it goes along. It has more resilience, more secrets in its armoury than perhaps we know, and its deadliest weapon is its sudden return.

Well! So Laura was to go into isolation. The evening was cold and crisp as Dad walked across the city that night from his office to the hospital. There was anticipation in the air that had reminded him of Christmas. He walked onto the ward. There was a buzz about the place as if the anticipation had followed him in through the swing doors and up the stairs. Young Peter had been told he was going home soon. Radella had been out of isolation for a few days and Radella's Mum was excited about the possibility of a few days at home before the next bout of treatment. Laura was giggling over some little game she was playing with Kit. He was not surprised when he arrived at Laura's bed to be told by Mum...

"We're going into our own cubicle tomorrow!"

Dad began to smile. Here was something to look forward to! Things began to take a positive tone. We could move forward. The hard work over the past few days had paid off. The treatment did work!

That evening Dad sat by Laura's bedside. She quite often stayed awake until nine or even ten o'clock. Sometimes she wanted to play or giggle or listen to a story. Other times she would become contemplative and curl up into an emotional little shell, quietly sucking her thumb. Tonight was just such an occasion. Dad had attempted to read her a story but she lost interest half way through. They were both watching the news on the television in the ward. Scenes of violent young men at a football match were projected across the half-light of the slumbering ward.

"Dad, why are those men being so naughty? You wouldn't be naughty like that would you? "

Dad looked at the scenes on the television screen and compared them to his surroundings.

"Well, it's like this, " he said, " Some people only ever want to hurt each other. Some people only see badness and naughtiness. It gives them pleasure to make other people unhappy, to make them sad and see them cry. They like to see a wounded rabbit or a bird caught in the claws of a tormenting cat. They smile when someone falls and breaks a leg. They like to bully and laugh at those who might be weak or unable to defend themselves. But these people don't know friendship and beauty. They don't see bright and pretty colours, only dullness, for they themselves are dull."

He paused and looked down at Laura, who gazed at him with a mixture of feelings. He smiled and she smiled back, her brown eyes sparkling over the top of the clenched fist, which encompassed her thumb sucking right hand.

"Some people, " he went on, " like to hold one another's hand. They take pleasure in helping each other, in being a friend. Some people like to take care of others and share their troubles and burdens. Some people like to look after those that are not well even if no one says thank you. Some people like me and Mum and all these others you see around us"

Laura looked around her. She saw Edward's Mum sitting by his side in silence, he lying in the comfort of her presence. She saw the young nurse comforting a screamingly difficult young baby whose parents had left for the evening. She saw the State Enrolled nurse, much older and wiser, cleaning up the vomit of poor distressed Arlain, fighting so courageously every precious last second of her young life. Arlain 's Dad leaned over her and gently cleansed her lips. Another nurse played with Peter whilst comforting a little baby on her knee. The sister stood at the nurse's station patiently listening to the complaints of a mother whose child had been brought onto the ward because it would not feed. She contrasted this young mother's minor irritation with the life threatened patients in her care and still managed to maintain her patience and goodwill. She saw Radella's Mum, come on the ward and organise a drink of tea for every one. She saw her Dad sitting by her side. She had a vision of her Mum at home with Kit preparing for her visit tomorrow. Some people care. She knew.

The ward sister changed. The new one said that fathers could not sleep on the ward when mothers were sleeping there. It was a rule of the hospital that should have been adhered to. Things would have to change.

Dad and the A.M.L boy's Dad made up camp beds in the playroom. The sister warned them to clear their beds by seven in the morning and leave the place tidy. As they made up their beds Dad felt it was an inappropriate place to sleep. With the children gone the toys looked forlorn and lost. Dad pitied them. The burgundy curtains looked limp and could not be closed properly. Outside they could see the lights from the adult wards on the other side of the building. The rocking horse in the corner near the sand pit was chipped and worn from many tiny legs. Beneath it the carpet was worn and bare. The room smelt like a schoolroom, of stale milk and musty books.

The man lay on top of his camp bed in a very old pair of pyjamas. He looked across at Dad.

"You seem like a man in control of his own destiny" he said, and waited for a response. None came.

"This must have been a terrible shock for you."

"Wasn't it a shock for you, for us all?"

"Of course, but less of a shock. When life has dealt you many cruel blows you lose the ability, the luxury of being shocked too much. I only wanted to know who or what was responsible for my boy's A.M.L, I only wanted to understand."

"Well, no one is responsible and no one knows the cause."

"Of course they do! You ARE naive! Mankind has systematically destroyed the environment, the world. We are a consequence of this destruction. You strike me as an educated person. Have you not heard of cause and effect?"

"But there could be many reasons for our children's cancer. It could be something generic, triggered off by an infection. It could be radiation, but if it was why only one of my two twins? It could be an inbuilt generic defect that was inevitable. The truth is we don't know for certain. We can only speculate."

"Exactly! We don't know, but someone does. The trouble is that the evidence is not conclusive. That's why we have clinical trials. We are part of an experiment to find the truth."

"Surely it is no bad thing to be a part of the quest for the truth. Once we find the truth then children will no longer suffer."

"By the time they find, and publish, the truth it will be too late for my son. Anyway, why don't they tell us what they know? It's our children yet they totally begrudge telling you anything. They only tell you when you ask and even then you have to ask the right questions."

"You sound pessimistic, almost without hope."

"Oh, I have hope. I always have hope. That is why I battle on, for his sake. If he sees me without hope then he will give up. I have to be one step ahead all the time. I have to lead him, consume his mind with positive thought, and more importantly, action related positive thought."

"Is that why you are always building things?"

"Yes I suppose it is. I believe in action-based therapy. I don't believe in sitting around watching TV or playing with those damned computers. Children's minds are like sponges. They soak up everything you throw at them. We have to keep their minds focussed, especially in here, otherwise they will give in."

"I guess we're all different in the way we bring up our children. I don't like building things for example."

The man laughed.

"Yes! I imagine you are more into books and painting and things. I've noticed you drawing and sketching with Laura. It's those parents who do nothing that concern me. The trouble is they are so dependant upon TV, and other stimulants that when they come into a place like this they are lost. They have no interests or hobbies."

"Well, we can't all be the same. I'm sure all those parents are doing their best for their children, as you and I are."

The man seemed content with this and returned to his previous concern; the environment.

"But don't you think, at the end of the day, that we are all guilty of polluting the atmosphere. We don't know what chemicals they're pumping out into the atmosphere or the affects on our bodies. You live in the country. You must have seen the chemicals they spray on the crops. What are they doing to us? I'm convinced that modern cancer is a direct result of our polluted environment."

So, they moved into isolation. Their chamber of privacy was cubicle 6. It became a haven and a home for the whole family. It also became the new battleground of their hopes and fears and Laura's pain. There were still drawings and paintings on the wall from the previous patient. When Mum enquired she was told the boy had finished his treatment and was now back on the ward. His father was a teacher and he had spent many hours making the pictures. Dad felt a little threatened by them, as he knew he could not compete on such a scale. They decided to leave the pictures up, less out of respect for the little boy than the fact that they brightened the rather dull walls. The little boy's Mum and Dad spent many hours on the ward with their son. Later Dad was to see his father often looking very weary on those long Sunday afternoons when the warmth of the ward and the endurance of the weekend would finally take it's toll.

The sister had decided to give Laura a bed in her cubicle, rather than a cot, as she had used a bed on the ward. Many children of her age were placed in cots in the cubicle for safety reasons. It was not possible for the nurses to keep a round the clock observation of the cubicles and they were afraid of younger children falling out. However the bed did have side rails, which could be raised when Laura was unattended. In the main, however, Mum or Dad was usually with her.

Laura became quite used to her bed. It was big and firm. The sheets were always clean. Sometimes they were changed twice a day. She liked the smell of the new sheets as it always made her feel cosy and sleepy and reminded her of when Mum put new sheets on the bed at home. She was beginning to feel more tired as the treatment progressed. However, her tiredness did not detract from the excitement of moving into a new home.

"Where will Dad sleep?" she asked Mum.

"Dad will be able to sleep right next to you. The nurses are going to bring him a special camp bed."

Mum and Laura then entered into a debate as to the most suitable place in the room for Dad to sleep. Laura chose a place right next to her bed.

"But if Dad puts his bed there the nurses and doctors will not be able to get at you."

Laura thought that sounded like a good idea.

"But I want my Dad there!"

Eventually they agreed that Dad would sleep at ninety degrees to Laura's bed and that he would put his bed up each night and put it away again in the morning. Laura was quite excited over these arrangements and looked forward to the first night in the cubicle. She was becoming institutionalised as were the rest of the family.

One of the major disadvantages of living in the cubicle was the lack of communication with other families on the ward. This problem was more acute for Laura as she could not leave the room at all. Some parents would appear sheepishly at the door of the cubicle and ask how Laura was. Others just stayed away, their own patients to care for. Mum was interested to note just how much parents were aware of other families on the ward. She had taken a great deal of time to get to know the other families, particularly those with a child undergoing similar treatment as she felt that the more she learned the more she could help Laura fight this disease.

Most parents accepted that the fate of their child lay in the right diagnosis and the professionalism of the medical staff. Their role was to act as nursing parents, a role supportive and in many ways subordinate to the clinicians and nurses. Their destiny was now out of their hands and they felt vulnerable and exposed. Their only hope was to place their trust in those who were trained and experienced in this field. They had lost the naivety of those who believe that courage and determination alone can overcome cancer and that those who eventually died of cancer were somehow weaker than the rest. Although they placed their trust in others they supported their children and the medical staff with a quiet determination and commitment that complemented the heroism of their children.

Some parents even gave up their jobs to look after their children. In fairness it was only those parents whose employers were not sympathetic to the flexibility required from them when an employee had a child suffering from cancer or those parents who were somewhat itinerant in their employment. The majority kept their jobs and in fact the paediatric oncology consultant advised most fathers to resume normal working as soon as possible as this brought some normality into the situation. Dad actually took one week away from work then resumed working on as near a normal basis as possible. Whatever, Dad was impressed with the way most parents cared for their children although there were one or two notable exceptions

Although the parents placed great trust in the doctors, the majority seemed afraid of them. They would tend to confide many of their anxieties in the nurses, perhaps because the nurses spent more time with the families, were more approachable and, more significantly, displayed their emotions and a commonality of feeling with the parents. Many parents used the nurses to feed their problems to the doctors. If they did not understand what a doctor had told them they would quite often ask a nurse to explain it more clearly and in language they could understand. Unfortunately, as Mum, in particular, was quick to realise, the vast majority of nurses on the ward were untrained in paediatric oncology and in many cases Mum was to display a better understanding of the nature of Leukaemia than some of the younger nurses.

Chapter 7

Vincristine

A song of Vincristine

The grass is green
The sky is blue
What have they done to you?

The sun does shine
The birds do sing
How come the white drugs sting?

The flowers flower
The dewdrops glow
Vincristine looks like snow.

It takes my life
To save my life
And makes my white cells grow.

Vincristine was a well-known vintage. It had been bottled successfully for a number of years. Most Vintners recommended it for its body more than its aroma. It is strong; there is no doubt about that. Most importantly it could clear the mind when others were struggling to do the same. It got to the heart of the matter. It was effective, but it was an evil cup to drink. It took away your complexion, liveliness and hair. It sounded so innocuous, so innocent, rather like a light red wine from a Beaujolais vineyard named after the childhood sweetheart of the vintner, or, if not, after some tender folk song dedicated to the lost love of a melancholic singer. The reality was terror, a drug that in its crusade to cure caused untold pain and horrors, yet despite this its reputation and pedigree were impressive. It could cure!

Things began to get worse.

The chemotherapy was taking its toll on Laura's little body. Although she willingly took on board the pain and sickness, the isolation began to bring her spirits down. In addition the continual bombardment of drugs, mouthwashes and blood tests began to drain her young resources.

She spent more time curled in a little ball sucking her thumb. It was difficult to keep her spirits up at times. Perhaps the most difficult part for Mum and Dad was not to know how the pain affected or how much she was suffering. She took it all. Without complaint, she took it all.

The doctors and nurses, the doctors in particular, were almost mechanical in the way they treated her. There was no apparent sympathy. They discussed her body whilst standing over her as if she was not there. One day the consultant turned to Dad.

"Does she understand what we are saying?"

"I don't think so. What are you saying? Is it something that might frighten her? Perhaps if you explained a little of what is happening we might all feel a bit better."

"This is perhaps the worst part of the treatment. Because her immunity is now very low she is susceptible to all kinds of infection. In particular she will suffer from mouth ulcers, but we can keep this under control by making sure she takes the mouthwashes regularly. That is up to you. She must not leave the room at all until her white cell improves which might take up to two weeks. I also advise you not to receive any visitors unless it is someone important to her like a grandparent."

"What happens if we get a cough or cold?"

"It's important that she sees you. By the time the cold is visible you will have already been infectious, anyway. If you are in doubt then discuss it with me. "

The consultant picked up one of Laura's charts and with a rather stern expression, went on, "I've been looking at her fluid balance. She is not taking enough liquids. She should be drinking at least a litre a day. "

A litre is an awful lot of liquid for a little girl. It might not seem a lot to beer drinkers, but perhaps if they had to drink water through an ulcerated mouth they might not be as keen. Laura sat silently on her bed, sucking her thumb. I know they are talking about me, she thought. If they are trying to say things are going to get worse I don't want to know. I don't understand why they have to make me feel so awful to make me better. They speak with words I don't understand and I don't think Mum and Dad understand either because they keep asking questions. Oh, Mum and Dad! You must be able to stop all this horrible pain and feeling sick. You can do anything. Why don't you do something now! But Mum and Dad always look so worried. I know they only pretend to be happy here. They really want to be at home and I make them stay here.

Here comes the drink.

Dad leaned over her with a glass half full of diluted orange juice. It was not in her cat cup, the plastic cup she acquired from the Happy Eater. The straw threateningly peered over its rim and leered at her as the glass approached in Dad's extended hand. She turned her head away. The thought of that straw scraping the ulcers in her mouth and the impact of the cold drink on her throat made her feel sick. Anyway she didn't have the energy for drinking, only sleeping.

"No! " she repeated in a drawling tone.

"It's only a little drink, Poppet. Please try to drink just a little. The doctor says you need to drink more to make you better."

"No!" she responded with emphasis and promptly turned on her side making it impossible to drink. Her thumb went to her mouth and Dad despaired knowing that thumb sucking made her mouth even drier and a worse breeding ground for the ulcers.

"Don't suck your thumb little girl. You'll make your mouth poorly."

He leaned over and gently removed it from her mouth. The thumb was inflamed and shrivelled with so much sucking. Eventually it would become very sore if not attended to or kept from her mouth. Dad despaired. If she cannot suck her thumb what other comfort can she have? The thought filled him with remorse and pity for her. He didn't know that she was thinking the same as he. Her thumb, or precisely, the thumb on her right hand was a lifeline, a safe haven in this strange world of pain and nausea. To suck it gave her such comfort that the awfulness of this place went into the background like a dull ache. She could escape and dream of other places and other times or even dream of nothing, letting her mind become blank, a void, a nothing.

Dad saw the moisture in her brown eyes as they appealed to him not to take her thumb from her. He released it. It went straight into her mouth, and was made secure by her left hand. She slowly closed her eyes and gradually shut out the noise, the place, the people, and the nausea and sank back into her world. Meanwhile the ulcers continued to unsettle her peace and only her immense will power overcame the pain they brought.

Eventually she closed her eyes completely and thought the deepest of thoughts. Her future looked bleak, Was she to be here forever. Mum and Dad had not talked about going home at all. Was this to be her new home? What about all these other children? How long had they been here? It wouldn't be so bad in here if they would just leave you alone, but they had to keep hurting you and giving you medicines that made you feel really sick. Really sick, not like the sickness when you eat too many Easter eggs, but an awful nauseous shivery kind of sickness that just hangs there and won't go away. You don't want to play or do anything just sleep and even when you are asleep they mess about with your body like it belonged to them. They wake you up when your mind has blacked out all the terrors of this place and you are back walking through the fields and down the lane with Dad and Kit and Pero the dog. You wake up to feel the needle going in, to have the thermometer under your arm or even worse to have that horrible yellow medicine forced down your throat.

And all the time these lumps in her mouth and throat made her want to cry. The pain in her arms where the needles had penetrated made her want to weep. The ache in her limbs and the awful, awful sickness in her stomach and bowels made her want to sob. Oh how she wanted to cry, to let the tears flow from her eyes in rivers taking with them the pain of this adult world that had been condensed into her young life.

She cried in her sleep but no one heard her. It was the cry of silent pain.

When she awoke, the dryness of her mouth jolted her and she gradually became aware of the presence of her ulcers as the pain overcame her again. She noticed Mum standing near the window. Standing by her side was Kit.

"Can I have my drink?" Laura appealed.

"Yes, of course. Here you are," said Mum passing her a glass of orange cordial.

Laura drank half of it then lay on her side again but this time with her eyes open looking at her brother Kit. She became intensely jealous of his situation and as a consequence angry with him for being there.

"Kit's looking at me!"

"That's because he's pleased to see you," said Mum.

"No, he's not," replied Laura sternly.

"Yes I am Laura," Kit said without the total conviction in his voice necessary to appease her

She turned from them and faced the wall, trying to escape back to her world but unfortunately she was now too wide-awake to do that.

"Where's my Dad?

"He's gone to his office."

"Can I have a cup of tea?"

Mum was pleased to hear this request, as it appeared to be an indication that either her appetite was getting better or her ulcers had started to diminish. To Laura it was simply an aspiration that could not be fulfilled for her ulcers were still there and growing. It was just that she dreamed she was at home in her kitchen drinking tea. When her hospital tea came she had lost the vision and hence the appetite for it. Mum was disappointed. Mum, who was looking for some sign of hope at every expression, every change in circumstance and every light in Laura's eyes. Mum who had borne her through hours of labour only to bring her into this place. Better she had never been born, thought Mum, than suffer in this way. Then the thought left her.

So the day passed. Many things happened on the ward. There were tears and screams, plenty enough, but there was also laughter and joy as some children made progress or were released. There was also joy for the sake of it. Children's joy, and false joy imposed by parents to make an unreal situation look normal.

Laura knew this happiness was unreal. It had a hollow and shallow tone to it like the ring of a moulded glass vase. She went along with it because she knew it was a charade that kept everyone sane in this crazy world of childhood cancer. Everyone played the charade and playing it did some good. It was almost as if this world was the normal world and everyone "outside" was abnormal. This was life at its sharpest and most real because life is meaningless unless related to death. Here in this place death was a silent reality. It was there, skulking, hiding, happening to other parent's poor sad children not to your own because your own have to survive and will survive, or so you believed.

The day ended with a misty golden haze piercing the southwest window. The sky was copper. The damp of the evening clung to the window with a moist comforting warmth that conveyed instincts of the coming winter and hibernation. Laura felt this more powerfully than Mum and Dad and yearned to sink into the warmth of a winter nest under the trees surrounding her village. She looked at the rapidly disappearing sun and soon these feelings left her. As they did she remembered this was the time when Mum left and Dad came to stay with her for the evening and the night. She liked it when he came back at night because he smelled different to when he left and he brought something special with him. It was the smell of the outside world. When he left in the morning he was freshly washed and still smelling of the soap and toothpaste and of the hospital, but, during his day in the outside world he came into contact with many places, things and people. He had, perhaps, eaten strange food in strange places. Whatever, he brought the outside world to her. It was exciting. His smells were titillating to her nasal pallet and she loved to nestle her head into his shoulder and take in these aromas of the outside living world where she longed to be. When he came back to her his hair was always a little untidy. His suit was a little creased and his eyebrows furrowed. His glasses would be at a slight angle as if he'd taken them off many times to wipe his eyes. Indeed he had, not to shed a tear but to wipe the sleep away.

"Hello little girl!" he said cheerfully, his eyes lighting up as he came closer.

She looked at him with pleasure but tried not to show it by turning her head away from him. Whether it was from shyness or a desire to contain her pleasure at seeing him he did not know. She lay quietly whilst Mum reported on the doings of the day. Dad listened attentively whilst keeping his eyes firmly fixed on Laura. She could feel his attention and quite liked the warm glowing feeling it gave her. It made her body tingle and helped subdue the discomforts of her predicament. Eventually he came and sat alongside her on the bed.

He knew the evening had to be planned, that her mind had to be occupied until she grew tired. It had to be occupied to distract her thoughts away from the rigours of the clinical regime she was under.

After Mum told him of the events of the day she left with Kit who by this time had become tired and wanted to leave the hospital. His life had also changed and he wondered if anyone was aware of him any more. Mum and Dad always seemed to be irritable with him and Dad did not want to play any more. He only wanted to be with Laura. So Kit was glad to get away from this place. At least when he was at home he would have Mum to himself and he would get some attention even though Mum tended to be distracted. However, he would probably get to sleep in her bed, which was nice, apart from when she cried in her sleep.

After they left Dad got changed. He did this in the cubicle, which meant keeping a look out for doctors or Nurses who seemed to appear at unexpected times with different forms of medication. Laura thought this was funny and Dad made a great play of it, pretending that a doctor or nurse was coming at any moment and that he would be caught in a state of undress.

"Dad! Don't be silly!" she would cry.

After he had changed they would play a game or he would read a story from a book. Most usually he would make up a story. Sometimes these stories would feature a little boy named Jimmy. Laura liked stories but could not maintain her attention for long.

The timing of the drugs was supposedly critical to the success of the clinical trial. This Mum and Dad found out later. However drugs were administered only when the doctors had time. This was particularly bad at night when the ward was completely in the hands of some junior doctor trying to cover this ward and ward 14. Often doctors had to be woken up to give drugs. However at this point Mum and Dad were fairly naive about the treatment and took everything at face value. Later they realised that the ward had appalling problems. Nevertheless the doctors and nurses all worked very hard

Laura did not like any of the nurses or doctors. She did not realise they were trying to make her better. To her they were the purveyors of pain. Their appearance belied their smiles and attempts at friendship. They looked and smelled of clinical terror. They were enveloped in an ambience of suffering from which they could not escape. Their proximity scared Laura and she froze when they came close. This must have made their job harder, but she did not care about this. She only wanted to be left alone. This was her dream, to be left in peace.

After he had played with her and told a few stories Dad prepared her evening medicine before she settled down to sleep for the night. She hated their medicines, especially the yellow one in the thin syringe, which she had to swallow. Dad said it would make her mouth ulcers better, but it didn't. They were still there and they still bled and still made her scream with pain when she attempted to eat. However, the ulcers were not the worst things.

Perhaps the worst thing was when she woke one morning to find some of her hair on the pillow. Her scalp had been very itchy all night, making it difficult to sleep. This itchiness had gradually crept through her body and made her scratch. At times it was like a million flies crawling over her. It was only the distractions of the pain in her mouth, the ache in her legs and the sickness in her stomach that took her mind and her fingers away.

She slowly ran her hands through her hair and as she did lumps of it came away in her hand. She had felt strands of hair come away from her when she was in the open ward but thought nothing of it. She was not expecting great big lumps of her own dear golden hair to suddenly fall from her head. Mum had told her that it was going to happen but it still came as an awesome shock to see so much so soon.

Dad watched her that morning as she picked up the hairs from her pillow. His heart bled, but he could do nothing. He knew it was to come. He leaned over her and smiled

"Come on little girl, let Daddy carry you "

She looked at him with appealing soft eyes.

"Carry me Daddy," she pleaded.

He picked her up and lifted her to his shoulder where she came to rest. The warmth of her small body against his gave him all the comfort he would ever need to maintain the strength of his love for her. She had such love for him that he felt it consume him. She felt secure, content and peaceful in his arms. She put one arm around his neck and the other across his chest. She rested her head against his cheek and looked behind him straight into the mirror on the wall near the door. She gasped and cried. She was quite bald.

Chapter 8

It's a miracle

The corpuscles song

Little by little, day after day
Red blood cells showed the way
They came and went, and went and came
But never went away.

Corpuscles know their strength.
When measured to the tenth
Of a tenth of ten percent

From red to white and back again
White Phantom lost the fight
To dominate the flow of life
That made her life cells grow.

White cells gave way to red
Who sleeping in their bed
Unguarded, dead, had never bred, now led.

"Good morning! I'm a voluntary worker. This is my very
first day. Do you think I could come in?"

"Yes, of course. " said Dad and then glancing toward the
floor. "This is Laura."

Laura very casually looked up from her position on the
blue play mat that lay on the floor next to her bed and took note
of the kindly face of this new intruder. Laura knew she was not
a doctor. She knew because the lady looked a little afraid of her.
The doctors were never afraid.

"What's your job in the hospital? " enquired Dad with a
lot of disinterest.

"Oh, I'm a voluntary worker. I used to be a headmistress of a primary school, but now that I've retired I wanted to do something useful. I thought I might enjoy working with sick children". She paused then continued " What's the matter with your daughter? Is it anything serious?"

"She has Leukaemia", he said politely but with a deliberate bitterness that was aimed to sting.

"Oh!"

The Voluntary Worker looked down on Laura with a dismay that projected throughout the sunlit room.

"I'm so sorry," she said.

"Sorry?" said Dad. "You must know that all the children on this ward have very serious diseases."

"Well, er, yes, I was told they're all quite ill."

"You know that most of them have Leukaemia or Cancer?"

"Erh, yes. sister said so."

"But you were not expecting to be confronted with one on your very first day. Well here you are! Why do you think Laura has no hair?

"I'm so sorry. I'll go and leave you with your daughter."

"No. Don't go. I didn't mean to rude, but you must appreciate it's very difficult for us all in here. Please stay and look after Laura for a few minutes until my wife gets here. I really should be at work."

The Voluntary Worker knelt down next to Laura and began to play with her

"It's my dolly!" said Laura, addressing the Voluntary Worker but not looking at her. "She's poorly."

"Shall we make her better?" said the Voluntary Worker with warmth that betrayed a combination of her sympathy and her experience as a teacher.

Within minutes new toys appeared on the play mat and gentle games of pretend were played. Laura felt comfortable. Here was a new Grandma in her life. Dad kissed her on her forehead, put on his jacket and with some reluctance left her for the day. What would today bring, he thought as he walked down the ward, away from Laura's room; a problem or some encouraging development? Certainly things appeared to be going as they should, according to the consultant in charge. But was she right? Who would know? Was he right? Who was accountable to whom? Had they carried out the most appropriate treatment?

The consultant's best song

Fifty or a hundred, what is the count?
What is the threshold of discontent?
B or C or D regime?
What is this thing with random scent?
That picks the day our life will end
B or C or D regime?
What matters, one white count or two
When trials physicians cannot bend?
B or C or D regime?
Microcosm microscope
One in many in this trial
What counts is not the count you know
What counts is that they want to know
Fifty or a hundred cells in three
Is that enough to make her free?

B or C or D, or any, if any, regime?

Laura felt sad when the Voluntary Worker said Goodbye for the day, but by then Mum had arrived with Kit. Laura was pleased to see Kit. She missed playing with him. She wanted to play with him today but still felt tired. She was happy just watching him play in her room.

"Oh Kit!" she would say when he did something she considered silly or foolish, and he would be especially silly just to please her. By pleasing her he pleased himself. He liked her attention. In fact he thrived on it.

She seems more pleased to see me today, he thought. I wonder if she's getting better? I'd better not say anything to Mum or Dad because they'll say she's not. If she does get better then she can come home.

It would be wonderful if she were at home like normal. Then I wouldn't have to come here every day and we could go to playschool and I could play with the little boy in the close. When she's in here everybody seems upset and I get shouted at for doing nothing. I hate it. I hate her being sick. I feel that I should be sick too and I'm sure I will be one day. We do everything together. Why are we not sick together? We came from the same place. Are our lives going separate ways already? But Laura is strong. Perhaps she's leading the way. I wish she didn't have so much of Mum and Dad though.

His mind was confused, although he didn't know it was confused. How could he? This situation in which they, the family, had found themselves was to Kit a part of life, a part of the natural course of events. How could he think anything else? He didn't know anything else. How was he to know that other children would not eventually come to this place? He soon learned, and as he learned the more he felt the need to save his sister. This feeling was already beginning to stir within him. Was he not the one who had lain by her side in the womb? Was he not the one who blocked her way out and made her wait for him? Was he not the one who had lain awkwardly at the door to life? Was not the confined space due to him, he who had compressed her so much that her head shape was temporarily, and minutely, distorted. Did he not breathe alongside her, sharing his breath and body fluids with her? And when they came out into the great light it was he that was always there for her. She needed him. He was her Captain when they played. He was responsible for her.

Laura was now utterly confined to her bed. She did not want to get out of it. She was rapidly sinking into complacency. Her span of concentration was very short. Stories would be half finished when she fell asleep or turned away with total disinterest. Mum and Dad used to get her out of bed but she simply collapsed on the floor, her legs buckling under her. She refused to do anything other than lie in her bed and take what ever was thrown at her. It was almost as if she had given up and this is what worried Mum and Dad the most.

Mum and Dad got her out of bed and put her on her feet. Dad held her hand and they started to move forward. Laura cried out in despair. Her legs collapsed. She had lost the ability to walk. She had forgotten. She had reverted back to infancy. She crawled.

Mum and Dad were desolate when they saw their three-year old daughter crawl across the floor to the door and look up at them appealingly like some young inexperienced puppy dog, begging to be let out. She was desperate.

"Please let me go!" she cried, crouching on all fours by the door. "Please open the door and let me go!"

They broke their hearts. She broke hers, but she wanted to go beyond the doors of her room and never come back. That was more important to her than walking.

Mum and Dad now realised they had another battle: to teach their daughter how to walk again.

By this time Mum and Dad found they were seeing each other less and less. They had a few minutes in the morning and evening, and all this time was consumed with discussing Laura. Eventually even this time began to disappear as Dad had to go to work earlier and came back later. They introduced a little system whereby they left messages for each other in a little notebook. For days at a time this was their only means of contact.

24 October
9.45am
Mum,
Laura has eaten nearly two bowls of Rice Krispies + 1 boiled egg + little toast. She has been playing all morning and has been quite cheerful. Paul says to walk her for a little around the room. She cries when I do it, perhaps you might have more luck. She might stand at the window and play with her toys. She has gone to sleep now. She has had her blood test. The Registrar has visited and says progress is satisfactory.

She has been drinking tea this morning.

Asparagines is due today.

If the workload is getting too much at home you could possibly leave Kit here for a while. I could collect him if necessary or meet you halfway.

Anyway keep cheerful...
Love Dad

24 October
4.15pm
Dad
The house doctor came to see us this afternoon and her blood test shows that her levels have gone down again, so sometime tomorrow she will be having a blood transfusion. I've been exercising her legs this afternoon so if you can carry on with that all the better. Don't forget to phone tonight.

See you tomorrow
Love Mum XXX

27 October
9.20am
Mum

I have exercised Laura's legs a little this morning but she gets very upset and will not stand on them. They gave her extra Lactryl to make her go in the night. She soiled her knickers but has not done much else. She has had no food and drink so is not very happy. The consultant is sick today. I have told the house doctor of her legs and upset tummy. He is going to tell the Registrar. We need the Physiotherapist I think, also a play mat for the floor from the play nurse. I exercised her legs by playing at riding a bike.

I will be in the office all morning. I will come around about lunchtime.

C.U. love Dad

28th October
Mum
doctor's visit

Good news this morning. Laura's white cell count is starting to go up again as a result of the first bout of treatment. The doctors were quite pleased and say it is encouraging. Her weight has increased slightly (11.61kg to 11.7). Her potassium count is down a little but this is not a concern. She will have some today in her medicine. Platelet count is going up a little.

The nurses are exercising her legs every two hours, can you make sure they keep it up.

She's still constipated and needs to drink more.

She has eaten one Weetabix + 1 toast & jam. I gave her a second piece before I left so if she eats that she's eaten 2 pieces!!

C.U. at 1 Love Dad

29th October
9.30am
Mum

Laura is a little tired this morning. She has eaten no breakfast but has drunk 2 cups of tea. The doctor has examined her tummy and says it's a minor problem and occurs quite often when children will not go to the toilet! He checked her legs and said they are OK

She needs to go to the toilet a.s.a.p.

Love Dad

So the battle continued to make Laura walk, to make her go to the toilet, to watch out for ulcers and to keep her spirits up. All these problems were symptomatic of the treatment of Leukaemia. Mum's and Dad's time was consumed with attending to these matters in the hope they would influence the chances of recovery. They did.

It was difficult to concentrate on both looking after Laura and giving Kit a normal upbringing. He had missed out on love and attention and needed topping up. He was not jealous. He knew the score. He was not unreal. She was sick. He wanted her to be well. He knew Mum and Dad had to work hard to make her better

He could not sleep. He missed the stories of Jimmy, the games of soldiers, the cuddles and fights at bedtime and most of all Mum and Dad and Laura and he being together. He hated this transient life and this flitting back and forth from the hospital. They were always on the move these days. No one seemed to have time for him. All he got from Mum and Dad was impatience. He was glad when the neighbours came around. They seemed relaxed and had time for him. Sometimes he went to their house to play. They had a grandson called Damien who was Irish. He was good to play with although he seemed especially to like Laura. Sometimes he would come over from Ireland and the three of them would play all day, happily and contentedly. He wished Damien were here now. He would like to tell him about Laura. Perhaps Damien could help her.

If only I could do more to help, thought Kit. I'm only so helpless because I'm such a little boy. There is not much a little boy of three can do other than being good and doing what Mum and Dad say.

It was a clear frosty night when Mum was driving back from the hospital. She had left the suburbs of this so called city that was more like a large market town with a Parish church as a cathedral and was driving through the blackness of the Belgraveshire countryside. The stars twinkled and shone like the lights on a Christmas tree. They hung in the sky as if beholden to the moon, clustering around it, subservient to its dominant radiance. It shone before her, in the windscreen of the car, almost lighting her way but not quite.

Kit was in the back. Thank God for Kit, she thought. At least with him beside me I am not alone. She drove mechanically. Her heart and mind were still back in the hospital with Laura. Barbara Dickson sang "The Crying Game" on the car radio. Mum made the words fit her situation and she cried, silently so that he would not hear. She wondered what Dad would be doing now. Most of all she wondered whether anything would develop over night. She wondered about the future, about what kind of future there was for Laura. She had stopped being angry about their predicament. She had stopped being angry with lots of things except the nature of the treatment. She had come to terms with the situation they were in but had difficulty in accepting that the clinical regime they had been assigned was necessarily the best. She had no foundation for this theory other than the fact that Laura was on a clinical trial and had been assigned a fairly low regime despite the increasingly obvious evidence that her white cell count was high. This fact preyed on her mind and as it did she thought of Laura's chances of survival. The consultant had said that Laura's chances of achieving remission were 90%. But what then? Would she grow to adulthood and what sort of adulthood?

She turned the car off the main road onto a side road to the village. The light from the two village pubs and garage shone before her. She slowed down as she approached the last junction before taking the road into The Close. As she drove down the Main Street of the village she saw familiar faces all busy in their daily routines. She wanted to tell them of her ordeal, for them to share in hers and Laura's suffering but knew she could not. She found it strange that they could still have normal lives whilst hers had become so abnormal.

She drove up to the house. It was dark and empty. It was probably cold as well. She could not remember whether she had left the central heating on. Probably not.

She opened the door. The heating was on. At least here was a welcome, of sorts. She unpacked Kit, gave him some crisps, which he half ate then poured herself a gin and Tonic. As the Gordons gin fell over the small cubes of ices clinging to the side of the tumbler she felt some comfort, some continuity with the normal things in life. The sparkle and bubble of the Schweppes slightly raised her spirits. She took a first healthy gulp of the life comforting liquid and felt the relaxation overcome her. She gave Kit a drink of lemonade and a biscuit to keep him going whilst she made some light supper for them both.

Kit went to watch television whilst she busied herself cleaning, washing and ironing clothes for tomorrow for the family. Amazing, she thought, even in this situation the washing and ironing does not stop. Dad had to have a clean shirt. Kit needed his clothes and Laura needed clean underwear and pyjamas. She also knew that she had to keep herself looking smart and attractive. By doing this she sent the right messages to Laura that she had not gone to pieces, that there was stability, normality, continuity. She also felt better for it and that made her perform her tasks so much better

It was only ten o'clock but she was already in bed eating her supper with Kit by her side fast asleep. She watched some programme on the television in the bedroom. She had dimmed the lights to allow Kit to sleep. She needed him with her. She hated sleeping without Dad. The light from the TV set flickered across Kit's face and she noticed how like his Dad he was. She cried, and cried. Oh how she missed Laura and Dad. She would do anything for them to be here right now, but they were not and would not be for a little while yet, and then what?

31st October
Mum
2.00pm
Your car is parked on the front, opposite to mine.

The results of the bone marrow have gone down greatly according to Stuart. He says he is happy with the results & is sure the consultant will be. The intensification treatment should clear it completely.

I will ring after 6.00pm in case we are meeting up.

Love Dad X

31st October
5.45pm

Give me a ring tonight. Leave it till after 7.00pm as I am hoping to get a takeaway.
Mum

3rd November
9.00am
    Mum
    Laura is fine. I have cut her nails on RH. LH needs doing before her platelets drop.

    She was OK with Dounarubacin although nurses woke me in the night because she was unsettled.

    After 5 days intensification it may be possible to take her home for a couple of days before her count drops.

    C.U. tonight. Dad

    It had been a long time since they had spent time together without the children. To hold hands, talk about life, their own needs, and love. The ward sister said they needed some quality time; on their own; re-charge batteries and all that. They agreed to meet at the White Hart in Sharnsby. Sharnsby was midway between Belgrave and North Peveril.

    He left Laura with one of the junior nurses. Mum had left hospital at teatime. She had arranged a baby sitter for Kit. As she drove home with Kit in his Mothercare car seat she felt a tremor of excitement at the prospect of meeting Dad on his own. She hoped they would be able to hold each other and indulge in a hug and kiss. She smiled at the wickedness of her indulgence.

    Sorting Kit's meal, getting changed and taking a warm bath sapped her enthusiasm and libido and as the hour approached for her to leave she felt overcome with lethargy and despondency. Bed, a book and a large gin and tonic lured her. She rang the hospital to cancel but he had already left.

    The babysitter arrived and she felt compelled to leave. As she turned the ignition in the car her despondency turned to irritation at being inconvenienced.

    His white XR4 was parked under the chestnut tree outside the pub. Its Michelin Sports wheels askew and front fog lights gave it an aggressive appearance. He was sat at the lounge bar talking to one of the locals in an animated fashion. He was clearly on form.

    He took her arm and escorted her to a table after ordering her a glass of dry white wine. She was happy again.

    The consultant walked in the room and looked at everyone with a smile.

    "Well, I've good news,"

"We'll have some good news!" said Mum "I think we deserve it don't we Laura?"

Laura didn't answer.

"Laura's count has started to come down nicely. The intensification will really knock it down. So I suggest you go home for a few days. It's her birthday soon isn't it?"

"Yes on the seventh. The timing couldn't be better," said Mum. She looked at Dad, then at Laura. "Did you hear that Laura? We can go home." She turned to the consultant. "When?"

"Tomorrow. Let me see her count after the blood test and if that and everything is all right you can go. I suggest you stay in the house or in the garden. This afternoon you can take her for a short walk as far as the lift."

"Can she mix with other children," said Mum, then addressing the sister, "can she go to see Radella?"

"No, not yet, let her just walk down the corridor and wave to her when you go by. When you are at home be careful about any coughs and colds other children might have. Otherwise she should be okay"

By the time they had left the small corridor that led to her cubicle, Laura wanted to walk by herself, aided only by Dad holding her hand. They walked slowly and carefully. Laura looked out for Radella, her ally in this fight, a fellow sufferer. As she walked past the ward of six beds she felt proud, oh so proud. She felt pride in herself but much more than that. She felt pride in the dignity of her position. Despite her physical humiliation at the hands of seemingly dispassionate doctors, she had survived. But it was more than that. She felt like a champion of the cause for children with cancer. She could not comprehend that there were others in this place with this malignant disease that may not survive. As she walked past the rows of on looking parents and children, pausing during their games of scrabble, their storytelling, their crying in each other's arms, their being normal, she felt as if the whole world was watching her. She saw them look up at her and was very conscious of their gaze. She felt as if she were leading the fight against this awful disease, that all eyes were on her, which indeed they were.

So she made it beyond the double doors to the lifts. The lifts were symbolic of the way out to her home. She returned slowly and painfully but with great joy in her tiny soul. She had made it. The next step was to go home.

When they came back to the cubicle Mum became very serious. She looked at Dad, sitting by a Laura who was exhausted by her short trip and was beginning to fall asleep.

"Can we talk?"

"Yes. What's the matter?" He began to panic that she had some bad news up her sleeve. Perhaps she had read some file somewhere or overheard what the doctors had been saying. He felt the perspiration on his brow.

"I went to the doctors this morning."

"What?" It was the classic introduction to the inevitable announcement. Surely it couldn't be happening now?

"It must have been that night in Sweden."

"Why then?"

"Come on! You know it was either then or on the ship, but I think he's a Scandinavian."

"You're sure you are expecting?"

"I'm sure. Are you pleased?"

"I don't know. I'm just surprised."

"Well. It's happened."

He thought for a few seconds. Another child. Another person. The timing was not good. Despite that a tremor of joy ran across his heart.

"Well?" she said leaning over toward him.

"Don't be silly. It's just that we thought our family was complete with having a twin boy and girl. Can you cope all right? It's easy for me."

She laughed.

"I know! You don't have the pain. Yes, of course I can cope. You told me I was born for motherhood."

"Well, at least we'll be kept busy. Keep our minds off things, perhaps," he said, not really believing it but saying it because he had to say something. He leaned over and squeezed her hand. She knew that was the greatest show of affection she could expect, but at least he seemed happy.

Chapter 9

Oh you lucky thing

Dad was glad to be home. She knew that. He was glad to be home, not just for her sake, but because he could attempt to resume some sort of normal life. He liked to go to his office. Laura wished he could stay at home but she was old enough to understand that Dads have to go to work. That was the normal world. So in that respect she was glad when he went to his office from home instead of from hospital.

There was another good reason for being at home. It was soon to be her birthday, and Kit's too! They were three years old. It felt such a long time since she left the warmth of the womb. In truth she could no longer recall those feelings that had stayed with her for such a long time after she was catapulted into the world.

"Please come inside," said Laura. "I don't like that banging noise. Please, please come inside."

It was November the fifth and they were letting off fireworks in the back garden.

Kit looked perplexed. He wasn't too fussed about the banging noises, but he'd rather have the sparkling lights and the ones that shoot up into the sky. They were exciting. The ones that banged just made you jump, that's all. Some had green lights, some had lights that looked like the stars and some just shone with a brightness that lit up the whole back garden, the walls of the house and the trees surrounding the garden. Those bright ones made the whole world seem totally unreal just for a few splendid minutes.

"I want to go in!" she screamed in despair as both parents tried to prolong the going in so Kit could enjoy the last of the fireworks. Eventually Kit became tired of the display and he asked to go in as well. It was fortunate that some local children came round. They took the remaining fireworks home with them. Dad heard them going off later in the evening.

For the twins' birthday Mum had arranged a party with some friends from the Close where they lived. Laura liked her friends and wanted to see them again. Some of them were really quite old, but not as old as Mum and Dad because they still went to school. It was a long time since Mum and Dad were at school, especially Dad. What she had not expected was that her friends would be afraid of her. They seemed so distant. She could not understand it. She also felt different towards them. Why had she to suffer when they did not? I'm only three, she thought, and I'm being hurt already.

One of the best parts of being at home was to sink into the familiar warmth of her bedroom, and to know that everything she touched, saw and smelt was hers and made for her. It was not for others before or after. It did not hold their touch or aroma. She sank into the comfortable ambience of her room and was immediately at peace.

It was also good to resume the routines she associated with home, which although repeated in hospital were never quite the same there. On Saturdays and special days Pillow Fairy came. She brought sweets for Kit and Laura when they had been especially good, which meant always because Dad's interpretation of good and bad was fairly flexible. Pillow Fairy placed the sweets under the twins' pillows after they had finished their evening meal. Dad would look out of the window and say, "Pillow Fairy's been". They would dash upstairs to find a special sweet or bar of chocolate. Sometimes Kit would look out of the window to see if he could spot Pillow Fairy but he never did. If Dad did not see Pillow Fairy he would telephone her or one of her assistants to see if she was coming. Sometimes he had to ask her to come. She always said yes. Laura tried to speak to her on the telephone once but she was not there. Pillow Fairy was a central figure in their home life.

It was the autumn. The back garden of her house was covered in golden leaves. The floor was stricken with them. They made a covering so dense she could not see or touch the grass beneath. The touch and smell of the leaves took her back to the time in France when she picked horse chestnuts. She should have known then that everything was not going to be straight forward in her life. There were feelings then that she could not understand. Perhaps they were a warning.

There were no horse chestnuts to be found in her back garden but the golden warmth of the season made her feel content. Tomorrow she would go to the harvest festival at the village church. It would be a time for rejoicing and thanksgiving. She knew they had all prayed for her at the Sunday services when she was in hospital. That gave her great comfort. The power of prayer is beyond the comprehension of most people, she knew that. She knew it because she felt something come to her from this village of hers, something that not only transmitted itself across the miles to her hospital but also lived and breathed deep within her. These kindly people with whom she shared her peace on a Sunday morning had risen to support her in prayers and words that had floated through hidden paths to reach her. She had felt and known their message. She had not understood the how and the why, but she knew it was good, and particularly good for her.

Dad went back to work. Mum spent time with Laura.

One day Mum took Kit and Laura for a walk. She decided to take the twins across the fields behind the church. Expecting Laura to get tired fairly quickly she took the twin buggy with her, whilst the twins walked alongside. Eventually Laura slowed down and began to suck her thumb. She looked up at her Mum and she was happily in the buggy before they reached the village shop. It was a fine mild day and good for walking. The leaves had almost completely fallen from the trees with the last few remaining hovering on the fingers of branches before a descent into the soft warm pillows below. The sun was hazy and distant, gloomily peering through the mist and the shades of late autumn. Nevertheless it was fresh and good to be out.

As they walked through the village lots of people stopped to speak to them.

"Hello! How is she?" said the old man from the house opposite the shop. He went on. "And how are you little girl? Better now? Glad to be out of that hospital I'll bet. Glad to be home with Mum and Dad and all your dollies, I'll bet."

Laura looked at him and sucked her thumb. Please Mum don't stop to talk. Lets walk on, she thought.

"She's been a brave girl hasn't she? We've all been thinking about you and praying for her. You know life brings us these challenges from time to time. I knew you'd pull through."

"Well, we do have to go back for the next stage of treatment. This is only the beginning. She is in remission but we have to consolidate the treatment."

"It's marvellous what they can do these days. Well, you take care little 'un, and I'll bet Father Christmas will bring you a special present this year."

I hope he does, thought Laura. I hope Father Christmas stops them from taking me back into that hospital again. I hope he comes and drives this Phantom that lives inside me away from me. I hope he comes and makes everything nice like it used to be, but perhaps even Father Christmas can't fight the Phantom.

"Hello Laura," said the lady with two sons who lived in their Close. "I'll bet you're glad to be home.

Laura looked at her and sucked her thumb.

"When did she come out?" asked the lady of Mum.

"Oh, only two days ago. We're just going for a walk to get some colour in our cheeks after being in hospital for so long, aren't we Laura?"

"I want to go to the swings!" pleaded Laura

"Oh she must be feeling better if she wants to go to the playground!" chuckled the lady.

Mum could have cried. If only, if only, she thought. If only the world were so simple that it could be so clearly defined as a ride on the swings. So clear, that one simple excursion was all that was needed to cleanse themselves of this haunting and brooding that pursued them still. You're sick and you get better. Is that what they thought? Lets hope they're right. If only we could step back in time, change things, do them differently; be in a different place at a particular time, she thought? Why did they have to make those decisions, to be there, then, and in that way? Someone once said to her that it was fate that brought her twins into the world. It was fate because she had met and loved a man who was older and they had wanted a family as soon as possible. The twins were a gift from heaven everyone said. If so, she thought, who is trying to take this gift away from her? Is it heaven, or its Keeper?

"Well it is nice to see you walking round the village again. Quite like old times," said the old lady from the cottage by the stream. "And how is our brave little girl? Quite the heroine, eh? We're all very proud of her, you know, and you of course!"

Laura stared hard for a few seconds, turned away and sucked her thumb.

"Mum! When are we going to the swings?"

"I thought we were going for a walk in fields?"

"I want to go on my swing!"

"We'll go to your swing Laura," said Kit reassuringly, cocking his head to one side and looking at her with sincerity.

After a visit to the swing park they walked toward the field behind the church. It is not possible to go to this field without passing the church. In fact the church dominates the village. Even more, it imposes. Its 12th century Norman structure demands to be acknowledged, but this is no more than any other parish church in these parts would demand. This part of the world was first inhabited by the Ancient Britons whose names are still embodied is such place names as Walcote and Walton, the Wal (Welsh) being the Anglo Saxon for foreigner, hence Welsh Cottages (cot). The Romans came and were overthrown by the Saxons and latterly and to some extent the Danes, who laid down their own laws yet only lived alongside the Saxons in places like Thorpe Lubenham and Althorp. The people were Saxon but after 1066 the architecture was Norman. Travel to any village in Belgraveshire and you will see the history of England. If there is any county in the country that truly epitomises England and its history this is it.

Kit was symbolic of this history. His looks were Saxon and Laura was his Saxon Princess. He was blonde and fair skinned. She had golden hair running in rippling rivers. He looked after his sister like a Saxon Princess should be looked after.

Mum stopped as they reached the church.

"Come on Mum," cried Kit, anxious to play in the field.

She heard music coming from inside. It was the same music she had heard many times before. It was a hymn, an incantation or even a sung psalm, yet this time there was another sound. There was a deep and enduring melody hidden beneath the normal dreariness of an English hymn sung by the small band of the faithful who kept the churches going. It drew her toward the door of the church to which she went, dragging the children along with her.

Inside the place was full. A packed church like she had never ever seen before. As she walked toward the Font, to which she felt drawn, all faces turned round to look at her. She expected a welcoming smile but got none. All she received was a beckoning pity that drew her deep into their midst. Their eyes pleaded with her to come forward. Why? She thought. Why are these people beckoning me in this way? What can they do for Laura? Why are they all here today? It's not Sunday.

She turned round. The children were no longer with her. They had got lost in the sea of faces. She heard them laughing. Then she saw them in someone else's arms looking at her as well, beckoning her. She walked forward and looked toward the altar.

They are here for Laura! She realised this as she saw the earnestness of their prayers. I don't believe in miracles she thought. These people and their God cannot possibly help us. I don't believe in miracles. This is a medical problem. Bravery and courage mean something, yes, of course, but at the end of the day it had to be clinical solution. I don't believe in miracles!

I walked past this place every day and am never drawn in apart from Sundays, she thought, yet, here I am. She felt the urge to go forward toward the altar. She did, and as she arrived there she saw the crucifix. A man lying bleeding looked down at her with sorrowful eyes. Eyes made sorrowful by the artist. Surely his face and eyes should be contorted in pain, she thought. She looked more closely and as she did she heard the strains of a bird singing in the trees surrounding the church whilst all inside seemed to be silent. As the bird elevated the pitch of its song, voices inside the church took up the harmony and swelled until they took over the melody completely. Mum was carried along by this harmony, which rose to a pitch that made her want to scream. She looked for Kit and Laura but they were not there. Instead they were in the congregation of singers. She felt alone, but still drawn toward the altar. She looked at it again. His face had changed. Now she saw the pain in his eyes, yet now he looked at her with a plea that was meant to be encouragement. She avoided his gaze. She looked back into the sea of faces. She saw pink globes surrounded by the sand coloured interior of this Norman church with its light oak beams and medieval drapes. She saw the florescence of the numerous candles secure in their silver holders donated by thankful worshippers throughout this ancient church's history. The words from a song by Barbara Dickson came to her mind. It was from a tape she often played in the car.

> *I walk alone along the road and past your door*
> *Then I remembered the things you said*
>
> *I don't believe in miracles*
> *But I thought you might show your face*
> *And have the grace to tell me where you are*

She felt the warmth of their prayers not because of its divinity but because she knew they cared. It was another weapon in the war. If it worked, it worked; she had nothing to lose and everything to gain. She stood looking at the altar for a few more minutes, or perhaps it was only seconds. When she turned round from east to west the church was empty, and cold. Laura ran up to her.

"What were you doing Mummy? Were you praying on your own? Can we go now?"

"Where's Kit?"

"Kit! Kit!" shouted Laura.

He appeared from behind the lectern with a smile.

They left the church for home and tea.

Chapter 10

Carry the lad that's born to be King

Mum and Dad sat by Laura's bed waiting for the consultant. They knew what was to be said. The consultant arrived with an entourage of nurses, junior doctors and students and they discussed various aspects of Laura's treatment in hushed tones.

"Well, I think Laura can go home now for a few days, " said the consultant in rather matter of fact tones. "She is in remission."

"Is everything as it should be," said Dad. "I mean, should she be in remission at this stage or is she late? Has it been difficult?"

The consultant looked at Dad apologetically.

"Everything is as it should be. I fully expected her to be in remission at some point. I think I told you that our success rate is 95% remission for children with A.L.L."

"What happens now?"

"What happens now is that you go home for a week and then come back to complete the treatment. We call it consolidation."

So it was that Laura went home. Mum and Dad thought the timing was significant and perhaps a sign of hope. It was the twins' birthday. They were three years old.

Laura could not contain her excitement and pleasure as they drove home. She knew they had to go back to make her properly better but this thought she put to the back of her mind. Now they were going home! Home! She had dreamed of it for so long and could not believe that it would really be the same, but it was; just the same as it always had been. Same smells, same warmth and her own dear bed.

Her birthday was good but her happiest times were getting up early in the morning so she could go downstairs to Dad. She would stand at the kitchen door with her pink pyjamas and pink slippers in her hand (she could never put them on) and would wait until Dad saw her through the glass of the door. Then she would smile. He would come for her, pick her up, plonk her down at the kitchen table and put on her slippers. These were magic moments, just the two of them in the quiet of that nice, warm and cosy kitchen with only the sound of the radio to disturb them. Eventually Kit would come down and the day would begin proper. Then everything would change and the world would come alive and she would be a part of it, carried along in its indeterminate path to nowhere that she cared to be.

The solitude of her life on the ward seemed a world away and she cared not to think about it. Mum and Dad had told her that she must return but she could not anticipate such an event in the timescale comprehended by her mind.

While they were at home Mum had to go singing at some church nearby. Dad was quite proud of her singing. He could sing himself but Mum was an accomplished soprano, trained in her craft. Dad just "had a go" as he would say. He tried to be modest about his singing and it was justifiably so. He could read music of sorts and make a musical note of sorts but he was hardly the accomplished singer.

"Where are we going?" said Laura, as Dad put her coat on.

"We're going to St What his name in Bisford to listen to your Mum do justice to a piece of Mendelssohn."

"Is she singing?" said Kit

"Yes, of course. We won't stay long but I thought you would like to hear Mum sing."

Mum was in full voice that night and sang as if her life depended upon it with an emotion that only Dad understood. He remembered her singing a few years previous. It was only a year after they were married.

"Come on! We're going to be late!" Dad was waiting to go to the concert. Mum was late as usual.

"I'm coming! Stop panicking! We've plenty of time," she said putting on her lipstick as she dashed down the stairs of their bright little cottage in Honeypot Lane.

"Hang on!" she exclaimed giving Dad the impression that he had done something wrong. "Where's my music?"

"I don't know. You had it only an hour ago"

"Oh! I know where it is." she gasped as she dashed into the bathroom.

"You've not been rehearsing in the bathroom have you?"

"Yes, of course I have. The acoustics are much better. What about you? Have you rehearsed your lines? I've not heard you."

They arrived at the school in Guilesborough with only a few minutes to spare.

"There! I told you we had plenty of time," said Mum as the dashed up the gravel pathway toward the staff common room that was being used as the changing room.

It was only the men who had to dress up. In fact 'dress up' was an exaggeration. They simply had to wear some hats in order to look jocular for they were to sing some Gilbert and Sullivan.

After a few excerpts of Pirates of Penzance the whole choir, women included, embarked upon a rendition of John German's Merrie England. Mum did not enjoy Gilbert and Sullivan and as a trained Opera Singer she approached Merrie England with some trepidation.

When the body of the choir had sang her introduction she stepped forward to take the part of Queen Elizabeth. She appeared as a young symbol of English womanhood. Her bright face encapsulated in a horseshoe of fair hair embodied the almost virginal epitome of youth, of hope and the future. The choir subsided and looked toward her. There was silence. She broke into song. Not suddenly. Not loudly. It was with the gentleness of a spring morning and the clarity of a new day. She had no vibrato. She sang with the purity of a treble voice or castrato. It was pure and untouched by operatic conformity. It was appropriate for her song, as well as for the mood, for it was the time when ships were sailing to the Falkland Isles to fight a war.

"Sword and buckler by my side" she sang.

The audience were gripped with emotion and uplifted by every word and note that she uttered.

She finished and bowed slightly. There was uproar. She had an encore. She knew it was unbridled patriotism but she didn't care. She relished the moment. After she had finished Dad took her home tired but happy.

"What about me?" he said. "Was I okay? Did you hear me get that top F?"

"You were brilliant. You just lack confidence"

"No. You were brilliant. I was just okay. That's fine by me. If I'm considered okay by you in music then I'm doing pretty darned well, I reckon"

She laughed.

"I've been trained! You haven't. So you can't expect to be the same. Anyway, lets not analyse tonight. Lets just enjoy it."

He agreed and within minutes they arrived back home. Nevertheless he was quite proud the next time they went shopping in Horbury Town to hear the praise of her singing from people they met in the Square, the Market, Flynns Bookshop and Amerson and East's Delicatessen.

It was time to go. It was a Sunday evening. They had to return to the hospital for the next batch of treatment. They prolonged the preparation for leaving until the last possible minute. Clothes had been washed and ironed in secret so she would not see and think about her inevitable return.

"We have to go now, little one," he said "But this is the last time you have to sleep at the hospital and Dad will be with you every night and Mum will be there every day. You're nearly better now. We just need to take a few more medicines and let the doctors look at you to make sure you're getting better"

"I don't want to go."

"I know. I don't want to go either, but we must to finish off the treatment. It would be silly not to go back now when we know everything is nearly finished. So, lets go."

"Can I take my toys?"

"Of course! You can take anything you want."

"I want to take Rupert."

"I'm sure Rupert would want to come back with you. Don't you remember I brought him to see you?"

"I think he's poorly like me."

"He's probably poorly because you are. You know, teddies and dollies are always sick when their children are sick. It's all part of being a teddy"

Laura thought about this for a while and it gave her some comfort that someone else should share her sickness. It seemed reasonable. After all, Rupert was dependant upon her and only came to life when she held him or when Dad put on

104

one of his puppet shows, which she knew were not very good but she enjoyed nevertheless. He had to come with her. Besides, Dad told her stories about Rupert and she knew that when he was with her he brought the whole of Nutwood village, Bill the Badger, Edward Pig, Pong Ping and all. For after all, Nutwood village was really their own village. She knew that. It was all rather obvious.

"When will we be there?" she asked Dad from her seat in the back of the car as she saw the night fly by them. They were still in the country. It was very black. She liked the black comfort of the country at night. It was like a warm blanket. The city was full of garish orange light that bounced off the streets and houses. People reflected the orange in their ashen wan faces.

"It won't be long, little girl. We'll soon be there and settle you in to a nice cosy bed. Perhaps Dad could tell you a Jimmy story tonight."

She liked Jimmy stories. They were the best because Dad made them up and they could go on for a long time if he was in the right mood. Sometimes he wasn't in the right mood and would yawn halfway through. The story would be boring when he was tired and she felt disappointed and wished she hadn't have asked for a story. Still, he told good stories. She settled back and began to suck her thumb, lost in thoughts of Jimmy, sleep and the surrounding night.

A song of Rupert Bear.

Oh no.
Tonight we must be there.
Why does he hurry?
Does he not care?
Why can't we stay, why can't we play
At home with Kit and Mum.

I know
I shall of course be there
But I'll be sorry
For Rupert Bear
He doesn't care
If he can play, he'll want to stay
With me and not with Mum

To show
Them all that we are here
And by tomorrow
We will not care
If we have to stay there every day
With Dad and Rupert Bear.

Whilst Dad was taking Laura back to the hospital, Mum
was about to embark upon an equally important and significant
journey.

The sun hung low over the sky as she drove the Ford
Sierra up the M1. Her thoughts were mixed. Most of all her mind
was still with Laura and Dad in Belgrave. She wanted to be with
them. As she drove through Holmfirth she felt some comfort in
knowing that she was close to Grandma and Grandad. Perhaps
here she could let herself go, tell people what it was really like,
and also relax and for a day and be free of this burden of care.
Even this she felt guilty of.

She took the Saddleworth turning out of Holmfirth.
She liked Holmfirth. They always came this way when they
went up North to mutual parents. It seemed so welcoming,
so friendly, yet so dignified and civilised. The Yorkshire stone
of its architecture conveyed an ambience of age and security.
Here was a place one could settle in and be happy. Even the
people you saw in the streets looked happy and content. She
remembered coming this way on a frosty Christmas morning
before the twins were born, when they used to spend Christmas
up North. There was a brass band standing in the street near
the bridge. It was playing 'O little town of Bethlehem'. She
remembered it well. The ruddy faces of the players, who had
probably indulged in some Christmas cheer donated by their
listening audience, combined with the lilt of the tenor cornets
and the atmosphere of goodwill made her happy. There was
something about brass bands and Christmas Carols. Perhaps
it was her northern upbringing. Whatever it was made her
sentimental. It made her feel warm and comfortable. She was
glad about her roots.

As she approached the summit of the Pennine hills
separating Yorkshire from Lancashire, she was aware of being
on a plateau of space and time between two worlds, for it was
well known that if it was raining in Yorkshire it would be sunny

in Lancashire and vice versa, and as such she felt free from care in a place of indifference. She knew these were two different peoples. Danish, Saxon and Viking bloods had never really mixed in these parts. The moor was bleak, but its bleakness was, if not beautiful, at least inspiring and awesome. One had to respect the moor. Because it was bleak its profile against the sky was sharp and intense. She had walked these moors many times with Dad, lost in a place between heaven and earth, where wildlife was rare save the startled grouse or moorland hare, where the sky touched the earth and the heather drank the sun and rain.

As she drove over the sweeping moors she remembered that this area was known as the Isle of Skye to the local people. She seemed to recall that there had been a sign but could not see it now. Words came into her head.

'Carry the lad that's born to be King.'

She remembered the words to the song. It was strange that it came to her. She had never thought of it before. Perhaps it was the new record album she had bought of Barbara Dickson. Didn't it contain this song? Still, it was strange that this part of the Yorkshire moor should take a Scottish name.

Perhaps this whole thing was relevant to Kit? Was he to achieve something honourable in all of this?

'Over the sea to Skye'

Perhaps taking him away was significant to the future success of Laura's care. Perhaps it was. Who was to know? All she really knew was that she would miss him terribly.

She stayed just one night. She talked to Grandma and Grandad until the words became hazy and she grew tired. They listened. They consoled. They offered comfort. They tried to offer hope.

Kit stayed at Grandmas and Grandad's for a few weeks whilst Laura underwent her second bout of treatment. He came back just before Christmas, when Laura had officially been released and put onto maintenance therapy. He came back with a deep pain in his little heart. He had enjoyed his brief respite but missed Laura terribly and dreamed of her very night. He was glad at the prospect of seeing her again. He didn't realise that she would have changed so much.

The intensification treatment had begun. The consultant said that this phase was difficult for both the patient and the parents. They had a role to play. They must avoid Laura getting mouth ulcers. That was number one priority.

"Why?" asked Dad.

"Because if she has mouth ulcers she will not be able to eat. She is going to lose her appetite anyway and feel very sick. She needs to eat and drink to keep up her energy. In addition some of the drugs work with the intake of food. That is why the timing of them is so important. She must eat."

They were in a different cubicle. Dad had toothache and was irritated. This cubicle was a little nicer. It had a small wardrobe with a mirror. The view was the same. There was also a TV

Laura had brought her own duvet with her as well as Rupert. When they arrived on the Sunday evening Dad laid out her duvet, put Rupert to bed and switched on the TV The room looked very cheerful and Laura felt quite comfortable. Dad told her Jimmy stories, then, when she fell asleep, he telephoned Mum from a mobile pay phone. Laura could hear him talking in the background as she sank into a deep sleep. It helped her feel secure, to know that he was there and hear his voice, to know that he was talking to Mum.

As usual she dreamt. She went to her usual dream place. Radella was not there. The other children seemed happy. They said Radella had gone home to get better, and then they carried on with their play, ignoring her. She felt left out. She wanted to be a part of them.

"We thought you were not coming back", one of them said. "We thought you were better."

A little girl with a white face and with only a few wisps of hair on her head came over to Laura.

"You should not have come back, but everyone does. There's no escape you know. He'll get you. He's too strong for us to fight. Our parents think we can overcome him by being strong and having the will to win. They know nothing. It is all up to the doctors. They are the only people who can beat him, and sometimes they don't want to. They just want to know more about him"

Laura felt sad and wanted to escape back to her bed and Dad but could not wake herself. She turned to flee and collided with the legs of a man in a robe. It was Jesus. He looked down at her and smiled, then looked across the room and scowled. Laura followed his gaze. The Phantom whom she thought was within her was standing by the door. He looked weaker than before. In fact he looked tired and disappointed. She no longer felt afraid of him. She turned to Jesus, but he was gone. She woke up. Dad was asleep. The ward was quiet. All was well.

The first few days of the treatment seemed to go very easily. All the nursing staff were in a happier mood knowing that Laura's chances of recovery were now good. They were impressed with her ability to accommodate all the treatment thrown at her. However as the days progressed the chemotherapy began its work again, extinguishing the last few hairs on her head and sending her reeling into spasms of vomiting and nausea.

18th November
Mum
8.10 am
Laura is a bit low this morning. She has done a wee and a poo and drank all her tea, but no food.

However, she has 2 ulcers in her mouth and still has a runny nose. The cough seems mainly due to the cold in her nose. Difflan and Nystatin diagnosed.

Please make sure the doctors keep an eye on her throat. They have taken swabs to make a culture & check for infection.
Love Dad

Dad had a camp bed at the bottom of Laura's bed. He would spend the evening reading to her then would make up his bed whilst she was still awake so that they could go to sleep at the same time. Sometimes this was not possible because the doctors and nurses did tests and checks regardless of the hours. Dad was enrolled to help them. Mostly Dad or Mum would give Laura her medicines.

One night she had to have a blood transfusion. Dad waited all night for the blood to arrive but eventually became tired and went to bed. The blood arrived at one o'clock in the morning. Dad was annoyed. Laura cried when they woke her up to put the drip in her arm. She screamed then eventually fell asleep again, the new blood slowly drip dripping into her tiny body. Dad stayed awake for the next hour to watch the blood go in drop by drop.

Chapter 11.

White Christmas

It was not the best of Decembers. The weather was indifferent, grey and sullen. There was not much rain but water hung in the air like wet washing on a damp day. Dad said that the wealthy people of the past used to emigrate for the winter months. He said they had the sense and the money. He said that the roads were just mud and people could not even get into Horbury Town by coach and horse so they went abroad until the weather got better. The poor people, like us, he said, just had to stay and endure the damp and the cold and the mud and walk to Horbury Town and usually got a cold in the head.

Laura was at home. Dad was at work again. He would come home early in the evening if he could. She longed to see him and was disappointed if he was late. Sometimes on a Friday he brought a little present. She liked it best when he had been to the Little Chef for breakfast on one of his long journeys. Then he would bring back a few sachets of sugar, which the twins would use in their morning tea on Saturday. Silly really, but it was as if he brought a part of his day back.

I love my Mum, she thought, just as I love my Dad; yet there is a burning warm feeling when Dad is near, a magical sense of wellbeing and goodness. But, she thought, her mind in a complexity of emotions, if I want real, real, proper, practical kind of help then; oh Mum I really need you to hug me and take the hurt away. But Dad, he is just happiness, that is all, and a special girl Dad kind of love.

She liked it best when she could sleep in his bed snuggled into his shoulder. That was usually when she had cried because she suddenly felt hot or there was a pain in her tummy or she just had a nightmare. He never moved when he slept and she felt comfortable all night even though she dreamed strange dreams. She wondered if the closeness of their two heads somehow merged their dreams. She thought this because sometimes her dreams were so complex they had to be grown up dreams. Sometimes they were so frightening that she woke up. The night would be silent; Mum and Dad asleep surrounded by an all-pervading blackness. She could hear the distant sounds of the countryside; an owl, a bat, the wind in the old horse chestnut tree and then silence. She wanted to wake Dad but he slept soundly. The dream was with her still. She lay down beside him and submerged once again into her dream.

There was a place she knew that she sometimes went to when she was asleep. Dad went there too. Sometimes he was with her. At other times she was quite alone. It was a place that was a mixture of tranquillity and the macabre. Here she met the strangest of people and animals.

As her mind turned to slumber she deliberately searched out this place. The same dream that she had dreamed before came back to her.

She ran. She looked for the way to her place. It was too dark for her to find a way there. The more she ran the darker it became. She knelt in despair. Her fulfilment lay in finding her place. The darkness turned her search into a melancholic frustration. She was trapped. There was no way out. Only darkness and beyond that, what? As despair entered her mind she became conscious of a faint but encroaching light. Over to her right was Jesus standing in the doorway holding a lamp. He smiled. He said "I am the truth, believe in me."

She arose and went forward into uncertainty. Jesus was alongside her, smiling. He pointed toward the way forward. She liked Jesus. He was nice, but she wished he would stay with her and not tell her to go alone.

In the corner of the room she had entered was a man playing a very large and grand piano. He played it rather well, Laura thought. It made a tinkling sound that gave her the instinct to dance. She danced. She was dancing with Dad, and then he was gone. Then she danced with the man from the piano, but yet the piano still played. They danced beautifully. She noticed for the first time that she was wearing a red frock. Pure red. The Piano Man wore a very nice suit. She stared at his tie. It was red. She gradually moved her gaze to his face. It was pure unblemished white, the same colour as his hair and his eyes. She cried, from sadness for this albino of the night rather than fear.

He whisked her away into a frantic dance. They span, and as they span she noticed the white flecks appear on her dress. As they danced the man's face began to flush and her dress continued to grow whiter.

"I am the Phantom", he said "Don't you know me? We met before at the hospital. I stole your blood. Remember me?"

He had a nice voice but his face was very unpleasant. Half of it was covered in a mask. Laura knew she had seen him before, in a picture that Mum and Dad had brought back from London. It unsettled her when she saw it.

He picked her up and continued to spin her round. As they spun her dress gradually became wholly white. She saw the redness drift away. She saw him absorb it. Eventually the dizziness became too much for her. She cried for him to stop.

"Please, please, I don't want to dance any more. I have a white dress now. I have to go home to show my Mum. Please stop!"

"It's all right Laura!"

She opened her eyes to see Dad's face framed by the darkness and safety of her own home.

"You must have been dreaming. Dad's here. Nobody's hurting you. It's okay"

Mum had awoken at this point.

"She must have been dreaming of the hospital," said Dad.

"Probably," said Mum.

Mum took Laura to the radiology department. It was actually called The oncology department but Mum felt that this title was not appropriate as oncology was all about the treatment of cancer and related diseases and radiation therapy was only a small part of that treatment. Already Mum was becoming quite knowledgeable about the diseases of cancer in children and the treatment of these diseases. This made some of the consultants very uncomfortable. They did not like to see a parent become too knowledgeable. It took away some of their mystique and authority. Parents also had one quality that the doctors had to some degree lost. Parents had objectivity. The doctors were too engrossed in the regime, in the need for clinical trials, and the never ending need for statistical proof. To these ends the children became a part of the clinical equation. They were almost laboratory experiments. Those that sacrificed their life or well being actually further advanced the cause of a cure for cancer in children; even of they did it unknowingly. They were like warriors in a great fight that was fought in silence and secrecy, but they were anonymous soldiers.

The route to the radiation department at the Belgrave Royal Infirmary is not a pleasant one. It involves a trip through miles of oppressive corridors canopied with clusters of pipes and cables. Dull orange lights flicker and dance along the walls. However when you arrive there the department is full of light and offers a bright and welcome reception. Laura did not mind going there, because the people were so friendly and made a fuss of her. She would rather be at home but she knew that she had to come to this hospital so she would rather come here than sleep upstairs on the ward.

The nurse in the corridor smiled when she arrived. She had dark hair and an olive skin. She introduced herself to Mum and Laura. They liked her and she liked them. They became friends straight away and Laura felt comfortable with her when she did things to her that were not quite pleasant.

She would take Laura into a special room where a cream and grey machine lived. She asked Laura to lie still for fifteen minutes whilst this machine hummed around her. She could cope with the whirl and the noise and the confinement. The most terrifying thing was that everyone left her during her fifteen minutes with the machine and watched her from behind a screen. Only the nurse would stay until the last minute and then she would disappear. However she was always the first to return. Laura felt frightened when she was on her own.

It was strange to lie there by herself. She could not understand why her Mum could not be with her. It would be nice if someone were here. Where was Dad? She thought. Why does he have to go to work? The place about her became silent save a faint humming noise, which she presumed was the machine that drew over her. Occasionally it made whirring noises as if something was moving. The room was quite large and the people in the glass window seemed a long way away. They stared and talked to each other. Her mind started to drift and as it did the whirring would stop and the nurse would return telling her she was a clever girl.

I don't know why I'm so clever, thought Laura; I've not really done very much. But then again neither have these grown ups. They've just watched me and wouldn't stay beside me. Perhaps I have been very, very clever after all.

Laura came every day for radiation therapy. In the end she got used to it and used to look forward to a little doze on the couch. Sometimes it made her feel a bit sickly, but not as sickly as on the ward. She shuddered when she thought of the ward, although, even there, she had some good times, when she was getting better that was.

Perhaps the best thing about the Radiation department was the kindliness of all the nursing staff. They made her feel very special. They said she was very brave and always took an interest in what she had to say. All the other people who came to this place sat around in nightgowns and looked very unhappy. Until Laura arrived that is. Then they would smile and talk to her. They began to talk to each other. They talked to the nurses. When they saw that Laura had lost her hair they made jokes amongst themselves and felt better. For after all if a three-year-old child can endure this and smile, then why couldn't they?

"At least with having no hair you don't have to wash it," said one man, taking off a green baseball hat.

Laura took off her scarf, which disappointed Mum as she had tied it specially. A lady in her 50s could not resist speaking.

"Just think. You're going to have brand new hair. I bet all your friends will be jealous."

Mum scowled. She didn't want Laura to be reminded of her alopecia.

Laura went to the oncology department every day for two weeks. After that she went to her most favourite place in the hospital, which was the clinic. This was a place that was full of toys and children like her. Children with no hair, with pale skins. Children who had pinpricks all over their tiny arms and hands where the needles had gone in. Children who didn't cry when they were injected but held out their arm with total compliance to the regime of clinical indoctrination which they had come to accept. Children who knew pain but cried inside themselves. Children who were brave but did not know it.

Laura went back to play school and her friends were pleased to see her. She felt very brave and special. She was glad it was all over apart from the visits to the clinic. Even though the weather was cold and damp she liked to play outside as much as possible. She knew she had a lot of playing to catch up on for the time in hospital. Sometimes she just liked to be in the garden with Mum and Dad while they busied themselves on gardening chores and Kit played with his bike or car.

One day Dad chopped down an apple tree. The tree had been blown down by the wind the day before. It fell on the wire that separated the orchard from the field where the horses grazed. It limply hung there, like some First World War soldier trapped and dying on the German barbed wire, Dad said. It hung there all morning, gently buffeted by the receding wind.

Dad didn't know it was an apple tree. It had neither flowered nor borne fruit since they moved into this house. A man came to help Dad cut it up. He said it was an apple tree. He said he knew this because he could smell its sweetness in the sap. He said it would fill the house with its sweetness when it was burned.

"Why did it have to fall down and die Dad?" asked Laura as they stood by the chopped up tree scattered across the grass.

"All things are born and all things die, Laura."

"But it was a nice tree. Now it won't be there any more. Trees don't go to heaven. They're just dead."

"Well that not quite true. You see this tree. Well this tree will live forever."

Laura laughed.

"Dad! A tree can't live forever!"

"Well this tree can and I'll tell you why."

"How can it? Tell me!"

"First of all we have the roots. The roots are still in the ground. They will still grow and may even shoot off new little branches which won't be new trees but will be like new hands reaching out to the sun and rain for nourishment and life. These shoots might be so small that you won't know they're there. They will live without your knowledge in a private little world of their own, happy and content, safe from the man with the chain saw."

"Will they have any apples on them?"

"No! They'll be far too small for that. Next we have the logs, which Dad has cut up. They will go on our fire and keep us warm. They will help sustain us and keep us from freezing to death and so the tree will live on through us."

Laura did not fully understand this.

"The warmth from the burning wood will help us to live. Without warmth we would all die"

"What about all these little pieces lying on the ground?"

"Well, Dad will collect them all and burn them in the vegetable garden. They will turn to ash. The ash will fertilise the ground and its goodness will go into our vegetables. You will eat those vegetables, except the sprouts of course, (Laura chuckled when he said that for she hated sprouts) and the goodness will go into you. So you see trees do live forever. Everything in life does. There was once a famous scientist who said that matter, or things, could neither be destroyed nor made, they only change. So this tree will only change. It will not die. Just like we won't die. We'll all go to heaven to be with Jesus. If we're good that is!"

Laura hoped she was good enough to go to heaven. She liked the thought of Jesus. He was a kindly if rather sad man. She thought he must be very sad because he had to worry about a lot of people and every time she saw his picture he was hanging from a cross. Dad said he was sad because not everyone believed in him. How could you not believe in someone who is real, she thought. It's a bit like not believing in the story of the apple tree. Perhaps other people had not seen him like her.

" I want to go in now. I'm cold. Can I play with my Doll's house?"

Laura liked to play with her Doll's house. She also liked to play at tea parties with her Dad and Kit. They would retire to her bedroom on a Sunday afternoon whilst Mum was busy in the kitchen or garden. Dad would get out all the teddy bears and dolls and lay out the tea set. Kit and Laura would give the toys tea.

Laura also had a toy cooker and she would make cakes and sausages for tea. All the toys enjoyed this very much, but not so much as Dad. As the game progressed they would be transported into a world of unreality. Dad would talk of Alice Through the Looking Glass, of the Cheshire Cat and the Mad March Hare. The toys about them would begin to take life and talk as well. Laura had a special teddy bear. In fact both Kit and Laura had a teddy bear. Although Laura liked her Teddy Bear she especially liked the white china doll she brought back from Germany. She put the little white doll on the dark wooden cabinet in her bedroom. It looked nice under the lamp. Its pale face seemed to shine. She also liked a doll that was capable of drinking and 'weeing'. She would chuckle when it wet its knickers. She would call it naughty and scold it, but really she was amused. Both these dollies joined the tea party.

Some of the dolls would want to play after their tea. Laura liked it best when they made a little show for her and Kit. Dad would hide behind the linen cupboard. Suddenly her nice dolly would appear and begin to recite a poem. Laura just knew that something was going to happen, and it did. Silently and stealthily the green crocodile would appear behind the dolly. Kit and Laura would shout a warning but not before the crocodile had taken a nip at dolly, whose name was Melanie. The crocodile and Melanie would pursue each other up and down the linen cupboard. Eventually other teddies and dollies would join in until it was total mayhem and they all collapsed in a heap upon the floor.

One day, Laura thought it was on her birthday; Dad came home with a Brio Train set. It was a very simple train set. It was one circle and a few coaches. But, oh! Such joy! To be able to push this little train around the track and pretend you were on a great journey was wonderful. Both Kit and Laura loved the little train. Kit loved it especially because it was a route to adventure; Laura liked it because it was a route of escape. Later Dad was to buy lots more Brio train equipment, but this little track was perhaps the best buy of all. Dad created games that took Kit and Laura into a pretend world of trains and the people who lived alongside them. It was almost as if he wanted to escape with them into another world.

"Can we play pretend?" Kit asked one Friday evening.

"Yes! Of course! Do you want to play Big Pretend or Little Pretend?" replied Dad.

"Big Pretend or Little Pretend?"

"Yes. Big Pretend is where we pretend to be someone and perhaps dress up and act the part. Little Pretend is where we play with trains, dolls or soldiers."

Laura liked Little Pretend the best, like with the doll's tea party, but Kit liked to act out parts and so liked Big Pretend, although he liked Little Pretend as well.

Dad used to play Big Pretend on Friday nights when he was a little boy and Grandma and Grandad had gone to the pictures. His cousins Alice, Janet, Bill and Percy (yes, Percy) would come around to baby-sit. One night they rigged up two chairs and a curtain across a broom handle over the chair backs to act as a theatre stage. Then everyone, except Dad and his brother who were very young, would make a little performance, a poem, a song or just pull a funny face. Dad and his brother sat very quietly enjoying the show when there was a special announcement.

"Especially tonight we have the famous star from the wireless who has come to then village to make a special appearance. See if you recognise her face"

The curtains opened and a bare bottom confronted Dad and his little brother.

"Alice!" Dad shouted, although he was not completely sure that it was she.

Kit and Laura thought this story was very funny but very naughty. Laura thought she could never do such a thing. Dad often told stories of when he was young. Kit wondered if he would have such stories to tell. Would he too have the adventures that Dad and his friends had or would life be less exciting. Dad said that he was sure Kit would have a lot to tell his children about.

Childhood is a strange thing. Laura had temporarily put the immediate past behind her. Sometimes it was difficult for her to believe she had undergone such horrendous treatment was it not for the fact of her lack of hair, the need to take medication three times a day and visit the clinic every week. However she did not often think of these things. There was no point in reflection. That was the sort of thing grown-ups did. They were always looking backwards or forwards. Life is today. That is all she knew. She awoke and lived each day. Her horizon only stretched as far as the next weekend. Beyond that is total uncertainty, incomprehension, the unknown. Life is today and life is good. Life is sweet.

She remembered one evening when Dad read a poem to Mum that said:

Life is not sweet.
One day it will be sweet
To shut our eyes and die
Nor feel the wild flowers blow,
Nor birds dart by
With flitting butterfly.

She thought this a strange poem, but sometimes Dad became melancholy and made everyone around him sad. He withdrew into himself and was reflective. During those times she would get special hugs and cuddles as would Kit. Then his melancholy would turn to joy and he would fill the house with his happiness. Laura knew the melancholy was not about her but about life itself. Mum liked to watch a film called "The Family Way". In the last scene an actor called John Mills, whom Mum liked, sat by the window crying. When his son asked him "What's the matter?" he simply replied "Life, lad. Just life."

She knew life had pain and sadness but nevertheless it was sweet in its entirety. Indeed, pain itself could have a strange morbid kind of sweetness, bittersweet. Pain is, after all, the counterpane of love. Knowledge is strong but love is sweet. Does love itself not bring its own pain? Can you have love without it? Laura wished she knew the answers to these questions. Her mind remained confused as to why she, and not others, had to suffer such pain.

To Laura love and life were made up of little moments. To be with Dad in the early morning, to surprise him as he is making his breakfast alone in the kitchen, to see the joy on his face and to be picked up and cuddled before he puts on the slippers she carries in her little hand and plants her on a chair for breakfast. From then on in everything is a game. Everyone else sleeps but these two make cornflakes, eggs and toast into the special meal of the day whilst the early morning sun rises over the Ash trees in the back garden and sprinkles through the kitchen window onto their table.

It was on one of these days that she thought that sunny days must be best. That is when you can really feel hopeful and good about life and the world, she thought. When everything is bathed in warm light against a backcloth of blue. However, she did like windy days and even wet days. On wet days Dad would take the twins for walks in their Wellies so they could splash the puddles made by the rain. But most of all she liked the brightness and warmth of the sun.

One Wednesday morning at clinic Mum and Dad were called into the consultant's office as usual to discuss the results of Laura's blood test. This morning her face was more serious than usual.

"I'm afraid her haemoglobin is a little bit lower than I would have liked," she said after reading out the results for them." It's not serious. It's just that, with Christmas coming up I would be happier if Laura had a top up to keep her going over the holiday period. I wouldn't like her haemoglobin to get too low."

"Is it normal for her haemoglobin count to go down at this stage in the treatment?" asked Mum. "I've not heard of the other children needing a top up."

"Well, I'm afraid nothing is normal in the treatment of Leukaemia. You cannot compare Laura to other children."

"Why not? She has been given the same treatment as other children. There must be similarities and comparisons that can be made."

"That may be the case, but you must remember that each child presents differently and so we cannot expect the same response to the treatment."

"Did Laura present differently?"

"Not particularly. Her white count was a bit high, that's all."

"What do you call high?"

"Anything over 100 is high, and Laura's was not as high as that."

"Was it as high as 50, because another consultant says that 50 is high."

"I don't know to whom you are referring but I am the consultant in charge here and can tell that Laura's count was not abnormally high."

The consultant hastily referred to a set of notes.

"If you could bring her on to the ward next Thursday morning, we'll give her a blood transfusion."

"But that's Christmas Eve," exclaimed Dad.

"We never close, and that's the day we do transfusions."

Mum and Dad left the office dismayed at this set back. Everything had seemed to be going so well. Was this the start of something sinister or were they over reacting?

They decided that this Christmas would be very special. It had to be; surely they all deserved a reward. There was a general feeling of relief. That the battle had been won and now was the time to celebrate. Yet, there was still this uncertainty. Could it really be going so well, and was the blood transfusion a set back or just a slight expected hiccup in the course of events.

It was agreed that Dad would take Laura into hospital on Christmas Eve. Mum stayed at home preparing Christmas. Both Laura and Dad were fairly relaxed about the day. They expected to be home just after lunch to help Mum with the final preparations. Perhaps with a little bit of luck they could be in time to go to the Carol Service at church.

The ward was quiet. Most children had been sent home for the holiday. The ones left were the serious cases and they didn't make much noise. They arrived at about 10 o'clock as requested. By midday Dad was becoming very angry because they had not yet been attended to. Apparently the haemoglobin had not been delivered. Mum telephoned.

"What time will you be back?"

"We haven't had the transfusion yet. It's probably going to be about 3 or 4 o'clock."

"Are you sure that everything is alright? " She was still not convinced that everything was as it should be. She had an inherent distrust of what she was told by the clinicians. "Can you ask them why her count has gone down and has it gone down any further. Shall I come in? It's awful sitting waiting at home."

"I think you are worrying unnecessarily. I'm sure everything's okay. It's just annoying that we have to wait so long. Apparently this is not untypical."

"You are too trusting. Ring me again in an hour"

Dad became unsettled by what Mum said and went off to pester the nursing staff for more information. He knew what they would say.

"We'll tell you as soon as it arrives."

Dad didn't ring Mum back. She rang him first. He knew she would. He knew she would not rest until this thing was sorted and her daughter was at home with her. Unbelievably the stuff had arrived and Laura was being prepared when she rang.

The transfusion took an awfully long time. Laura was very apprehensive about it and just hoped that it was not more chemotherapy in disguise. She did so want to be at home with Kit and Mum for Christmas. She was also worried about whether Father Christmas would remember to come if he realised she was not at home. Perhaps he checked up on which boys and girls were at home for Christmas Eve before he got their presents ready. I hope he realises that I'm coming home, she thought.

"Dad?"

"Yes, Laura?"

"Will I have to stay in hospital tonight?"

Dad looked at the drip in her arm. It was about halfway through and it was 5 o'clock. It had suddenly gone dark outside. He hadn't really noticed until now because a combination of streetlights and a clear sky meant it had remained fairly bright. He imagined Mum preparing their Christmas buffet at home. In the background the TV or radio would be playing some Christmas Music. There would be the smell of mince pies and the anticipation of Christmas. Kit would be getting quite excited about the prospect of Christmas day. He thought of the time when he was he was a boy on Christmas Eve. His mother preparing food, ironing her best frock for her big day, waiting for Dad to come home. Christmas Eve was the best part of Christmas. Like all things the anticipation is always more satisfying than the event. And they were still here on the ward!

"No. You won't have to stay in hospital. We're going home just as soon as your drip has finished."

Angry that they were still here he dashed off to see a nurse.

"Yes, can I help?"

"How long before the drip finishes?"

"Not long now. Before 6 o'clock. But we need to keep Laura here a little while afterward to make sure that everything is all right. Just to check her blood pressure etc. I don't know if doctors will want her in for a blood test."

Dad's face fell in dismay.

"Well, how long will all that take? It's Christmas Eve!"

"We don't close on Christmas Eve, you know."

"You may not close, but Laura and I do."

"Don't worry. We'll get you home as soon as possible. I'll check with Staff nurse when you can go."

Dad returned to Laura. A black and white film flickered on the large and rather ancient TV set standing between the two outside windows. Bing Crosby was singing. It looks like the Holiday Inn, thought Dad. Laura was asleep.

Dad couldn't remember whether it was before or after Bing Crosby sang "White Christmas" when the nurse came to say they could go. He remembered thinking that it was a significant and perhaps symbolic moment and one that was full of hope. He felt very happy and telephoned Mum to say that he and Laura were coming home for Christmas and didn't have to come back to clinic for two weeks.

Chapter 12.

The clinic

One day after Christmas the family went to London. It was a quiet Sunday. The twins were excited about the trip, especially Kit. His favourite toy was a miniature London black cab. He played with it constantly. He enjoyed holding it. He liked its shape, its uniformity, the smooth edges and the brave front of its bonnet. It was a comfortable toy. One to go back and play with time and time again. Like an old friend. He hoped he would see such a cab in London.

They drove to London, parked at Hyde Park then took the Tube to Trafalgar Square. When they came to the surface Kit was confronted by a flock of black taxicabs. They all appeared to converge on their little party. He was glad when Dad briskly whisked them over the road into the Square to feed the pigeons.

Laura was not happy about the pigeons sitting on her head. Their audacity surprised even Dad who recalled his experience as a child with the pigeons many years ago. Perhaps they have the confidence of today's youth, he thought.

They left Trafalgar Square and stood opposite St Martins. Dad waved for a cab. Very quickly one stopped in front of them. Kit cried. He was overwhelmed with the prospect of actually entering into one of his beloved toys. Dad had to lift him in with legs kicking and tears pouring down his face.

"Harrods please," said Dad.

"I want to get out!" screamed Kit.

"We'll soon be there. I thought you liked black cabs. This is meant to be your special treat."

"Why can't we walk?" Kit asked.

Laura looked at him with despair tinged with concern: "Don't worry Kit. It's just like being in Dad's car. We won't go in a black cab again if you don't want"

125

This prospect, of not travelling ever again in a cab was too much for Kit. He became quiet and contemplative. Perhaps it wasn't so bad after all.

They arrived in Knightsbridge. As they dashed into Harrods they were pursued by the cab driver. Mum thought that Dad might not have tipped him.

"You left your camera, Sir."

"Thank you," said Dad. "Thank you very much."

Dad's faith in humankind was rekindled, but he should have known London cab drivers much better. Are they not the best and most honest in the world?

In Harrods they bought a few small things, mainly in order to obtain carrier bags with the Harrods name, Dad said. In reality it was to take back a few luxuries; a scarf, a pair of socks, some pate, bread, cheese and for Mum, a hat.

They took a cab back to Whitehall, saw Downing Street and the Horse Guards Parade then went for lunch at that little Pizza place near Trafalgar Square.

Laura wore her hat all day. Nevertheless, the coolness of the day got through and made her poor baldhead so cold that she was conscious of it constantly. It was like a toothache. She felt as if everyone must know that she had no hair. When they went into the Pizza Place she just hoped that Mum or Dad would not make her take her hat off. When Mum asked her she screamed, sucked her thumb and looked out of the window. Don't they know? She thought, how I hate my body. The marks on my skin from those injections. My brown face from all that radiation and my head with no hair. How horrid I must look. I thought girls were supposed to be pretty. How can I be pretty?

Dad was glad to be back at work. Life had to go on, he was told. But surely the sickness of Laura was part of life. Life was going on anyway. What could he do to influence things? He felt helpless amongst the clinicians. Their advice was dictated more than given. How could he know he was getting the best for Laura? Should he believe them or were there internal politics at play here amongst the medical profession? What was the real significance of a clinical trial? They talked to you as if you were without rational thought. He hated their bedside patronising manner. The way they clustered together when challenged and dismissed your questions as if they came from a child and were not worthy of an intelligent answer.

Thank goodness Mum had embarked upon a programme of learning. She was now asking intelligent questions and the clinicians had to respond with some answers.

Dad did a little research as well. He once sat beside Laura on the ward reading a book on chemotherapy drugs. The matron told him he was not allowed to read this book. It was one that was used by medical staff. She asked him to hand it over. He told her he had borrowed it from the library. She stood her ground. So did he. Eventually she half relented and said " If you read it, then read it where no one can see you. The doctors will take it off you."

After this he read it with greater interest. He read of the horrendous side affects of the treatment. He read of the damage the drugs were doing to the rest of Laura's body in their mission to kill the Leukaemia cells.

At what price are they killing the cancer, he thought.

He read about the success rates of these drugs and the possibilities of a return of the disease. He read of their inability to kill every known Leukaemia cell in every child. Most importantly he read of how critical, how vital, it was to administer the drugs at certain times of the day in relation to the body cycle and he realised that he did not know if this was done.

Wednesday morning was the most important time of the week for the family. This was the day they visited the outpatient's clinic at the hospital. The days approaching were anxious ones. They were days and hours of worry, of fear and anxiety. Would the blood tests reveal the news that everyone dreaded? Surely she was limping a little at the weekend? Did she not spike a temperature the other night? She looks a little pale. She is lethargic. She keeps sucking her thumb. It must be coming back! Oh God! It must be coming back!

But there was some relief in going to the clinic. At least now they would know for certain. It can't come back just yet. We've only just finished the treatment. Anyway, she has the best form of Leukaemia.

It was a great comfort to meet the other parents. They felt like the closest of friends, of allies in a battle. At least with them one could be free. Even so you did not utter your innermost fears. You didn't because you knew that they had the same fears and anxieties. They suppressed their worries as you did. Everyone talked positively about the future. But you knew there was a hidden agenda in the discussion. When they talked about their child doing well they were really saying, " I hope to God the blood test results will be all right! Please don't give me bad news!"

Dad normally took Laura in for her blood test. He liked to get there early so she could have her blood test early and they could get away as soon as possible. She was good. She sat and took the needle from the Outpatients sister who was ever so gentle, a true professional. There was always a sweet at the end from a little bowl. They were not the best of sweets but they tasted like the best to Laura. It was a just reward.

Mum and Dad treated the clinic like a little club. They chatted to all the other parents who were there and would compare notes. The health visitor would be there and would be a focal point for parents. She would comfort, cajole and, on occasions, scold parents. She had been looking after families with childhood cancer for twenty-five years. She remembered years ago when they all used to die. Now half of them live. At least then you knew you had no hope. It is the fact of having some hope that is the greatest source of pain and anxiety amongst the parents. Will we be one of the lucky ones? Will our child live or die? They had to understand that their own situations were merely microcosms of the great battle against cancer. They were all helping win it and the health visitor was determined to play her part in this battle whilst at the same time carrying and supporting the parents and their families. It was a battle that she loved, but at the same time it drained her heart and soul and body.

Dad would play with Laura on the rocking horse or the fort after the blood test. Kit came too and played with the other children. Mum would wait impatiently for the result. Eventually a ward clerk would arrive outside the consultant's office with the children's files, having taken down the results by telephone. Sometimes Mum would manage to sneak a look. She was greatly relieved to see a good result and whispered to Dad what she had seen.

After the result was confirmed at the little meeting with the consultant Mum and Dad were filled with relief. They dared not think of next Wednesday's clinic. Instead they comforted themselves with the thought that they now had at least a few days of respite. The white cell count was good. The Neutrophils were okay. Platelets were as high as they should be. The consultant looked pleased. Surely everything must be going all right. That evening they would be able to relax, enjoy life and attempt to be normal again until the fears started to set in again on a Sunday night or a Monday morning. They left the consultant's office with a smile and chatted to the other parents. Some had heard good news, some were still waiting. It was rare to hear bad news. But this was a delusion. Those with bad news didn't speak. They simply went home.

One day at clinic they were waiting for their results when they heard a scream from the consulting room. Later another Mum and Dad came out with red faces. Their little boy was waiting for them by the rocking horse.

"Can we go to MacDonald's, please?" he asked.

"Of course you can go to MacDonald's," said his Mum, "Oh, of course you can. You can go as often as you like you lovely little boy."

He didn't come to clinic anymore. When all the other parents asked why, they were told "No more treatment". They knew what this meant. They didn't ask. They just knew. No more treatment. There was no point.

Chapter 13

Happy Days

Oh such happy days to be at home in North Peveril. There were meadowlarks in the field and yellow-headed wagtails skimming the hedges. Lambs were growing and the calves were beginning to look like young adults. The winter wheat and barley were deep green and growing a few extra inches every day. The beech and ash were in leaf and the oak was thinking of doing the same in the gradual and grand way that oaks come into leaf. Bluebell Wood was a sudden carpet of blue. Nests of robins and wrens appeared throughout the garden, hedgerow, spinney and coppice. Hedgehogs poked their noses out of piles of leaves and the hares in the field became brave now that the shooting season was over. The countryside was coming alive. It was spring. Laura's hair was growing. It had changed from gold to black, but it was growing. She began to feel better about herself.

Laura's first song

> Can I see life beyond the sun
> Where shadows have not yet begun
> To cast autumnal thoughts
> Upon the hopes I hope are real
> And feelings that are not yet surreal
> Betrayals of doomed destiny.
>
> The light that once had gone from me
> Has settled in uncertainty.
> And comes to me again.
> I have few fears. I'm only young
> He says that Spring has sprung
> And hope returns again.

The sun is shining. Wagtails hop.
Across the searching budding crop.
And optimism blooms.
Can I resume my world again
Dispensing memory and pain
That beckon me
I will be free.
I will be free,
Again.

They walked through the churchyard and climbed the wall into the meadow.

"It's yellow!" Kit stood and looked.

He saw a green speckled sea of yellow rolling over the crests of ridge and furrow in this ancient meadow that stretched to the woodland hiding the distant hills. The breeze sailed mellow and warm over the deep yellow dancing flowers.

"They are buttercups Kit," said Dad.

Laura let go of his hand and ran to the yellow field. She bent amongst the flowers. Kit knelt beside her and together they held the small buttercup heads in their hands. Their faces reflected orange light.

"It means you like butter," said their Dad.

Life in the country is for boys and girls. They can find adventure in a coppice, excitement in a stream and beauty amongst the animals whether they are in a farm or field. Laura liked the lambs. She laughed a deep throaty laugh when she saw them hop and jump. Dad took her and Kit into the field behind the church as often as he could. She consumed as much of what she saw as ravenously as she could. The hospital was a long way away but now she was here, in her own dear countryside. clinic was the only connection with the past but even that was a place of hope. She had so many friends there. She only thought of it when the time came to go to clinic.

Although she had learned to walk again fairly quickly she now found that she could not walk very far. She liked especially for Dad to carry her and had her own special position in his arms.

As they were walking Laura would feel an aching in her limbs. She thought of how comfortable it was in Dad's arms.

"Carry me, Daddy."

He would smile, look down at her and then sweep her up into her favourite place. The joy of being there. Sometimes she would just snuggle her head into his neck for comfort, but only for a few minutes. Otherwise she would chatter to him. She would point and lean in the direction she wanted to go and he would take her. He would talk to her and constantly feed her with small kisses to lips and cheek. It was almost as if she was walking alongside him. She sometimes forgot that she was being carried and that he was much taller than her.

Her body relaxed when she was in his arms. She experienced feelings of peace that could only come from the closeness and familiarity of his body, his form and his warmth. Sometimes she experienced this familiarity with Kit.

> There's blood between us, love, my love,
> There's father's blood, there's brother's blood;
> And blood's a bar I cannot pass.

Dad felt a great comfort in carrying her. He was her protector. But it was more than that. He liked to feel the closeness of her small form nestled into his arms. He was as close to her as a Dad could be to his little girl. Being close to her gave him great satisfaction and feeling of sublime contentment. He knew that these moments were as precious as any he would experience in his life.

Physical contact between a parent and child has its own particular sensuality, unlike that of any other physical contact. These arms and legs, tummy, hair, eyes and lips all come from the same source. Their affinity is natural. When they touch it is a product of love, the greatest love. When Dad was close to Laura he wished for nothing else in the world. All material things seemed unimportant and of little consequence. He fell into a complacency of body and soul. His personal needs were of no consequence.

Every day Laura had to have medication. This was part of the maintenance therapy. It was important that she took this medication correctly; so little charts appeared in the kitchen reminding Mum, which drugs to give and in what quantities. Syringes appeared, swabs and other clinical artefacts. Mum became adept at administering these things. To Laura they were a constant reminder that she had not fully escaped from this evil thing within her, this phantom, this white devil who used to haunt her so terribly. Now he lay dormant in the background. In two years he would be gone completely said Mum. So, it was not long to wait and Laura appeared to be well on the way to recovery.

Dad became very busy with his work and began arriving home quite late, which both Kit and Laura did not like. Some nights he did not come home at all. He said he was building a tunnel under the sea to France and one day he would take them through it. Laura did not fancy the idea of going in a tunnel under the sea. Dad seemed excited about and would tell the twins of the big machines he had seen, and how they cut the earth and rocks away.

Kit noticed that Mum was getting a fat tummy. She had told both him and Laura that there was to be a new baby in the family and he was quite excited by this. He was secretly hoping for a brother but he didn't tell anyone this. It would be nice to have another boy to play with; someone to show things to; someone who would look up to him. Dad had a younger brother. That was the normal way of things. Then he would have both a brother and a sister. Perhaps they should have a baby girl as well so Laura could have a younger sister. He sometimes wondered why the Baby had to grow in Mum's tummy. Other children at playschool laughed when he told them. They said that brothers and sisters came from heaven. Well most of them said that. Kit knew babies grew in Mummies' tummies.

He and Laura were playing in her bedroom. They quite often played in her room because originally that was the nursery and it had a nice welcoming feel about it. Even three-year-old children can be nostalgic.

"Mum has a baby growing in her tummy," he said to Laura.

"I know, Kit!"

"Well, do you want a boy or a girl Laura?"

She had not thought about until now. A baby was a baby. She hadn't realised that they were of different sexes until she was confronted with the possibility.

"A boy!"

"I want a boy too, then I can play with him."

"Don't be silly Kit. You can't play with a baby"

"Well I can when he grows up. Why do you want a boy Laura?"

"Because I can be like his Mum and look after him. Perhaps Mum will have a girl as well."

"That's what I thought Laura. Do you think we should tell her?"

"I think we should"

They went downstairs. Mum was in the kitchen preparing a bowl of food for Pero the dog, who was dribbling from her mouth in anticipation.

"Mum!" Kit said. "Can we have a baby boy, and perhaps later a girl as well?"

Mum stopped what she was doing. Pero looked at her with despair and at the children with annoyance. Her dinner hung in the air at the end of Mum's arm. She gently tapped Mum's thigh with her paw. To no avail, Mum put the bowl down on the work surface. Pero began to whine.

"Now that is an interesting question. It just so happens that Dad and I went to the hospital this morning. They have a special machine there which looks inside Mum's tummy. We took a peek at the new baby and you'll never guess! We think it's going to be a...."

"A boy! A boy!"

"Yes! A boy. Now this is not guaranteed but I'm pretty sure. You must not tell anyone though" She turned to Pero, who was still whining. "Be quiet! Oh! I'm sorry! Your dinner!"

Pero ate her dinner as quickly as possible in case Mum picked it up again.

One day Dad came home early. He did not look very happy. Mum also had been unhappy all day. They changed their clothes into a more sombre attire. They took the children round to a neighbour's house.

"Where are you going?" asked Kit. "Can't we come too?"

"Yes, we want to come too!" piped up Laura in support.

"We are only going to church." Mum responded comfortingly.

"But it's not Sunday!"

"I know. But this is a special service for someone who has been very sick in your hospital."

When Mum told Dad that the boy had died he was very sad. He knew it would happen. He remembered seeing him on the ward. He saw the acceptance in the eyes of his parents. He remembered when they were told "No more Treatment". He remembered so vividly long conversations about life and death with his father, who throughout the futility of it all still retained hope. Not hope of survival but hope in the future, hope for mankind, that we will all learn from these bitter moments in our lives.

Mum and Dad sat at the back of the church. There were few tears amongst the immediate family. His father helped carry him in, walking with his head held high, with dignity. His mother walked quietly behind, her face set hard, her eyes to the front and a look of determination and resolution. Dad could not avoid shedding a tear. He wanted to do something bold and magnanimous. He vowed that at least the father and mother could be aunt and uncle to their own children.

It was two o'clock on a Saturday morning when a new and free spirit appeared in time and space.

Dad decided to get an electronic pager so that Mum could forewarn him if she had to rush into hospital to give birth.

The call came one Friday evening when he was in his office in Birmingham. He telephoned Mum.

"Don't worry," she said. "The contractions are more severe. I think my water has broken. Don't rush back, just come as soon as possible."

He shouted across to one of his colleagues.

"I've got to go. My wife is in labour"

"Good luck!"

He was home within the hour but Mum was quite relaxed when he arrived and appeared in control. They packed a case and arranged for a neighbour to look after the twins for the night. She came over at about seven o'clock. Mum and Dad went to the General Hospital.

It wasn't long before a little blue faced baby greeted them, screaming for life and air. Dad was startled by his blueness. Was this normal? The midwife said it was quite usual for some babies to look blue when they were born.

The blueness went. He continued to scream and cry. Perhaps he was angry at being dragged in pain from his dark fluid home. Perhaps he was afraid. Who could tell? He could make a lot of noise. His was a declaration of intent. It was like he was the first baby in the world. It was appropriate that his name was Adam. He would not suffer temptation easily. He was a free spirit and would always be so.

Mum stayed in the hospital over the weekend. She was happy and content. She had given birth naturally. The twins had come into the world through Caesarean operation. Although she was delighted and relieved at their birth she nevertheless registered a small amount of disappointment that she had not quite done it by herself. Next time, she vowed, I will. She did, smoothly and courageously, but also with grace and a lot of love and passion for this newborn soul of the world.

He was the most beautiful baby. Dad thought he looked like an angel. His cherub features did have a ring of divinity about them. He was also a very good baby. Reluctantly Mum and Dad had to concede that he was easier to manage than the twins. He took everything in his stride. He was good and he was beautiful. What else could parents wish for? Dad pondered over him and wondered what he would be.

Adam's song

Some child are you
Some throwback to an independent age
You know your way
Life's disarray
Now let us share this great secret.

You will be wild
I know you will, I know you will
But I can cope
A misanthrope
I hope you will not be.

Adam's homecoming was an opportunity to celebrate. Laura loved him the moment she first saw him. He was the living doll of her imagination. Sometimes Mum would allow her to nurse him. These were very special occasions for her. She loved to feel his warm little body against hers and hear his faint warm muzzling against her chest. She sat with him across her lap, afraid to touch him in case his fragility was broken. She placed her finger in the clutch of his hand and laughed out loud when he would not let go. She examined every one of his features. His face, eyes and ears looked so fresh and new, which of course they were, but best of all she liked his hands. She found it fascinating the way his fingers moved. So grown up yet, so young. His hands were so perfectly formed. They were like the hands of an older child. The rest of his body was that of an infant. His hands were older. Perhaps they were made first, she thought.

Well, Adam was born into the world and all was well with Laura. She continued to grow stronger and stronger. The days on the hospital ward seemed a long time ago. Mum and Dad looked forward to the completion of Laura's maintenance therapy in about eighteen months. Although she would never be considered cured by the medical profession, Mum and Dad knew that completion of the maintenance therapy meant that she should be clear of the cancer for good. Everything was going to plan. The whole family put the hospital behind them and concentrated on living.

They decided to go to Bournemouth for a holiday. They had thought of going abroad but Mum and Dad were nervous of being away from the hospital for too long. The consultant said it would be all right, providing they stayed in Western Europe or the U.S.A. There were other constraints as well. There was not much money in the bank. Dad had not earned as much. Anyway Bournemouth was nice. Dad said it was like an up market Blackpool.

Laura remembered a trip to Blackpool before she got sick. They had come to see the illuminations. Mum and Dad called them 'the lights'.

"Wrap up well. We're going to walk along the golden mile. We're not sitting in a queue of cars."

Dad had just parked the car in a side street close to the South Beach and an excellent looking fish and chip shop. The aroma from it tickled Kit's nostrils.

"Can we have Fish and chips Mum?"

"Yes of course you can."

She turned to Dad.

"What are you looking so gloomy about?"

"It's going to take us absolutely ages to walk the lights. We always drove when I was a child."

"Well, it must have been nice to have been so well off. We walked."

"Can we drive?" enquired Kit with a pensive expression.

"No!" said Mum emphatically. "Listen. When I was a little girl, I remember walking the lights when it was so windy that they rocked and swayed violently and bulbs came crashing down around us. The sea was so stormy that the water washed right over the wall onto the front. We got soaked. It's a wonder we were not washed away. We had to wrap up really warm. We couldn't see the lights properly because they were swaying that much."

"Why didn't you just go home?" enquired Laura

"We were happy! We had Fish and chips to keep us warm and the dark, the swaying lights and crashing bulbs and the spray of the sea excited us. We were like explorers in a fantasyland. It was wonderful."

The twins became quiet. Kit hoped the same weather conditions would prevail tonight, but they didn't. It was blustery and cold but there were no crashing bulbs. There were Fish and chips but they didn't quite taste the same as he imagined they did in Mum's day. That's the trouble with grownups, he thought. They make their own childhood sound so wonderful that your own can never compare. Although it was interesting to hear their stories they nevertheless left you with a feeling of being unfulfilled and a disappointment with your own experiences.

Dad always said that childhood is an important time. It is not a time for growing up, because that simply meant it was merely a stepping stone and accordingly not an accomplishment. No, Dad said it was a time and a life in isolation. When we are children we are our true self. Enjoy childhood for the sake of it, not simply as a building block for the future. Your memories will last forever; they will sustain and carry you through the bitter disappointments of adult life. For adult life is the successive and continual contrast of disappointment and hope. It is a meaningless quest toward oblivion and the possible source of truth and light. Only the end will reveal the worthiness of the journey.

Dad said his childhood was happy. Furthermore, he saw no connection between his childhood and his adulthood. He said his childhood and the way he lived it did not make him the person he is today. Perhaps they were different people, Laura thought. Perhaps we all have different people inside us.

As they drove into Bournemouth the sun began to shine.

"Look!" shouted Dad pointing through the windscreen at the silhouetted forms of red aeroplanes moving across the sky in formation. "The Red Arrows have come to meet us. What a welcome!"

Kit and Laura peered out of the window to see. Laura was very excited.

"Can we see some more of them Dad?" She looked through the windscreen anxiously. Dad sped toward the town centre and the beach.

Laura liked the hotel. They all slept in one room. Adam had a cot. He was very quiet but Laura didn't like the smell of dirty nappies when he had to be changed. In the morning they went downstairs for breakfast into the large restaurant where they had dinner the night before. Laura liked her breakfast times at home, but this breakfast time in the hotel was magnificent. There was a large table, the like of which she had never seen before. It contained every known cereal in the world. There were Cornflakes, Weetabix, Muesli and Coco Pops. There were eggs, toast and lots of little containers of butter and jam. There was orange juice with bits in and a great bowl of milk into which people dipped ladles for their cereal. Breakfast was a feast. Best of all there were oodles of tea and Dad could have his favourite egg and bacon, which Laura could share.

Poor old Pero had come on holiday too but she could not sleep in the bedroom or go on the beach. She slept in the car, which was under cover, and Dad took her for lots of long walks.

Laura loved the beach. The sand was so white and clean. She liked especially to build castles and walk on the edge of the water. Kit loved to stand at the water's edge and wait until the tide hit his feet before he ran away. Eventually he moved further into the sea until Mum became anxious. He could not yet swim. He enjoyed the sudden cold splash of water on his legs and the anxiety as the larger waves rushed toward him.

In the evening they would play around the swimming pool of the hotel. Dad would take them down the slide, which made their tummies tickle and to some degree frightened them.

After dinner in the restaurant Laura always felt tired. When she got upstairs she lost her tiredness and wanted to talk with Kit. Dad read a story and her tiredness returned. She quickly fell into a deep sleep.

She was walking along a white sandy beach, which seemed to stretch in a long straight line as far as she could see before it disappeared over the horizon. It reminded her of the beach she knew in Spain in that it was warm and welcoming. As she walked the sand became hotter and hotter. She began to run but could feel the heat following her. Eventually she collapsed with fatigue. The sand became cool again so she arose and started to walk. She stopped in despair and dismay. He was there. The Phantom.

It was the Phantom whom she had known so well in hospital. This time he looked different. He smiled as he always did but was somehow afraid to come too close.

She walked forward cautiously. He walked beside her. She quickened her pace and he kept up with her. She became frightened and ran so fast that the salt air and the salt of her tears of fear blinded her eyes. She kept running as fast as she could, but could still feel his presence.

Suddenly she felt the ground beneath her give away. When she opened her eyes she was confronted by a void of emptiness set in the silvery sand. It was the bottomless pit she had heard so much about. She began to fall.

Her descent was suddenly halted. She was lifted up and placed back on the sand by two strong arms. She felt the sweet breath of her rescuer on her forehead. She opened her eyes to greet him. It was Jesus. Jesus from the picture smiling with the lamp still in his hand. She nestled into his warm, welcoming white robes.

"I am the way", he said. "Believe in me."

She sat up. He was gone. The room was quiet. Adam was sucking his thumb in his sleep. Mum and Kit were murmuring the sounds of deep slumber. She looked around the room. Dad was lying with his head on his arm and was looking directly at her.

"Go to sleep Laura. It's only a dream"

She looked at him silently for a few seconds, then lay her head on the pillow and fell asleep.

Laura liked to be on the beach. It was a world so different from the sleepy claustrophobia of a summer in the countryside. She liked her countryside. The humming bees, the thick heavy scent of wheat and barley, the wagtails skimming the hedgerow. It absorbed and consumed her into complacency. She was consumed in peace, sweet tranquil peace. But here, beside the sea, she felt liberation and the wild excitement of unexpected freedom. Perhaps it was the freedom associated with the expansive space of the sea. To Laura the sea and sky seemed as one. Even the sand was expansive and appeared to be a part of sea and sky.

The sand was a wonderful medium to play with. She could build, dig, bury or just let it run through her fingers like minute crystals of gold. To be able to stay on the beach all day was a great delight. They had lunch, drinks, and ice cream on the sand and Dad fell asleep whilst reading his book. Adam lay in his pram under a blue parasol, blinked at the blueness of the sea, then slept and dreamed of ships and gulls and buccaneers. They were lazy glorious times. No timetable beckoned. The only governors were hunger and tiredness. On occasions they momentarily left the beach to browse shops and seaside arcades. Dad had a go on the air rifles, Mum tried the darts. The twins went on roundabouts and swings and Adam continued to sleep and dream.

On the last night they organised a little party in the hotel room. Mum had bought some party food, sausage rolls, crisps and things. She laid them out in a little display. Dad was sent downstairs to buy some "nice drinks from the bar". He decided to have a pint of beer whilst he was there. Other male residents stood at the bar discussing the weather and cricket. Dad joined them. When he had finished his drink he ordered a bottle of sparkling white wine and two glasses.

One of the men, seeing the wine, turned to him with a look of some envy.

"It's all right for you young married couples. Wait until you have children. Then you'll be glad to escape for a pint and a few minutes peace."

Dad turned to the barman.

"Can I have two bottles of Coke with straws and a glass of orange cordial for the children?"

"That's what I call duty" said the man.

"That's what I call life." said Dad, and smiled. He was glad to get back upstairs.

Chapter 14

All children catch colds

Mum kept busy during the remaining weeks of summer. She took the twins to playschool and began Adam's development. He came off the breast after a few weeks. Dad began to share in feeding him. He liked especially to get up for the early morning feed. Dad and Adam would sit in the kitchen at five o'clock in the morning, just as the sun climbed the poplar trees and reached its golden fingers through the kitchen window. Dad would read a book as Adam took his early dawn breakfast. They were peaceful quiet times and Dad became bonded to Adam.

Mum continued to worry about Laura. The weekly clinic continued. One day she became so worried that the sickness was coming back that she asked Dad to go and see the consultant. The consultant was busy. Instead Dad talked to the health visitor. She assured him that everything was all right. With her experience she could tell when a child was going to relapse. Laura was not such a child. Dad hoped that Mum would be content with this. Certainly her blood tests had been satisfactory. The trouble with blood tests is that they are too late. By the time the Leukaemia gets into the blood there is very little the clinicians can do. They need to detect the leukaemia cells in the marrow but are unwilling to take too many bone marrow samples, as they are afraid to unsettle the child.

Laura continued to grow stronger.

Dad liked to watch her grow. He would silently watch her movements, her limbs, the way she walked and the gentleness of her gesticulations. She was a little person. Her contours fascinated him. Her movements were rapid and responsive. She never paused. Yet she could move with grace. He especially liked to see her when she felt she was unobserved. When she ran her head bobbed in tune with her body. Her legs moved as rapidly as possible. Her arms swung in harmony. Her whole body was in tune with getting where she wanted to be as quickly as possible. When she got there she settled quickly and waited for something to happen.

"Are you happy Laura?" Dad asked as they sat in the garden one Sunday evening.

It was near her bedtime. Kit was playing a game with Mum. They had enjoyed a day in the garden. Laura looked morose. She looked at Dad silently and made no answer.

"Did you enjoy today?" he pursued.

"Yes Dad!" she replied with some annoyance.

What is on her mind? He thought.

Today has been so nice, she thought, yet, I feel as if there is something wrong. It's the way they look at me, especially Mum. I have not dreamed for several weeks yet I feel a foreboding sense of an imminent threat. It's as if someone wants to take me away from my happiness.

She tried to think of Jesus with his lamp, but she could not bring him to mind. Instead she thought of the man in the white mask and how much he wanted to dance with her. She pushed him to the back of her mind and concentrated on Jesus. He was not there. She felt sleepy.

"Bed!" she demanded of Dad.

He swooped her up into his arms and took her upstairs.

"Don't be sad Laura" he said as he closed her Clifford the Sheep book. "You are doing ever so well. The doctors are very pleased with you and soon your treatment will end."

She was surprised at what he said. She had not been thinking of the treatment. She had been thinking about the way she was different to Kit. His happiness was directly relative to the way he was treated and the mood of the day. Hers was attributable to the mood of her mind. Sometimes she felt very sad and did not understand the reason. Sometimes she worried about her body and the way it felt. She did not know why. Still she worried. She heard grown ups call it depression. Children don't become depressed. She felt sad, teary even, and the tears turned into anger and resentment of those who loved her and those she thought she ought to love. This in itself made her even angrier and she fell into a spiral of despair which only sleep could dispel.

When she awoke the sun was shining on the house opposite her bedroom. Everywhere was quiet save a distant noise downstairs. It was Dad preparing his breakfast. She had awoken in a panic. She did not remember going to sleep, only a vague recollection of Dad leaning over her.

Was today the day he went to work or was it the day he stayed at home. She could not recollect where she was in the week even though she had learned all the days. She climbed out of bed and picking up her pink slippers made her way downstairs to Dad.

She stood at the kitchen door and watched him through the glass as he busied himself, tidying, cleaning and preparing breakfast. She sucked her thumb and watched. Eventually he turned to notice her. He opened the door with a look of delight on his face.

"Hello baby! Have you come to see Daddy?"

She did not answer. It was not really a question.

"What day is it today?" he asked plonking her down on her usual chair.

She did not know and as a consequence stayed silent, upset that she did not know.

"It's Saturday! What does Daddy do on a Saturday?"

"Stay at home," she said mumbling through her thumb.

"What does Daddy do?"

"Stays at home!" she said more loudly, with a laugh and without the thumb in her mouth.

"Yes, of course he does. It's a pity today is Friday"

She looked dejected.

"It's Saturday. Of course it is! Would Daddy tell fibs?"

"Yes!" Laura shouted and chuckled with resonant pleasure.

Laura grew in strength as Adam grew in size and awareness. She watched him grow. He was a doll to her and she liked to cuddle and love him. She liked it best when he was put on her knee. His baby vanilla like smell was good. The taste of his flesh as she kissed him was exquisite joy to her. His gentle murmurings and sighs gave her comfort.

Her own body she likened to his. It was as if she had started to grow again. Her hair was new. The scars and marks of the treatment had disappeared from her body. She felt good about life, when she was awake that is, for she still dreamt, though not as often.

Mum continued with her concerts throughout the summer. However most of her time was spent on rehearsal. St Matthew's Passion was the next big one. Dad would be singing too. Her heart was not in her singing. She often thought of the songs she and Dad composed together. They were love songs. No time now. Now I am confined to the home, a dog biting my feet and a meal to prepare. No time for composition.

Most nights now she would go to bed alone. Dad would stay downstairs playing his music. Usually melancholic music. Sometimes he played some of his own compositions. It's a pity he's not a better singer, she thought, but she always lay awake to listen.

I wonder if you wonder
How I felt about you
When I met you on that day
We walked for miles and talked for hours
And jumped the puddles in the lane.

You came across serenely
In the photographs I took
Though smiling rather shyly
Like the images I keep.

Oh girl you are a precious thing
It's painful loving you
No glance, no sharp response
Can stop me wanting you, I need you.

Summer turned to autumn, gradually, slowly and positively. The leaves and sky began to change in colour, perspective and clarity. The air was moist and mysterious. Laura had feelings of nostalgia. The gold and bronze of the trees were reflected in the air.

She knew that Dad had these feelings also. He constantly played Brahms symphonies. They were autumnal he said. Avenues of trees and things he said. Reminiscences from the past, from Hapsburg, from a different life, a different age, an age he never knew. His nostalgia fed hers.

Autumn is a strange time. The Americans call it 'The Fall'. Dad said that this was a better name for it. It not only symbolised the fall of the foliage but the decline into winter and the descent of complacent quiet into reflection and nostalgia. Dad liked the 'Fall'. It was a strange thing to like, but Dad sometimes had strange likings, Laura thought.

One evening as the sun began to fall over the treetops and Mum was about to call the twins in from playing she got a telephone call from Radella's Mum. She rang many times. Mum was always pleased to speak to her. They shared the same ideals but expressed them in different ways. This time she did not sound the same. Mum knew that there had been problems with Radella and that she had needed more treatment. Things had not gone well.

"We're on the ward. She's relapsed. We knew she had. They said the treatment was not working too well. She was just not responding"

Mum had a long conversation with Radella's Mum. She was upset, and so was Dad when he was told. Mum decided to tell Laura because she wanted to visit Radella next time she was at clinic at the hospital. Laura went quiet when she heard.

"Radella has something different to your illness. It's a totally different thing altogether. The doctors and Nurses want to make absolutely sure that Radella has no sickness left inside her so they are giving a little bit more treatment. That means she be spending a few days in hospital. Would you like to go and see her next time we go to clinic?"

Laura was sucking her thumb whilst Mum spoke to her. She nodded. Then, taking the thumb out of her mouth she said, "Can Kit come too?"

Laura remembered the Sunday in the summer when Radella had come to see her. The three children played together all afternoon. First they rode tricycles and pedal cars outside. Then they came inside to play with trains and dolls. Laura's Mum and Radella's Mum sat with a bottle of wine and chatted all afternoon. Dad and Radella's Dad played with the children.

They invented crazy stupid little games that made the children laugh. They rolled on their backs on the floor whilst Radella, Kit and Laura climbed all over them.

"I don't know who are the bigger children?" observed Mum when Dad was pretending to be a horse with Kit on his back.

For tea Mum had made the twins' favourite; a buffet. This comprised of sausages on sticks, cucumber slices, little squares of cheese, strips of celery and carrot, small crackers with an assortment of toppings and lots and lots of different flavours of potato crisps. The grown ups had smoked salmon and Ardennes pate. Laura tried some of the smoked salmon but wasn't very enthusiastic about it.

Laura enjoyed that day. It was a day of pure indulgence.

So the autumn began to settle in and around the village. Tractors were out every day ploughing the fields, after the harvest, to make ready for the winter wheat and barley. The apple trees were full of fruit and Mum and Laura boxed them. Kit preferred to help with stringing the onions. The vegetable garden that had once looked so rich now looked depleted and forlorn as the last few green beans began to shrivel and the late lettuce plants sprang up into long shoots. The air became damp and cold. Each morning the grass was wet and there were little tracks where nocturnal creatures had made their way. Hedgehogs began to feed at the back door and some of the old familiar bird songs were no longer there. At the weekends the guns could be heard across toward Crow Spinney and the Hall. Some evenings Dad would walk out with his gun but always came back empty handed. Horses filled the meadow with riders in black and red. A whole new season had started and with it a change in the weather.

Laura caught a cold.

Chapter 15

Mum knows best

Laura's cold made her feel very tired. It sometimes made her feel very hot, but the heat soon turned to cold and she would be shivering. Dad said that colds were a nuisance. When he had one he was always grumpy, he said. Laura could understand that because she felt grumpy too. Mum did not like Laura to have any kind of sickness, even a simple cold, whilst she was on her maintenance therapy.

The next time she went to clinic they said her count was 'a bit low'. They said she had better come on the ward for a few days to clear up her infection. This had obviously caused her count to drop a bit. These things happen. A few days on antibiotics under observation would sort it out.

Mum did not like it. She was not comfortable with the situation and she said so. They smiled at her and said she was over reacting.

"You have been very fortunate so far," said the consultant. "Laura has been at home for a good few months. Many children have to come back to hospital for treatment."

"You are worrying unnecessarily", said the health visitor. "I'm sure it will be fine.

"They don't want to take any risks," said Dad. " A few days on the ward will clear it up. We'll be back home by weekend."

Mum took her in on the Monday morning. Radella was still on the ward.

They gave her antibiotics. They checked her blood every day. It was erratic. The readings varied. Only one reading had continuity. Her white cells increased.

"Of course they will!" they said. "She needs more white cells to fight the infection."

Of course she did!

Dad stayed every night at the hospital. Like in the old days, he thought, but at least we will be out of here in a few days. A few days of discomfort with the weekend at home as a reward.

Laura was quite happy to be back on the ward. When Mum said they had to go back in she was frightened. I'm going to be sick again, she thought, all those terrible drugs. I don't want it. In fact she felt quite well apart from the cold, which began to get better now that she was on antibiotics. The only thing she didn't like was the blood test every day. To be on the ward and feel quite well was a strange sensation for Laura. She felt confident. She was also pleased to see some of the nurses she had known previously. Then she had not liked them all. Now she did and she smiled and laughed with them. Some of the children were the same. She assumed that they, like her, had come back for a check up but felt a little sadness when she saw how unwell some of them looked.

Mum did not like the way the blood test results went. The consultant repeatedly told her that this was quite normal with an infection.

"How do you know it hasn't come back?" she asked on one of the morning ward rounds.

The consultant stopped reading the chart and calmly looked at her.

"We don't know. But I'm sure it hasn't."

Laura had been on the ward for four days. The lack of communication from the consultants was worrying. Laura's count continued to drop. Mum rang Dad whilst he was with a client. He found he could not concentrate on his meeting and excused himself. They looked at him strangely as he left.

When he arrived at the hospital everything seemed fine. Laura seemed cheerful and pleased to see him. He could not understand why Mum was so worried.

"She's had a bone marrow test, that's why I'm worried. Why should they give her a test if they did not suspect something"

"Perhaps because you have spent all week pestering them to give her a test. You said it was the only way they could really know. A blood test is too late. When the Leukaemia is in the blood it's too late, you said."

"Well it is. But the fact they have agreed must indicate that they are worried"

The consultant came to see Laura. She was checked over by the consultant and a colleague.

"Have you the results yet?" asked Mum

"These things take time. We'll let you know as soon as possible. You just concentrate on looking after Laura. She looks fine. You are doing a good job"

He turned to Laura and smiled.

If only they could spot these things earlier, thought Mum. In the United States and some other Health Authorities they have blood tests earlier in order to eliminate the options of cancer. They also do regular bone marrow tests to monitor what is happening in the marrow. Here we have to wait until something goes wrong and then we fight back.

She asked the consultant about this.

"If we gave the children blood tests and bone marrow aspirations for the sake of monitoring what is going on think of the discomfort the child would go through. In most cases it would be for nothing and a totally unnecessary worry for the parents as well as discomfort for the child."

"But isn't it better to have some discomfort now, even if it might be unnecessary? From what I've read, in the United States they eliminate all the worst possible options as soon as possible."

"So! You have been doing some reading. Now that is very good but you cannot compare what goes on in America to Belgrave."

"Why not?" butted in Dad.

"Because we don't have to pay for health care in this country."

"What difference does that mean?" Dad pursued.

"It means we have to balance our decisions against what is economical and likely to yield a result."

"You mean we don't have these tests because it would cost too much?"

"That's one way of putting it but I'm afraid that's far too simplistic. We have to cater for the majority and not put everyone under discomfort when in the majority of cases it is not necessary."

"I think you are digging yourself a hole," Dad continued with resignation and a shake of the head.

Mum made as if to speak.

"I had to insist on Laura having a blood test when she first became ill. Now I have to insist on a bone marrow test. Is that right?"

"It's very commendable of you. I think we are all aware of the amount of reading up you have done and the way you both take a keen and active role in Laura's treatment."

Dad stepped forward.

"What do you expect? Should we resign ourselves to leaving her entirely at the disposition of other people? It's not a question of us not trusting you. We have to. We have no other choice. We simply want the best for her. We are talking of life, not of buying something off a shelf."

"When will the results be ready?" asked Mum in a calm but resolute voice looking at Dad with an expression that told him to calm down.

"As soon as possible."

The consultant began to walk away, then after a few steps paused and looked back.

"About tea time."

The consultant turned and walked directly to the nurses' station where he conferred with the ward sister. She looked at Mum and Dad, then looked at the consultant and nodded. The consultant left her and walked into the ward office, closing the door after him.

"See. The consultant doesn't seem unduly worried. It's you. You are almost willing it back."

Immediately after saying it he regretted it. Perhaps he felt that if he willed this thing not to happen then it wouldn't. Anyway, if it was to happen again perhaps they were better off not knowing.

"They know something is wrong already," said Mum observing the nurse's eye movement.

"I think you are jumping to conclusions," said Dad.

One of the other mothers came across to Laura's bed.

"When are you going home? Have you heard anything yet?"

"We don't know. Laura had a bone marrow test today," said Mum.

"Oh. I'm sorry. Still, she looks so well. I'm sure it's just a precaution."

"We hope so."

They sat and waited. Dad read Laura a story but his heart was not in it and she knew it. Kit tried to cheer everyone up by fooling around.

"Kit! Don't!" cried Laura.

Tea Time came and went. There was no sign of a consultant. The nurses knew nothing. The sky went dark and the ward lights came on.

The consultant appeared on the ward. Like all good consultants the body language betrayed nothing. He walked the circuit of beds and spoke to al the parents apart from Mum and Dad. The children's charts were read and discussed. There must have been a joke because one of the parents laughed. A little boy's tummy was examined. The little boy didn't like it but tolerated it. The consultant nodded something to the parents, smiled at the boy and walked over toward the nurses' station. On the way across one or two more children and adults were acknowledged.

All this time Mum and Dad waited for the consultant to come to them. But that didn't happen. Mum's and Dad's mouths must have been wide open; they were so aghast that they had not been spoken to. Dad began to complain to Mum. She was becoming very upset. To wait like this was one of the worst possible pains. The uncertainty, vulnerability and exposure of their situation were unbearable. The next few hours would determine the course of events for the rest of their lives, of that she was sure. The outcome could be good or bad news. They would be either devastated with sadness or overcome with joy. The extremes of these emotions were nightmarish. It made her want to scream. There was a dull persistent pain in her head. Her body felt sick. She just wanted to escape. Surely all this anguish has been for nothing. Really bad things cannot happen to a family like us. We have suffered enough. Everyone said that Laura looked fine. Surely it cannot have come back?

By this time Laura had decided to go off and play with Kit who had wandered toward the playroom. Radella went running after her.

Dad sat by Mum. She knew his thoughts must be the same. He didn't speak, but sat twiddling his hair, rubbing his eyes, anything to ease the tension. He wondered what brought them here. Why are we in this situation, he thought? He suddenly hated God. He thought of the words of Jesus on the Cross. Why have you forsaken me? God was never there when you wanted him. Anyway, what could God do about this situation? If the cancer was in Laura it was in Laura. God could not take it way, only chemotherapy could do that. Chemotherapy was the new Saviour. But why couldn't God take it away? If he indeed did create life why could he not change the course of events of nature? Is he so powerless, or is he in perpetual conflict with evil, with the devil, and is this evil personified in the form of human sickness and frailty?

The consultant smiled at the ward sister. She smiled back. Still there was no attempt to come over. Eventually Dad could tolerate it no longer. He walked over to the Nurses Station.

"Excuse me," he said in an apologetic and conspicuous tone.

"Just a moment," said the consultant, and continued with the discussion with the nurse for several minutes.

Dad looked at Mum. She was perturbed. Dad could see that she was also getting angry.

"Excuse me, could I have a word"," Dad said a little more firmly.

The consultant said a final word to the nurse who walked away.

"Yes?"

"It's just that...well...it's just that we expected someone to come and see us before now. You said tea time and we know that other people have had their test results."

"We are very busy. These things cannot be hurried and we are not used to being harassed by parents over test results. The laboratory has a set procedure and we just have to wait," the consultant said with a polite smile.

"Do you have Laura's results yet?"

The consultant looked at Dad closely.

"I was actually going to speak to you later. But, being as you have approached me, I might as well tell you now. Your wife has been very clever. They say a Mum knows best. It looks as if the Leukaemia is creeping back." He smiled benignly.

"What?"

Dad's mind began to swim.

"What? What are you saying?"

"It looks as if Laura's Leukaemia is coming back. As I say your wife appears to have known all along and we didn't. That's rather clever of her isn't it?"

Dad looked over to Mum appealingly. She knew something was wrong and was already on her way over, a look of alarm in her face. Dad waited for her to arrive before he spoke again. Then he turned to her.

"It's come back! It's come back! They said she had a good chance, but it's come back." He looked at the consultant. "It was A.L.L. Other A.L.L children don't relapse."

The consultant ignored him not through a lack of courtesy but because of a preoccupation with trying to calm these difficult parents. I must remember to put a note on the file about their attitude, the consultant thought. Difficult parents. Anti-the medical profession. The consultant looked at Mum and smiled.

"Well! Aren't we a clever girl! You were right all along, sadly and unfortunately."

"I knew it! I knew it!"

"Yes you did! But I must confess we didn't expect it. You were ahead of us. But we must have hope, you know"

"You must have expected it! You knew her count on admission was high. I saw the notes," she said.

"Did you indeed? And who showed you the notes?"

"No one. I just saw them."

Dad turned to the consultant who by this time looked worried and wanted to pursue the matter of the reading of the notes a little further.

"So! Where do we go from here? What are you going to do?"

Mum began to cry.

The consultant began to edge away. They were not to know. The mind of this medical practitioner had been reeling with the options that were available to them and to the little girl. The consultant could still see the lab results scribbled down in the familiar handwriting and remembered thinking how strange it was that whether the results or good or bad, whether they mean life or death, the form is still the same and the handwriting never varies. But this is a science. It's the chemistry of the human body and of the blood. It's another problem to be solved, one that will keep me awake until I solve it. It's another variant and if I can treat it then it's another one off the list.

" I haven't thought of anything yet. I was as surprised by the results as you were. It's not that common for A.L.L patients to relapse this early unless there are other....."

"Perhaps if you'd listened to my wife in......."

"Well, we can't just decide everything on what the parents think can we? I must go."

The consultant was going to say that A.L.L. patients tend not to relapse as early as others unless there are other factors involved. What she said about the high white count was worrying and the consultant knew it but colleagues disagreed.

With that the consultant turned and walked away.

Mum and Dad stood by the nurse's desk in absolute disbelief. It was a dream. It was unreal. They continued to stand there without speaking for seconds that felt like minutes. Life around them continued. Nurses busied themselves with children and parents. Drips were put up. The medicine trolley arrived. Temperatures were taken and the telephone rang. The florescent lights blinked and flickered.

They made their way back to Laura's bed. It was empty. She was playing with Kit, not realising what had started to grow again inside her.

All the parents on the ward knew there was something wrong. The place was quiet. They looked across at Laura's bed and spoke quietly amongst themselves. Radella's Mum and Dad came over.

"What's wrong?" said Radella's Mum, "as if I didn't know"

"It's come back! Oh! It's come back!"

Radella's Mum leaned over and hugged Mum. The parents on the ward must have heard or guessed what Mum had said. There were murmurs of despair around the ward. Mothers protectively clung to their sons and fathers to their daughters. Some children were newly diagnosed; others had come in for checkups. Some had relapsed. Laura had relapsed. Mum turned to Dad, almost accusingly. Radella's Mum was holding her hand.

"You know what this means don't you. You do know?"

Dad was confused. He did not reply. He just looked at her.

"She has relapsed on treatment. The treatment did not work. It didn't work! They got it wrong! They got it horribly wrong! They said her white cell count was okay. I knew it was high. Those damned clinical trials! These damned consultants. This damned poor man's excuse for an oncology unit staffed by untrained personnel. What chance do we stand here? You realise her chances now are not good, if they exist at all. Our only hope now is a bone marrow transplant. Oh my God! Oh No!"

Dad felt empty of feeling, devoid of emotion. He felt it was his fault even though he knew Mum's accusations were not directed at him but at the world.

The attention of the ward became focussed on Laura's bed. Everyone knew there was bad news and they shared it.

Just then a saviour arrived. It was the health visitor; a stupid job title, Dad thought, considering she was the life soul of the ward. She briskly walked directly to Laura's bed.

"I've heard. What a mess! But we've got to look forward. We're all surprised, but there is still hope"

"But you should have heard what the consultant said"

"I can imagine, consultants! They haven't got a bloody clue about how to talk to people, especially where children are concerned. I've been covering up for them for over twenty years and they've never known it. They're bloody useless. What's going to be done?"

Dad stopped talking to Radella's Dad.

"We don't know. The consultant just walked off," he said.

"I just can't believe it's happened to Laura," said the health visitor.

The sound of childish laughter entered the ward.

"Dad! Dad! Help! Kit's coming to get me!" Laura screamed with delight as Kit pursued her up the ward. She threw her arms around Dad's legs. Mum looked away. She didn't want Laura to see her so upset. Kit tried to grab at Laura through Dad's legs.

"What are you talking about?" Laura asked, looking up at grown up faces set in grey. "What's the matter with Mum?"

"She doesn't feel very well," The health visitor replied putting on the softest friendliest voice she could muster and trying to avoid a total out and out lie. Experience had taught her that children could haunt you with your lies. It was always better to tell some half-truth if the truth itself was not palatable. Laura seemed temporarily satisfied.

Radella's Mum enticed Kit and Laura away to play with Radella. Laura looked back at the group of grown ups in serious discussion. She didn't like it. She was not sure what could be wrong but things were certainly not right. After all, I am three, she thought. I hope Mum isn't really poorly because then we might have to stay in here a bit longer to make her better. She conjured up a picture of Mum sitting in a hospital bed but she knew that couldn't be right. Mums don't come to this place to be made better. She thought of home and felt a tingle of excitement at the prospect of the weekend. The Saturday morning walk to the swing park with Dad, perhaps a walk in the field. If the weather was bad they might have a dollies tea party. Best of all she hoped they would go swimming. She loved to swim, sitting on Dad and pretending he was a ship whilst he floated around the little children's pool. Kicking her legs in the water and feeling the sensation of movement. Jumping in to be caught in Dad's arms. It was so good.

"Lets play swimming, Kit!"

"But we haven't got our water wings, Laura."

"And you haven't got any water!" giggled Radella, and her and Kit fell about laughing.

Laura looked put out.

"We don't need water, look!"

She waved her arms around and made little swimming movements toward the corridor. She was at Hinckley Swimming Pool. There was Dad in front. She would swim to him. She could hear the echoing noise of the other children. The water was warm and there were lots of waves because the pool was full today. It was Saturday, the day that Dad stayed at home. The other two, still giggling, began to wave their arms in the same swimming motions. Laura led their laughter and became lost in a world of play. They abandoned the ward to a new sorrow. Radella's Mum followed them at a distance.

The ward sister came over. She was concerned at the deteriorating atmosphere on the ward.

"Come on," said the health visitor. "Lets go in the office at the end of the corridor. It's empty."

Mum, Dad, the health visitor, the ward sister and Radella's Mum piled into the office.

"Why? Why? Oh why?" Mum demanded.

"It seems so unfair. She was doing so well," said the health visitor. She then promptly disappeared through the door. Dad wondered where she had gone. Within seconds she re-appeared with a bottle of beer and a packet of cigarettes.

"These might take the edge off things."

"I don't smoke," said Mum.

"No, but I do" said the health visitor. "I stopped ten years ago but I need one now."

She poured some beer in a cup and handed to Dad. He sipped at it automatically. He probably would have done anything that anyone told him. His mind was numb, incapable of rational thought.

Mum tore the curtains open, and then flung them to one side.

"I'm sorry," she said.

"It's all right! Tear them. It doesn't matter. Wreck the place if you want. Do whatever you want if it helps," the health visitor said.

"I just want Laura to be well, that's all. I can't believe this has happened to us again."

"We came in this office to be told that Laura had Leukaemia and that she had a fighting chance. What chance have we now?" asked Dad.

"We are here," said Radella's Mum quietly.

"I don't want to go home tonight," said Mum. She remembered the very first time Laura came in. They both went home that night. It seemed the right thing to do, but Mum had doubts afterwards.

"Can't we all stay?" asked Dad.

The ward sister looked concerned. Where will they all fit, she thought?

The health visitor knew a place.

"Look. I'll sort something out. The whole family can stay in the Seminar Room. There's enough room."

"We could put Laura in there as well. Just for tonight," said the ward sister, wanting to contribute something.

"What happens now?" asked Dad.

"We need to ask the consultant," said the health visitor.

"I don't think the consultant knows yet. I don't think this thing has been worked out."

The health visitor left the room to fetch the consultant.

The air was a little calmer. There was a smell of cigarette smoke and beer that caused the consultant to frown slightly. The smell was unpalatable to a clinical nostril. The consultant was on the defensive, expecting a full frontal attack from Mum and Dad. There was one. They demanded to know the course of action that was planned.

"There is no automatic way forward. When Laura was first diagnosed, the course of treatment was straightforward. She was put on a clinical trial and regime B was considered the right one. Now we are in a totally different situation. There are no clinical trials. She has relapsed on treatment. It's not going to be easy but what I do want to say is that there are many options open to us. For example, coming up in the Lift I was thinking about a bone marrow transplant. Now with a transplant the problem is usually finding a suitable donor. So we usually have to think very carefully before putting someone on a fairly horrendous course of treatment to get him or her ready for the transplant. Sometimes we have to think very carefully about the quality of life. It is often better not to go ahead with difficult treatment if the chances of a happy outcome are not good."

"So. What are you saying? "Asked Dad.

"I'm saying there are lots of options and we have to think very carefully about what is the best for Laura."

"But are you saying that perhaps there might be no treatment, that perhaps we should let her, let her..."

"That is for you to decide. Terminal care might be the best way. I say might. But lets not discuss that now. There are a lot more things to consider. Now I thought about a bone marrow transplant because Laura is a twin. More than that she is a non identical twin. Kit might be a good match."

"I would have thought that an identical twin would have been a better match."

"No. No. With an identical twin there is always the possibility of them having the same problem."

The atmosphere in the room became strangely calm. There was some hope.

The consultant went on to say. "All this is a little hypothetical at the moment. We first of all have to get her into remission. Once we do that then we consider further treatment, transplants, whatever. So I would like to commence induction remission tomorrow. Is that all right?"

Mum and Dad spoke in unison.

"Yes, yes, of course."

"Good! Excellent! Now I have some other patients to see. Please be assured we shall do everything we can, everything that is appropriate. But I have to emphasise we are in a very serious situation. We are all in God's hands from now on"

"God's?" queried Dad "No! I think we are all in your hands and the hands of your colleagues."

"Well. Whatever, but a little divine help or inspiration would not come amiss"

With that he left.

"Why God?" Dad asked of the health visitor.

"He may be aware that you are church goers."

"Why? Is it on the file?" asked Mum with a cynical smile.

Chapter 16

So be it

The nurses emptied the meeting room and moved in Laura's bed and drip. They erected camp beds for the rest of the family. They brought tea and biscuits. They played with Kit and Laura whilst Mum and Dad sorted themselves out.

"Take him across to the pub for an hour," the health visitor said to Radella's dad.

Dad sorted out his feelings with another man. He felt better for it. He knew they had started yet another battle in this awful campaign, this campaign against an unseen enemy. An enemy who only showed himself when he was winning. When he got back in the hospital the meeting room had become a private ward. They all settled down for the night. Adam went in an old ward pram for the night.

Dad turned off the lights and within a few seconds everyone was asleep with the exception of Mum and Dad. They both lay awake staring at the ceiling, consumed with their own private thoughts. They did not reach for each other or comfort one another. How could they? Did they not share the same pain within the same window of time? They thought of what they, and in particular Laura, had to go through from today was horrible and bleak. They were faced with total uncertainty. A long, long battle. Could they sustain it? Could Laura take it? They both fell in and out of sleep, waking fitfully into a living nightmare and falling into dreams of horror and perplexity.

Laura lay awake too. Mum and Dad thought she was asleep. She heard them both cry. They tried to do it silently, but she could hear the stifled sobs beneath their flimsy hospital blankets. She was frightened. Eventually she could fight the sleep no longer and fell into a deep dream.

She was sailing high and low on her swing. Dad pushed her, higher and higher she went. So high she could see over the treetops and Dad was but a small insignificant thing on the ground. She was not afraid. She felt exhilarated and happy. She was close to the clouds and the sky. This was her favourite time. It was Saturday. Dad was at home and he had taken her to her favourite swing. There would be a walk afterwards and something nice for lunch. After that perhaps a bike ride, or, better still, a dollies tea party.

Suddenly things changed. Dad turned and walked away. She saw him walk out of the playground. She was alone. She screamed for him to come back.

"It's all right Laura, I'm here"

Kit was in the next swing to her. She had forgotten him.

"I'll look after you Laura. I love you as well"

"Get me down, Kit. Please get me down"

"We can't get down Laura. We have to wait for Dad to come back"

Just then she saw a figure walk into the park. The swing slowed down and gradually stopped. The figure stooped down to pick her up. As soon as she felt his breath on her hands she knew whom it was. She cried for her Dad. The figure stepped back. As he did so Laura saw another figure by the gate. It was Jesus. He looked sad.

"Jesus! Come here!" she cried, but he didn't. He stayed where he was, his head bowed. Laura felt despair. Just then the swing began to ascend again. The phantom was pushing it.

"I am in control now'" he said.

As she rose higher she could once again see above the treetops. Kit was still below her looking up. In the distance she saw the figure of Dad running toward the playground.

"Hurry Dad! Hurry!" she cried. She watched him for many minutes but he never seemed to arrive.

She woke with a start. Dad was leaning on his elbow watching her.

"Another dream Laura?"

"Another dream Dad!"

He came over and lay next to her until she fell asleep. He could tell by her breathing that she was sleeping in peace. He went back to his camp bed and dozed until the grey light filtered through the chinks in the burgundy curtains and he could hear the sound of trolleys on the ward. It was a new day. They were back in reality. Now the fight to save his daughter's life had begun once again. He felt brave. He felt proud to be here at her side. But above all he felt a deep pervading grief that consumed his heart. It was a trough out of which he must lift himself. All that counted now was the well being of Laura. Everything they did now had to be through the love of Laura.

The next day, which was a Saturday, was spent in the commencement of a new regime of induction chemotherapy.

In the evening they decided to have fish and chips.

"You had better ask the ward sister if is all right to bring fish and chips in" said Mum after she had suggested the idea.

The ward sister nodded in approval when asked. It was not strictly allowed but who is going to refuse a family in this predicament?

Dad went to buy the fish and chips from a local shop. It was not the best Fish and Chip shop, but they tasted like the outside world. They represented normality and home.

The ward was quiet that evening. The ward sister was a general nurse. Mum asked her about the timing of the drugs for now Laura was on chemotherapy once again to induce remission. It soon became evident that the sister knew little about leukaemia.

"I only work nights'" she said. "I heard about Laura's illness so I got a book out about Leukaemia."

"What the hell are we doing here," said Dad when the nurse had gone, "You know more about it than she does"

They carried on eating their fish and chips. Adam could eat none. He was still on the bottle. Everyone was quiet and worried. How could they hope to succeed? There were no doctors around save a Junior. The nurses knew nothing of Laura's illness. They had not seen a consultant for days. They were depressed. They ate in silence. In the background the television flickered. The windows reflected the blackness of the evening.

Suddenly Laura began giggling. The giggling broke into a deep throaty laugh, which was her trademark. The laughter turned hysterical.

"Kit! Kit!" she chortled and choked.

Mum and Dad turned to look at Kit.

He sat quietly and serenely staring straight forward with a look of sincerity and seriousness. A potato chip protruded from each of his ears.

Mum and Dad choked on their food and burst into laughter.

"Oh Kit!" cried Mum. "It's not very hygienic, but who cares. Oh Kit!"

"Well done Kit!"

"Why? What have I done?" Kit said, taking the chips out of his ears and eating them.

"One day you will know," replied Dad.

Chapter 17

Do they know better?

Sunday morning eventually sneaked in behind a veil of medical ambivalence. Mum's and Dad's concerns had not been eased by the night's course of events. The drugs should have been administered just after tea. Dad had to chase the junior doctor who was working all weekend and who was trying to look after four wards. Chemotherapy drugs have to be applied at precise times to coincide with the body's food cycle. They are more effective if taken this way, according to the clinicians, and they should know. Laura's drugs were eventually given to her at midnight.

He complained to the night sister about the late administration of the drug.

"I'm sure it will be all right," she said.

"Do you understand the nature of Laura's situation?" Dad asked her aggressively.

"Well I know she has Leukaemia"

"What else do you know?"

"Not much more. I am afraid I am not trained in paediatric oncology. I am a general medical nurse. You two seem to know quite a lot. What is the prognosis for Laura."

Mum handed her a book.

"Perhaps you ought to read this. It will tell you all about the different forms of childhood leukaemia.'

"And when you have read it," Dad said, 'Perhaps you can think about which ward you ought to be working on."

"I did not choose to come on this ward. I was sent. I am a bank nurse."

She walked away with the book that she duly and thoroughly read.

The injection, when it came, was painful to Laura. She was stirred from her sleep. She happened to be in the middle of a wonderfully happy dream. She was made to cry and went to sleep unsettled. It was unlikely that the drug was at its most effective under these conditions, Dad thought. What chance do we stand? Was this to be a futile battle?

It was a typical Autumn Sunday morning in any provincial hospital. It was quiet. The weather outside was miserable. If it wasn't it certainly felt as if it ought to be. Even in hospital everyone believed they really ought to be at home lying in bed reading the Sunday newspapers and taking a late breakfast. This mood conflicted with the regime and culture of the ward. No time for lazing around here. Nevertheless the mood prevailed and there was a general, if slight, relaxing of the rules. The nursing staff would rather be at home for the weekend. The parents and children wanted to be home also. Everyone made the best of it.

There were few consultants around at weekend apart from those dedicated paediatricians and doctors on call. consultants with private practices usually had something else to do. Everything was down to the nursing staff supported by junior doctors who had to be available twenty-four hours each day and sleep when they could. In reality it was the nurses who ran the ward. They were closest to the parents and the patients. They were the interface with the consultants. They made it happen.

Mum and Dad were still very keen to have a discussion with someone about Laura's prospects. No one was around.

"Where are we going?" said Dad to Mum." No one talks to us. What courses of treatment are we suppose to be on?"

"You had better speak to the first consultant to arrive on the ward. Surely they must have decided upon a course of treatment by now."

Laura, by this time, was becoming worried about how long she was to be here. Mum and Dad had said little. How could they? They knew little. I have come back in here because I had a cold, thought Laura. Mum and Dad said I must stay a little longer. They said I was still poorly.

There were two new nurses on secondment to the ward. They had been trained at Westminster and Great Ormond Street Children's hospitals. They were a part of the hospital's policy of improving the calibre and appropriate qualifications of the paediatric oncology nursing team. These two nurses were well advanced in terms of their understanding of the nature and treatment of cancer in children. They quickly developed a relationship with Mum and Dad and empathised with their views as to how things should be on a children's oncology ward. They were also outspoken and expressed a high degree of confidence in terms of their dealings with the consultants that the other nurses did not have. Perhaps they could do this because they were not local and had the pedigree of Great Ormond Street behind them.

Mum and Dad waited all morning for something to happen, for some advancement to be made in Laura's treatment.

Eventually a consultant walked on the ward and began talking to the nurses at the nurse's station. Dad dashed across the ward to speak.

"Excuse me! Have you any news regarding Laura's diagnosis and prognosis."

The consultant turned to Dad, took some time to reflect on what he had asked and then went on.

"The diagnosis is that she has A.L.L. As you know, she has relapsed. As for the prognosis; who is to know? As I said we are all in the hands of God, or if you prefer, fate."

"I'm sorry" said Dad, "that is not good enough. What do you have planned for Laura?"

"As soon as I work something out you will be the first to know. These things take time I'm afraid."

"But it has been three days! We need to know what is going on!"

"What is going on is that your daughter is undergoing induction therapy. That has to happen no matter what course of action we decide upon."

"No. That is not true. If the final outcome is totally negative then we should not even be thinking about treatment. Quality of life is important."

"That is for you to decide."

"How can we decide without access to the facts?"

"I cannot give you facts until I have fully considered all the options and researched the possibilities."

"That sounds like a cop out for doing nothing."

"Look, I think this conversation is leading us nowhere. If you don't like the way we do things here, there are other hospitals."

"I think it is a bit late for that, don't you?"

"In which case, you will have to trust me won't you?"

"I will trust you when I know what you plan for my daughter."

By this time Mum had joined the conversation. She had quietly been standing in the wings listening to the conversation.

"We want to know what her chances are!"

"I cannot say that! Look. This conversation is leading us all nowhere. I have other people to see. I really must go."

With that the consultant walked off the ward. One of the new nurses came across.

"I heard that" she said, "I was disgusted. If that is the way that parents are treated in the provinces then there is a lot to be learned."

She was a beautiful young woman with fair hair. The kind of woman who has a career. The kind of woman who was full of determination and all those positive things that makes a career person. Yet, she also had the ability to understand the real issues. She was pragmatic. She was straight to the point.

Mum began to cry.

"I cannot believe the way we are treated. It's almost as if it's our fault or Laura's fault. They make us feel guilty. It's almost as if we are an inconvenience if we start to ask questions about what they plan to do."

"I'll tell you," said Dad, "This time around things will be different. This time around we will make damned sure we have the best team available. In fact that is what we ought to do. Lets gather a team of people to care for Laura; the consultant, the ward sister, the health visitor, the Registrar, the child psychologist, whoever."

Mum looked at Dad and smiled. He then knew this was the right approach. Why could they not take a lead role in the management of Laura's care and treatment? They could and they did.

On the Monday when the Registrar carried out his ward visit Dad insisted on a meeting with everyone concerned. The Registrar agreed and said that he would arrange it. That afternoon. Dad became nervous as to what he should say at the meeting and what he could expect from it.

The time arrived and Mum and Dad went into the ward office. Many eyes watched them. This was something new. They knew that a special meeting had been arranged. Why?

Mum and Dad sat down ringed by many professionals with files, folders and clipboards. Outside Laura played with Kit and Radella. They were supervised by Radella's Mum who kept one eye on the ward Office door and wondered what was happening. She knew she would be told everything. She was an ally.

There was silence in the office. Dad waited. The clipboards stared at him. No one spoke. Mum looked at Dad. Dad continued to stare at the clipboards and files. Someone fiddled with a pen. Eventually the consultant spoke.

"Yes? What would you like to discuss?"

"I'm sorry?" said Dad in confusion.

"You arranged this meeting. What would you like to discuss?"

The health visitor was there. She looked at Dad and nodded her encouragement. 'Go on' he could see her mutter under her breath. So he did. He breathed deeply.

"I called this meeting to discuss the future options for Laura. I asked for you all to be here because I want the best for my girl and as I see it you will all be involved to some degree or other. So, we would first like to know what options are available."

Everyone looked at the consultant.

"Well, first of all we are not used to parents, or patients for that matter, managing the treatment but if that is what you want to do we will leave the decisions entirely with you."

At this statement Dad froze.

The consultant realised his predicament and went on.

"There are a number of options open to you. Firstly we could go for further chemotherapy and radiation treatment. This would be rather lengthy and painful. It may or it may not work. Secondly we could consider a bone marrow transplant. To do this we would still have to undergo the chemotherapy and radiation. Thirdly we could consider Laura's quality of life and consider terminal care."

"If we go for the first what chance do we stand?" asked Mum.

"Difficult to answer that, but not much I would have thought. It depends how capable Laura is of enduring the treatment. This time it will be very, very hard. Ten, twenty percent. I really don't know. We are now in the unknown. Every child is different."

"What about the transplant?"

"Now we really are in the unknown. It all depends on whether we can get a donor. If we can't get one in the family then it will be hard. We can of course try the Anthony Nolan Trust."

"Who are they?" asked Dad.

"It's a Trust set up to supply bone marrow donors."

"And what are our chances of long term survival?" asked Dad.

"Better but not good."

"So, what do you recommend?"

"What do I recommend?" he replied with an emphasis on the 'I'. He looked at the clipboards and smiled. "You called the meeting. I would like to know what you recommend!"

There was a new ward sister in the meeting. She was from Birmingham Children's Hospital. She looked uncomfortable throughout the meeting. She spoke up.

"I think Laura's parents are not as well qualified as you in the treatment of childhood cancers. I think they simply want your advice."

"My advice is for them to think about what I have said and decide on which option they prefer."

The discussion went on for perhaps a further hour where Mum and Dad explored the implications of each option. The consultant and the other clip boards left. They were left with the new ward sister and the health visitor. Mum cried.

"That was disgusting!" said the health visitor

"I only want the best for Laura!" cried Dad in desperation. "Can't people understand that?"

"The irony is that we have a bloody good consultant. Probably the best. You have hurt someone's ego. This is the problem with all consultants. They don't like to be challenged. They like you to show an interest, but not too much of an interest."

"Look," said the new ward sister, "it would appear that the transplant is the best option for you. You have to go through chemotherapy anyway. However, I recommend that you get a second opinion."

"A second opinion!" exclaimed Mum.

"Of course!" said Dad. "You are right. Why shouldn't we?"

"I recommend this person." The new ward sister handed Dad a name and hospital address. "This is a major centre. You will get the best advice. I know. I used to work there."

"That is what we will do!" said Mum.

Later on that day the consultant returned to check on Laura's condition.

"We would like a second opinion."

"Totally unnecessary."

"We would like one nevertheless"

"That is up to you but I cannot release Laura from hospital whilst she is on treatment."

"We shall need her case notes to send in advance," said Dad with information supplied by the health visitor.

"That is not possible. Laura is undergoing treatment here and I cannot release her case notes."

The consultant left for the evening.

That night Dad secretly arranged with a member of staff to have the case notes passed to him. He organised his secretary from work to photocopy them and bind them. The originals were returned the next day in secrecy. The copy was despatched by a driver hired by Dad to the consultant giving the second opinion. After the family doctor had sent a note a meeting was arranged with another consultant in another hospital.

Mum and Dad took Laura off the ward. They signed a document to say that she was now in their care and not with the hospital. The case notes had been sent in advance. The health visitor came with them. Laura sat in the back of the Ford Granada sucking her thumb.

When they arrived at the large hospital its sheer scale overwhelmed them. So many children with cancer! They waited for an hour. They visited the drinks machine. Kit was with them. Of course! He had to be there. This was his battle too. Kit liked the drinks machine. He tried to play with the toys that lay around but they were old and soiled.

They should have felt less alone surrounded by these families undergoing the same pain and uncertainty. They did not. They felt more alone than ever. They did not know the people around. The presence of so many children with cancer in one room frightened them. There must have been fifty or so families. Some of these will die, Dad thought. That frightened him even more. For his was the great certainty. Some would die. He looked at the faces of different children. He observed their mothers and fathers and tried to imagine how their lives might be. He looked at one teenage boy and thought, perhaps you will die. Am I now confronted by death?

Their name was called. The health visitor guided them to the consultant's office. All the while she had been discussing the excellence of the facilities here and comparing them to the inadequacies of their own hospital. Mum agreed but wanted to know why things could not be improved in Belgrave. Were they not building a new hospital wing?

The consultant wore a white overall. The case notes were on the desk. Mum was asked to put Laura on the couch and remove her blouse. Laura had been dressed very smartly for the occasion. She was very confused as to why she was here. She did not like all the noise and bustle. They took me out of my hospital only to bring me to another place so awesome and threatening, she thought. I believed I was going home for a rest. It was so good to sleep in my own bed last night. Am I to sleep in this big and noisy place tonight? Surely not?

The stethoscope felt cold on her chest. It always did. The consultant's hands were also cold and smelt of something strange, a hospital kind of smell. Laura hated these examinations. It all seemed so pointless. She withdrew herself into her own world, thought of the village, of walking in the field and sucked her thumb.

The examination was over. The notes were read. There was silence.

"I shall be frank. The chances are not good. What course of action has been recommended to you?"

Dad replied. "At the moment we are undergoing induction remission therapy. Then we may go for intensive chemotherapy or possibly a bone marrow transplant."

"I trust you appreciate that Laura will have to undergo a very aggressive and difficult course of chemo and radiation therapy prior to any transplant. She may not," she paused and looked at Kit and Laura, then went on. "I think perhaps Laura could play outside with her brother whilst we talk."

The health visitor took Kit and Laura out to play on the mats just outside the office.

"I was going to say that Laura might not survive this course of treatment. She may die in hospital whilst undergoing treatment. You now what that means?"

Dad knew exactly what it meant. Laura dying with no hair; locked in a room tied to drips and the hospital machinery. A battle lost.

"I understand that you are hoping to get a marrow donor from within the family. I must point out that if you do not get a donor from within the family then your chances are slim indeed."

"To be frank, I really think you must consider quality of life for Laura and think seriously about terminal care"

The dismay on Mum's and Dad's faces was apparent to the consultant.

"I am sorry to give you bad news but that is how I see it. Of course you can go ahead with treatment. It may work out all right. These things are never cut and dried."

"Would you treat Laura here at this hospital?" asked Dad.

"No, I would not. I think you will find that most other hospitals would say the same."

"Even Great Ormond Street?"

"Even Great Ormond Street. It does not matter where you go. We all work to a national regime under U.K.A.L.L. Anyway we're all full up. You also started your treatment at Belgrave so it is difficult to change now."

Dad did not believe this. He and Mum believed and wanted to believe that Laura had a good chance of survival. It seemed too early to give up. Nevertheless they were despondent and full of gloom when they left the hospital. Dad wondered if Laura was being offered treatment simply because they had put the consultants under pressure. Perhaps this really was the time to let go. Perhaps her time had come? Further treatment sounded as if it would be horrendous. Could Laura, could they, take it?

They had the rest of the day at home. Laura was due back the following day. At least this second opinion had brought the bonus of a day off from the Infirmary. Dad took the health visitor home then Mum and Dad enjoyed a meal at home with the children preceded by a few Gins and Tonics in the usual fashion and much discussion.

The following day was one of those bleak uninteresting grey days that occur in late autumn. The sky was sullen and low. The car windows were wet. The air was damp. Dad tried to be cheerful. It was difficult. His heart sank. The prospects were not good. He wondered at the reception he would get when he took Laura back.

They welcomed her then adopted her. They took over. "Welcome back," they said. They pampered her and gave her one of the best cubicles. They knew. They knew it could be hard from here on in, but they were going to try. So Laura started her second battle of this war against cancer. Would she win?

The body of a child grows. Its growing cells are strong. They are capable of combating infection and disease where grownups fail. Her diagnosis was that she still had Acute Lymphoblastic Leukaemia, the childhood cancer. But it was an unknown, prevalent type. The prognosis said a transplant was the only way if there was a way. Would they find a donor? Who might it be? And would it be worthwhile? Did not some people say she ought to be left to die in peace? Perhaps they were right. After all quality of life is the most important thing.

Chapter 18

Life is strange

Life is a strange bird, Dad would say. It flies its own course despite your best endeavours. Why bother to try? Why not go with the flow? The trouble is Dad tried to change the course of life and destiny. It did not work out for him. Life knew its way. It would not be distracted.

Laura felt as if she was on a conveyance of inevitability. Where she was going she knew not, but she knew she was on a journey. She did not try to fight her destiny, but whatever it was she was determined to survive it. She would float on the water not fight it. It could also keep her alive if she knew how to work with it. Water is a supporting not a drowning substance.

When they arrived back on the ward, Dad introduced Laura to Susan. Susan lived in the mirror. She looked like Laura and had a Dad of similar looks to Laura's Dad. Susan's feelings reflected those of Laura. She was a good friend. Dad and Laura would talk to her quite often. When Laura woke in the morning and had her hair brushed she would ask to see Susan, to counsel her opinion about her hair, her clothes, and her general demeanour. Susan always concurred with the populist view.

"Susan!" Laura would say with amused disbelief when Susan had expressed an opinion about her hair or clothes. Susan had no voice but spoke through Dad or in silence.

Laura liked to take Susan everywhere with her. Whichever room she was in she would look out for her. Some people thought that Susan was, in fact, Laura. They were mistaken. Susan was Susan. She was Laura's friend. How could she be Laura?

The new cubicle was nice.

The health visitor came to settle them in. Laura was exploring a large red toy car in the corridor with Kit.

"This is the best cubicle on the ward. They wanted to give it to someone else. I stuck out for you. It will help give you a good start. It has an en suite bathroom. The view is not as good as on the other side but at least you have some space."

"Now. Can we discuss Laura's treatment? It is going to be very, very difficult. She relapsed on treatment..."

"I told you!" exclaimed Mum. "Which means that we first have to get her in remission. If we don't, then...well...er."

"She will die," interspersed Dad

"Yes," said the health visitor. "You have to think about whether the price is worth it"

"But, what is the price? Weeks, months of horrendous treatment for what? A 1% chance or a 50% chance?"

"It all depends on whether we can get her into induction remission and, if we do, whether we can go for a bone marrow transplant. You have already started a course for induction remission. Assuming we get her into remission we can then make a decision about going for the transplant. Lets take one step at a time. For now, concentrate on getting Laura into remission"

"But, what are her chances if we go for a transplant?" asked Mum. "I don't want her to die in hospital"

"I can quote a figure but at the end of the day it is up to you as to whether you go ahead. Come here."

She took Mum and Dad to the door and opened it. Laura was playing happily with Kit in the corridor.

"She already has had two weeks of treatment. She is coping well. I think she will continue to cope. Can you? That will be the real test. It will be the most difficult part of your life, and Laura's. I think she can cope with your help, and I believe you are the right parents for such a fight"

Mum looked at Laura.

"We want to do the best for her. We don't want to do the best for us. I mean we don't want to fight an unnecessary fight for the sake of appearing to do the right thing. We want to do the right thing. For Laura."

"We don't want to battle on when there is only the remotest chance. I would rather she had just a few weeks and months of quality life than go from us in cloud of pain and unhappiness. There is such a thing as dignity in death, you know. She is entitled to quality of life but she also has the right to a good death."

Mum was earnest in her attempt to convince the health visitor that they wanted to take a rational not an emotional approach. It is easy to say you will fight for your child's life even if the chances are slim. You are not the combatant. It is the child who has to suffer and fight the fight. At the end of the day it is the child's fight not yours. Are we all not guilty of thinking of our own suffering? Measuring things by what we can bear. And at the end of the day is it not quality of life concluded with a dignified death all that we human beings aspire to?

The consultant came to see them.

"I think this time we should fit Laura with a Hickman line. It will go straight into her chest so that we can inject the drugs directly into a main vein without all the difficulties of injections and clotting veins. I propose a double Hickman. Two tubes. It's not normal but it gives us more flexibility and scope considering the intensity of her treatment. It will mean an operation under ananaesthetic I'm afraid, but I think it's for the best. We have ordered one from the United States. It will take a couple of days"

Mum and Dad did not like the idea of the Hickman Line. It was the disfigurement of her pure young body that hurt them the most. She would have to wear it for several months. It would be a protrusion from her chest that had to be cared and catered for. It would dictate how and when she could bathe and the clothes she wore. No more swimming for a while, thought Dad. He knew Laura enjoyed her swimming. Still, it was for the best. The alternative was, as the consultant implied, unending injections, bruising and the eternal search for a 'good vein'. Better the Hickman Line. She would get used to it. They all would.

So she went down to the main operating theatre. In fact there was a whole embankment of theatres. They shared a common reception area. This was a wide-open space without daylight. On one side was a green line painted on the floor. This marked the boundary between the world of surgery and the rest of the hospital. It was a significant threshold. Crossing it meant going into a world where the knife was the only way.

The reception area looked like an enormous billiard room with trolleys evenly spaced upon which lay recumbent visitors to the various theatres. A nurse attended some. On the others the somnolent visitor occasionally protruded a head like a turtle looking for daylight.

Dad took Laura to the Theatre himself accompanied by a porter to comply with regulations. He pushed the trolley to the green line and waited. A theatre nurse eventually arrived. Theatre nurses are not normal nurses. They are used to the knife. They see blood every day and the proximity of death permeates their mind so that it means little. They are there not to care, rather to rescue and recover, to make well in an instant. They are the miracle workers, when things go well. Sometimes it goes wrong. So they have to be tough, to survive as people and go on to continue doing their job. Dad thought this as the nurse approached. She looked totally unlike any nurse he had seen. She was dressed entirely in green. Boots, cap and mask completed an aura of mystery and fear that bordered on terror.

"Pass her to me," she said after the formalities had been completed. "I'll take her to Theatre. We'll let you know when to collect her."

"No!" said Dad. "I want to be with her when you operate. She is my daughter after all."

The nurse paused. She did not expect this.

"I'm afraid that is not possible. We cannot have anyone coming into Theatre. You must appreciate that we have to be clinically clean."

"I can be clean. Give me the robes or whatever I need, but I am not letting her go without me."

"I'm sorry. It's not possible. Pass me your daughter."

Laura began to cry.

"No!"

"In that case I shall have to speak to sister."

"Don't bother. Who is the surgeon?"

She gave him a name.

"I know him. He has treated Laura before. Send him to me."

"Send him? I shall ask him if he wants to speak to you. We do have a tight schedule and have allocated half an hour for this operation, which is very straight forward, by the way. Any further delays might mean a postponement or other, more serious, operations being put back. I'll ask. That is all I can do."

The surgeon arrived looking a little flustered and annoyed. He recognised Dad, shook his head and smiled.

"Kit him up," he instructed the nurse", and lets get on with it. We're behind."

Laura was very frightened. The argument at the green line made her even more afraid. Surely if Dad would not let her go alone meant that it must be very dangerous? Nevertheless she was glad he was there when she fell asleep for she hated the emptiness into which she sank and over which she had no control. That was the most fearful moment, when her face was covered and she breathed in a deep sleep full of bizarre dreams. She was also glad that he was there when she awoke full of dizziness and a throbbing pain in her chest.

Her body had changed. Now she had to carry a foreign body that was to become so familiar that she would eventually treat it with a familiarity that bordered on affection. Was it not here to help make her better?

The Hickman Line felt peculiar. When she breathed her chest became tight. The nurses would examine it regularly, clean it and put new plasters around it to secure it to her chest. One morning Laura woke up feeling very hot and dizzy. She tried to sit up but could not and collapsed back onto her pillow. Mum put her hand on her forehead.

"She has a temperature," she said to Dad and called for a nurse. The nurse took her temperature and confirmed that it was high.

"Give her some Calpol," she said.

Laura was given Calpol. The temperature dropped but rose again later. She became sick and vomited what little food she had swallowed. Her temperature continued to rise. The doctor took a swab from her mouth to grow a culture and find out what was wrong. In the meantime Antibiotics were prescribed. Her condition worsened and her respiration deteriorated. She was given intermittent oxygen.

Was this how it was to end? Here in this hospital bed before the real treatment had even started?

The culture was grown. The consultant called Mum and Dad into the office.

"She has an infection"

"We know that. Where has it come from?"

"The infection is called Septicaemia. It sometimes happens after an operation; no matter what precautions we take. We will need to remove the Hickman Line and replace it with another. However we cannot do that until Laura recovers."

"If she recovers. She is not making much progress at the moment."

"As I say this sometimes happens after an operation. Let's give the Antibiotics time to work shall we?"

Laura did recover but had lost weight, strength and the will to go on. When Mum told her she had to go for another operation she despaired.

Three days later Dad took her once gain to the Green Line. This time it was a different surgeon. Laura was carried away crying.

The grey days turned to darkness as winter settled in. It wrapped the hospital in a clinging cold vapour. The hospital ward was warm and dry. Dad got a cold.

He would come back onto the ward each evening to see the gradual deterioration in Laura's condition. He saw Mum became more tired with the strain of the day. Kit's complexion was pale through lack of fresh air. Dad vowed to take him outside this coming weekend. Spend time with him. Poor Kit! How he must have hated this life, yet he never showed it. He kept cheerful and tried to make the best of things. Everyone was short tempered. He knew that from when he had spilt his drink on Laura's bedspread. He was only leaning over to talk to her, to comfort her. Mum and Dad screamed at him then sank back into silence.

Worst of all were the mealtimes. How could anyone eat in these conditions? Food seemed secondary, yet, there were times when he felt absolutely famished and he would have his little plate filled up at the trolley. Then, when he got it on his knee in Laura's cubicle, he lost his appetite and Mum and Dad would shout. Still, he could eat when he got home.

Laura also lost interest in the hospital food but Dad had a remedy.

One evening when she would not eat he went out of the hospital to the fish and chip shop. Chicken and chips. He knew she liked chicken. She ate it with enthusiasm whilst Dad ate a meat pie. After that he went out for food two or three times a week.

One evening as Dad was dashing back with an armful of chicken and chips a consultant who detected the smell of hot food stopped him.

"I hope it's all right?" Dad said apologetically. "She eats it when she won't eat hospital food."

"It's fine," the consultant replied. "In fact, it smells rather good! As long as she keeps eating and we have a balanced diet that is the main thing. Do whatever you would do at home."

However, one evening Dad went too far. He brought back some chicken for Laura and Chicken Tikka Masala from the Indian restaurant for himself. The aroma filtered out onto the ward and very soon the ward sister popped her head round the door of the cubicle.

"I thought so! Fish and chips are fine but an Indian takeaway? If you must, please find a dish with a less pervasive odour. You are making us all hungry out there."

She laughed and walked away. Dad took this as a mild and diplomatic rebuke from a ward sister who did not want things to get too much out of control.

Once again Laura embarked upon a regime of toxic drugs, of battles against ulcers, sickness and diarrhoea. It was a battle she sustained. She maintained her dignity throughout and fought the fight with quiet courage. It was a re-run of their first encounter with chemotherapy. This time there were many more tests to monitor progress. This time her hair came out more quickly and Dad quietly cried when he saw the first golden strands lying on her pillow.

Eventually the time came for a bone marrow test to establish if the drugs had worked and Laura was in remission. Then she could go on with the fight. Things looked good when Dad once again took her into the treatment room. It was Thursday. The day of blood tests She had responded well to the treatment. Blood tests had looked encouraging. She was fairly fit.

Dad held her tight as the consultant extracted the marrow from her spine. He watched the little red drops as they were carefully placed on little glass trays. A lot of little glass trays, Dad thought. He prayed that the samples contained healthy cells. They looked good.

He took Laura back into the ward. How many times had they done this? He wondered. How many more times would they have to do it? Mum was waiting for them in the ward. Laura slept. Eventually she woke and was hungry. Mum gave her some food. The rest of the day she felt sleepy and lacking in energy. She had no enthusiasm for playing or listening to Dad's stories. Did they know how she felt after what was, after all, an operation? Did they know about the pain and drowsiness? The wanting and need for sleep, escape and the oblivion, the dull burrowing pain in her back and the ache in her bowels.

She remembered the first time they gave her this test. Then, there was no ananaesthetic, only pain. She shuddered to think of it. Nevertheless the after affects then were not as bad as having the ananaesthetic. After the first test she had lots of pain and suffering to go through. This time she was on her third test and had become used to the pain. She felt a strange kind of pride in herself. She had done it before and got through. This time she would do it better. This time she would beat the pain. She would smile through it and win.

Mum and Dad waited all that Thursday for the visit from the consultant with the result of Laura's test. They felt buoyant. Laura was happy. She was in control.

Other parents sat in nervous tension by the bedside of their children waiting for their own results, good or bad. The consultant made a point of visiting them first. He gave them news of various kinds. Not all were critical. Some tests were routine. There were no tears.

The consultant came over to Mum and Dad with a smile. At last! The treatment was not working, he said. She was not in remission. We would have to think again.

The noise from the ward seemed to float away from them and their minds swam in total unreality. Their hopes were dashed. This was not the news that was expected. They could not even think of the consequences. The consultant stood before them with an inane smile that was trying to become an apology or at least say 'I am sorry'. They heard the clatter of small feet running down the corridor. It was Kit and Laura running toward them as part of some game.

"Mum, can we go home soon?" said Laura as she dashed back into the ward. "I feel much better now."

The consultant looked at Mum and Dad. He smiled, gently but sadly.

"It's the Prednisilone, the Steroids. Sometimes it makes them feel good, hyperactive even. It's false, it's unreal. That's the irony of it. It's like a sick joke. The Leukaemia is still there"

Chapter 19

The next step

Life is full of setbacks. Everyone must experience them. In most cases you pick yourself up, dust yourself down and start all over again as the song goes. But that's a song for you. Sometimes you cannot get up again and if you do the world around you has changed. Sometimes the setback becomes a catastrophe. Then you have to re-think the purpose of your life and realise that what has gone before can never be the same again. The past is the past and will never return.

You walk the treadmill of life alternating between peace and sorrow and joy and ignorance. Better to be ignorant and happy than explore the depths of your mind and find the truth. The truth is that life is as sharp as an axe and you live on its blade, on a precipice between hope and fear. Life has taken its chosen course. Who can change it? God? Did the truth not come from above?

Life is full of crossroads. We fumble along and kid ourselves we know the way, even when we get horrendously lost. We try to get back to the road we started on but it is no longer there. Instead we find ourselves on a brand new journey, a journey of perplexity, confusion and wild hope.

Life is an irony that is full of surprises. Just when you think things are going well, disaster strikes. You say the car is running well and it breaks down two minutes afterwards. You mend it and say the traffic is very light today and you run into a hold up seconds after you drive onto the motorway.

Some people think life is wonderful and say you should live it to the full. In reality life is a bewildering tunnel, a bottomless pit of confused ideals and hopes. It is only wonderful because we hang on to it. We have nothing else. We know nothing else.

Life is an obstacle course. It slows us down and pulls us into swamps of hindering frustration. But we overcome it. We make decisions as we make our way through life. Some wrong, some right. It might be job or money, finance or marriage, to buy or sell, to move or stay, to believe or not to believe. We continue going forward for that is the only direction we know. Otherwise we sink into the swamp of self-pity.

Making decisions about ourselves through life's maze of obstacles is hard enough. Making decisions about others is harder. But imagine trying to decide if a child of four should suffer pain, or should live or die. Such a decision cannot, should not, ever be made by a mortal being. Only God could decide such a thing, but where was he?

Chapter 20

Christmas is only a date in the calendar

Laura had many dreams during this period. The consultants said that the steroids would make her dream, and they were right. The Phantom she had known in those early days had gone away. He was replaced by something more sinister. It was an inward terror that tore into her heart. It was a fear that was both fathomless and far-reaching. It was a terror that shocked and frightened her. It was something that lay before her, that stretched out and beyond into a distant mist. It was the future; her future.

She dreamed she was at home.

She walked with Dad to the Swing Park. They took their bikes, she and Kit. Dad was sad and therefore very quiet. She knew he would be happy when she was in her swing. Dad liked to watch her sail and glide through the air. He smiled with pleasure to see her hair lifted by the gentle breeze created by the turbulence of the swing. He would push her and she would sail even higher. Higher and higher until she was above his head and could see the school, the church and the fields.

As she looked down on him she could see the sadness rapidly drawn away to be replaced by a warm glow and inner happiness. When he was happy she was happy.

As she sailed higher she gazed high into the sky. She felt she could reach the clouds and stretched her arms accordingly. She heard Dad cry, "Hold on Laura!" but when she looked down he was not there. Instead he was walking to the gate at the far end of the Swing Park where Mum was waiting. They talked. As they talked her swing began to slow down. The sailing turned to a gentle glide. She shouted Dad to push her but he did not hear. Instead he was more interested in a long discussion with Mum. Laura became angry. She began to lose height. She saw other people join them. They all became involved in the discussion. As they talked they looked at her. She angrily cried out for Dad to come back. The swing was almost at a halt.

"It's all right Laura. I'm here"

It was Kit. He began to push her. It was hard for him. This was a big swing and Laura needed a lot of help to regain the height that made her happy. He pushed. Oh how he pushed. His small frame pulsated with energy to overcome his lack of muscular strength. He pushed and pushed. Gradually she began to move. Very slowly at first but at least she moved.

"Faster Kit, faster!"

"Lean back, Laura. Lean your head back and stretch your legs forward when I push. That way you will go higher."

She leaned her head back but it gave her a feeling of dizziness that partly frightened and exhilarated her.

She began to rise. Like the lark she began to rise. Slowly at first but at least she was getting higher. Kit exerted himself and as the swing began to glide he ran with it.

"I can push you Laura. I can push you as high as you want to go. Believe me."

She rose higher and looked down on him. She could see the tension in his face as he threw all his physical and mental energy into raising her higher. She was happy. She looked for Mum and Dad. They were no longer involved in a group. Instead they were walking toward her looking very happy and encouraged by something.

"Well done Kit!" said Mum." See, Laura, your brother can look after you when we are not here"

"And I can push her on the swing!" chirped in Kit.

"Push her?" said Dad. "You can do more than that. You can make her fly!"

Kit was pleased. He really had made her fly after all. If he could do that he could anything for her. When Laura awoke she was not sure that it was a dream. She felt certain that the events had happened in reality and she thought about it all day. She explained it to her Dad, but he said it was only a dream.

Laura often wondered where Jesus was. He had not been to visit her for a long time. Mum and Dad did not seem to go to church as often as they used to and she wondered if that was something to do with it. She liked church although she was not used to seeing Jesus in church, only his pictures. She wondered why he did not come to see her when she slept. She felt there was something he had to say that had been unsaid for a long time. Something very important. But she knew she would have to wait.

After the consultant had been to see Mum and Dad that Thursday evening Laura became unhappy. She knew there was something wrong. Mum and Dad were in frequent huddles of conversation and at these times she was packed off to the playroom with one of the Nursery Nurses. The strange thing was that she felt so well, yet she knew it could not last. She remembered this feeling from the last time. It was mixed with a sense of foreboding. Yet, this time had to be different. She was filled with a strange confidence. Last time she was afraid of the unknown. This time she knew what to expect, but it was much more. It was a positive feeling. It was a feeling of hope and determination, a feeling that everything must work out well.

Mum and Dad had a meeting with the consultant and the health visitor. They all had to decide what to do. Laura was still feeling very good.

"We have started this treatment so we should continue. Although she is not in remission she has responded very well. By that I mean she can cope with the chemotherapy."

"What is the next step?" asked Dad

The consultant looked at the health visitor. Clearly they had rehearsed this meeting thought Mum as she observed the glance. Was it a conspiracy or just a sharing of knowledge?

"The Maze," said the consultant.

This time Mum and Dad looked at each other. They knew what he meant. Instinctively they knew. It was a new course of treatment. Because of its name it must have an uncertain outcome if, indeed, there was a way out. Nevertheless they realised they had to ask.

"What is the Maze?" enquired Dad.

The consultant was relieved to hear the expected question.

"It's a level of chemotherapy designed for adults and for Myeloid Leukaemia in severe cases."

"But Laura does not have Myeloid Leukaemia. A.M.L. that is. She has acute Lymphoblastic Leukaemia, A.L.L. so why should she need this new treatment?"

"We need to aggressively attack the leukaemia cells. This is the best way. It's the only way left. I have no confidence that another course of conventional chemotherapy will work. I need to kill the leukaemia cells. In fact I need to overkill."

Mum was pleased to hear this. She had long believed that Laura had needed more aggressive treatment due to her initial high white count.

The health visitor interrupted to say, "This treatment will be as difficult for you as it is for Laura. What she has suffered so far will pale into insignificance compared to what she will have to go through in the Maze. She will not eat. She will lose a lot of weight. She will have to cope with severe ulcers in her stomach and mouth and she will be in a lot of pain."

"Steady on," said the consultant. "The treatment is not that bad."

"Yes it is, you don't see it as I see it, as a nurse," said the health visitor. "I am telling it as it is. How it will be for them, not how it might compare to files of success and failure in your casebook or the statistics that you live by. I have seen it. I have been there with the parents, day-by-day, hour-by-hour, on the ward and in their homes. You only see them on your ward rounds and in carefully constructed interviews and meetings."

"I do not think we ought to be having this discussion in front of, er, parents."

"Why not? We are not dealing with your typical family here, but one that is testing our ability to treat their daughter. They have every right to question and challenge us. We have promised the best. We have to deliver it."

The health visitor turned to Mum and Dad.

"I know you, Laura and Kit and Adam can make it. It will be hard but you have everything going for you. It's worth a try. I think the odds are on your side."

"There is only one thing, one condition if you like," said Dad.

They looked at him. Mum knew what he was going to say. They had discussed it.

"If we embark on this treatment we are assuming Laura will go forward for a bone marrow transplant. As yet we do not have a donor. At the same time as we give her the treatment we must find a donor. We must all be tested for a suitable match."

"Yes. I agree," said the consultant. "I was going to suggest that. We will test you all."

"Even little Adam?" asked Dad in surprise.

"Yes, even the baby. It will not hurt him to donate his marrow."

Mum and Dad reflected on this for a moment and both hoped that they might be the donors. However the chances were that Kit would be the best bet, but it had to be a perfect match for any chance of success.

So it was that Laura embarked upon the most difficult journey of her life. They were given a break for a few days at home to re-charge batteries. They made the most of it, cramming a week of living into three days, lingering until the last moment before, yet again; Dad drove on the road to Belgrave with his little girl in the back seat. This time she took her own duvet from her bed, and, of course, Rupert Bear. This time the whole family came. This time Laura felt proud as she walked back onto the ward. A room had been prepared for her. As they processed down the corridor to the ward Kit switched on his portable cassette player and they were accompanied by the sound of "The Snowman". Laura felt confident. This family of mine can achieve anything, she thought. Why should I fear what is unknown. I am not on my own. I have my whole family. There is strength in numbers. We will go on from here and beat this thing that terrorises me.

At this point in her thinking she realised that it was not only she that this thing terrorised, but also her whole family. She was not the only sufferer and, as a consequence, not the only adversary. They had to work together, as a team, as a family. But she would be the focal point, the striker in the game. She would also be the battleground and the ultimate winner or loser.

They said the treatment would be horrendous. It was, but they buckled down and coped. Mum and Dad threw all their energy, love and attention into the care of Laura. Kit suffered, of that there was no doubt. He also coped and it made him strong, as a boy and ultimately as a man, for was he not equal to a man in his ability to love and care for Laura?

The chemotherapy bombarded her. It attacked every cell of her tiny fragile body. There was no sympathy, no let up.

One day when Mum and Dad and Kit and Adam were together in the cubicle with Laura when the consultant arrived to talk to them.

"Now is the time for you all to be tested in order to see if we can find a match."

The nurse came in and laid out her paraphernalia. Laura watched things apprehensively.

"Your Mum and Dad are going to have a blood test now," said the consultant.

This amused Laura and even more amused her when Dad made a fuss and pretended that it hurt him. Little Adam did not make a murmur, just a short grimace. He is getting too used to this place, thought Dad. The samples were taken away and everyone hoped that theirs would be the perfect match, everyone except Adam of course. He was too young to know, but at least he had made his contribution.

Dad slept with Laura every night as usual. His life became focussed around the ward. He modified his working day to accommodate the regime of treatment. Mum had to do the same with her singing. The treatment had gone according to plan. Laura had responded well. Inevitably there were problems. She had blood transfers, when her blood count went down. Eventually her platelet count went down. These affect bruising in the body. Low platelet counts mean it takes a long time to recover from a bruise or a cut. This was more serious. Transplants of platelets can cause a reaction, a very negative reaction.

It was a cold December evening approaching Christmas. They had to go singing. It was a Christmas concert. It included a selection by Vaughan Williams; pastoral carols that carried you back to advent evenings of bitter cold and log fires; of rosehips shining in the hedgerows and crows in frosty flight above the silhouetted treetops. Like no other composer Vaughan Williams could convey the pure sentiment and emotion of the English countryside, which is, perhaps, at its best in the wintertime.

It was very frosty with a whisper of mist when they left the hospital to go to the concert.

"She will be fine," said the nurse just before they left. "We will not transfer the platelets until you come back. You go and do something different for a change. It will do both you and Laura good. You need your batteries recharging."

They left with an eased but still guilty conscience. Dad was wearing his black suit and bow tie. Mum was dressed in a long black dress.

The cathedral was already full when they arrived. No time to rehearse. There had been precious little time to rehearse the past few days, but everyone expected the best, especially of Mum. Was she not the trained singer? As they prepared themselves in the vestry Dad made some noises in an attempt to prepare himself which sounded more like the clearing of his throat. After a few minutes the concert began and they were in the thick of it.

The platelets arrived at the goods inwards office at nine o'clock. They were in a transparent bag contained in a Jiffy bag. It was a special delivery from Leeds. Specially sealed and coded. It sat in the office for only a few minutes before it was collected for delivery to the ward. The system worked well. This was a routine event. The ward sister received them and looked at her watch.

"Transfer them now," she said. "There should be no problem."

The tenors began to sing.

This is the truth sent from above
The truth of God, the God of love
Therefore do not turn...

The candles flickered in this medieval church, which only recently had acquired the status of city Cathedral. The music assumed its own buoyancy and lifted to the Norman windows. Warmth filled the building, which was further fed by the emotion of love, a love of Christmas, Christ and music. The music lifted into the cold winter night and floated across the ancient part of the city that once formed the castle. It touched the roofs of varied tiles and drifted past the old Armoury along the river to settle in the grounds of a Royal Infirmary first erected in 1771.

The nurse applied the drip as she was taught. Platelet transfers were not that common, but, surely, they were no different to blood transfers? She came back after ten minutes and everything was fine. "Keep an eye on her temperature and blood pressure," the ward sister had said.

The cathedral was warm. The audience, or congregation, Dad was never quite sure what to call them, were relaxed and enjoying the evening as a prelude to Christmas.

The first thing, which I will relate
Is that God did man create.

The next thing, which to you I tell
Woman is made with man to dwell.

Mum stood and waited for her part. It was straightforward. She had not rehearsed it very well, but she felt confident she could do it justice. The good thing about Vaughan Williams music was that it suited her lack of vibrato. She had a pure crystal voice that could only be copied by a treble voice or an Italian Castrate. She knew hers was a voice of distinction and she was proud of it.

Dad was pleased when the tenor part was coming to an end. He looked up at the carvings in the Lady Chapel and thought of the hospital ward.

Laura's temperature had risen. After taking it the nurse rushed to see the ward sister who told her to check blood pressure. The consultant was called for.

And they did eat which was a sin and thus their ruin did begin;
Through in themselves both you and me ....

The concert had not quite finished. Mum and Dad looked at each other. They both knew they ought to be elsewhere. It was a sudden feeling. A compulsion. They knew it was not right to be here. Something drew them elsewhere; a something that had crept into the Cathedral and tugged at their sense of reality.

...And thus did God interpose?

Laura's temperature continued to rise to a dangerous point. Her blood pressure went up. A doctor was called. They stripped her of all clothes and applied tepid water to her body to cool her down.

"Oxygen! Give her some oxygen!" said the young doctor. "She is not breathing properly. And turn the platelet drip off!"

She gasped for breath. Her eyes were glazed. She felt as if a strange substance had entered and taken over her body. She felt it in every limb and blood vessel. It made her go hot and cold. It was nauseating. It was the return of the Phantom. This time he had come with a grimace and a vengeance from which she knew there was no escape. Her mind swam in a mist of dizziness that sent her reeling into the depths of hopelessness. Then she began to float. The nausea left her.

They left the cathedral and ran down with the street the music riding alongside them like the wind of life.

Where am I? Laura thought. Where am I going? I knew the Phantom would return, but not this way. Now he has entered my body and is intent on destroying me. I cannot give into this.

She saw the swing. She was sailing again, high above the rooftops of her village. Kit was there. He smiled then ran away over to the church. She looked for him. In the distance she saw him. Standing by the West door. He was talking to someone she knew. It was Jesus. Suddenly Jesus began to run to her.

Mum and Dad dashed through the corridors of the hospital, Dad stripping off his bow tie as he ran. They came to the lifts. People stood around waiting. Dad could still hear the music in his mind.

...Till God the Lord did interpose

"Come on!" said Dad and they rushed up the stairs.

...That he would redeem us by his son

On the fourth floor they bounded down the final corridor and burst through the double doors into the ward. Nursing staff and parents stopped to stare. They pushed open the door of Laura's cubicle. They saw the platelet bag hanging from the drip. It was half empty. The light was dimmed and the room was peaceful and calm. A nurse sat by Laura, quietly reading her a story.

"She's fine," she said. "She had a reaction to the platelets. It sometimes happens. Do you want to finish the story? I think she's almost asleep."

"We told you to wait until we were here! Why didn't you!" demanded Dad, quietly but firmly.

"These are routine things. We cannot always wait for parents to be around."

"But one of us is always here. For two hours you could have waited."

"The outcome would not have changed with you being here. She was not in any real danger."

"That's not the point," said Dad. "If something goes wrong, and it might, we need to be here."

"I'll leave you with Laura. Please check her temperature on a regular basis and write it in the chart as we showed you."

With that she left the room.

"There's no point in taking it out on the nurse. I knew we should not have gone," cried Mum angrily. "Never again! Henceforth we are with her night and day, seven days a week without exception"

Laura reacted against the platelets because the batch was contaminated. Sometimes this happens. Mum and Dad realised they and Laura were living on a razor edge. Mistakes could be fatal.

Dad sat by her side after Mum had left for home. He could not sleep. He sat there all night and watched her. She became conscious of his staring and turned to look at him. She sucked her thumb. Her brown eyes gazed into his and she suddenly smiled. It was a smile that was deep and warm. It lingered on her lips. Dad could almost feel it touch him. He smiled back.

Look at me

Look at me and with your eyes
Talk to me
Look at me and see me
Within you for I know
We grow and sow the same name
That lets us know

I care for you
Know that I am with you
Impressed by your love
Of life.

Look at me
I see your eyes but not your mind
I know you well
We are together
We are the one
But not the same.

I can cope
With life and hope
With help I'm not alone
Love conquers all
Your eyes tell all
Give me all I need.

Look through my eyes
Look at this soul
Of inspiration for you
Without you
I was nothing,
I am nothing.

Your eyes say it all.

The daily battles continued. They hoped the second phase of treatment would finish at Christmas so that everyone could be at home. It was not to be. There was no such luck. Luck was not something they counted on. If anything it worked against them. Luck favours those who don't need it. It carries certain random selected people through life. People who are not in need of it because it comes their way anyway. Others say of them "they always fall on their feet". They say of themselves "I've done it with sheer hard work and effort, and a bit of luck. It's really all down to my personal brilliance". Some people have to fight every inch of the way through life, overcoming obstacles as they arise only to be faced by another obstacle or setback. Mum and Dad belonged to this group of people but would have preferred to belong to the former.

Christmas was just around the corner. They took her to the hospital party. She tried her best to be interested but the sickness overwhelmed her. It nagged at her continually. The only time she sparkled was at the end of the party when everyone rushed downstairs and into the forecourt to greet Father Christmas. Dad held Laura tightly wrapped in her brown winter coat. Her head was uncovered because she did not want to wear a hat. Eventually they saw the twinkle of lights from the sleigh and he appeared. Laura liked the lights surrounding the sleigh and enjoyed touching the reindeer, a reindeer whose life began when there was no treatment for Leukaemia and who had become a great tradition of this city. It was a misty mysterious evening and the lights cast small beams into the surrounding gloom. In other circumstances it would have been a magical evening.

Mum and Dad hated the party. Parents whose children had fared better came to see them to offer sympathy over Laura's relapse. Everyone, including Laura, was quite glad to escape back to the institutionalised comfort of the cubicle. When they did Dad played with Laura and the mobile home. They escaped into their own world, free of other people, relapses and even hospital.

It was the weekend before Christmas. It was a Friday night. The treatment, phase two, was now complete.

The consultant came to see them.

"I have received the results from Leeds on your blood tests."

He handed Mum and Dad a piece of paper. They snatched at it and eagerly scanned down the page.

Laura	HLA: A2, A3, B7, B35
Mother	HLA: A2, A28, B7, B14
Father	HLA: A2, A3, B5, B35
Adam	HLA: A3, A28, B14, B35
Kit	HLA: A2, A3, B7, B35

Kit was a perfect match. A 100% match. Now they could win.

"We can go ahead now. We have every chance. As I've told you before a good match from non-identical twins is the best kind of match. You are very fortunate. "

He said they could go home for the weekend. Have a break and recharge the batteries. They had better take the time out now, as they would need to come in over Christmas to start the final and most critical stages of treatment. There was no other way of doing it. Christmas is only a date on the carols, the health visitor said. Laura's life is something else.

Mum and Dad decided to change the carols. They decided to bring Christmas forward a week.

Chapter 21

Life is a gin and tonic

"Go and get a Christmas tree," Mum said to Dad.

He went. In the meantime she packed Laura's things.

Dad drove down Belgrave Road looking for a tree. He saw an Off Licence advertising trees.

"Sixteen pounds please."

"But it's only four feet and I could buy it for seven or eight pound on Belgrave market."

"I'm sorry but that's the price and we close soon. If you don't want it then you can try the market."

"I have to have it now. It's for my daughter."

"Well that's the price the boss told me to charge. Sixteen pounds."

"I shall pay it but I think you are taking advantage of my situation."

"I'm sorry you think that but that is the price we charge regardless of who we sell to."

The tree was sparse but it would do.

Mum was ready when Dad arrived back at the hospital. Laura was standing at the cubicle door dressed in her red coat. The hood was up to protecting her thinly covered head from the cold winter night. Kit was standing by her side. Adam was lying on the bed waiting to be packaged ready for a journey to the car.

Laura sat in the back of Dad's car.

"It's Christmas Eve tomorrow night!" said Dad.

"Will Father Christmas come?" Laura asked in earnest. There is no point in Christmas Eve unless Father Christmas comes.

"Of course he will!"

"But of I haven't told him what I want!"

Of course she hadn't. When had there been time for writing to Father Christmas , let alone visiting him in his Grotto in Lewis's. "Perhaps you can tell him tonight, we'll go to see his grotto in Belgrave," said Dad.

They arrived at Town Hall Square. Dad drove straight into the car park in front of the Town Hall. Mum followed in the Ford Sierra. Two cars in the Mayoral slot. The whole of Belgrave was lit up. They are probably the best lights in the country, or so Dad believed. He should know. He had travelled. Laura loved them. She was overwhelmed by the brilliance of them and could not wait to get out of the car to fill her mind with their light and twinkling happiness.

As Dad closed the car door an Official approached him from the Town Hall.

"You can't park here, Sir," said the Official.

Dad explained their predicament. There was no point in doing otherwise. It was the truth. It was Truth. It was reality. Why should others not share it? They did not have time for car parks, tickets and all that time wasting. Minutes were life. Life now was to see the Christmas lights of Belgrave, the finest brightest lights in the country.

The Official agreed. That was his view of life. Sod the Mayor's space, he said.

In the centre of the display opposite the fountain was a model Father Christmas.

"That's not the real Father Christmas!" said Laura.

"I know," replied Dad. "But he is one of Father Christmas's helpers. He will take your message to the real Father Christmas."

Laura looked at the model and wished a secret wish and was happy.

They walked back to the cars. The Salvation Army Band was adjacent. They played 'The Coventry Carol" at Dad's request. He liked that. It made him both sad and happy. He thought Laura might like it too. He knew it was one of Mum's favourites. They played it beautifully and sensitively as only the Salvation Army can do for it means something more than music to them. Mum and Dad stood together and quietly sang the words. Dad harmonised with Mum. Their lonely duo of sound drifted like snow across the square.

It was quite misty and frosty as they drove home. This was real Christmas weather. Laura was happy. Home! For how long did not matter. Time had no perspective in these things. Does the office or factory worker think of Monday when he or she leaves work on a Friday night? Neither did Laura think of returning to the hospital. After all, it was Christmas. A time of optimism and anticipation. A time for reconciliation with past anxieties and a resolution to go forward in hope.

Within half an hour Dad had trimmed the tree. The lights blinked unexpectedly in the hall; surprised to be dragged from their hibernation in the attic so early. In the meantime Mum had strewn holly and ivy over the picture frames and began to sing her favourite carols. It was Christmas!

"Read us something from the Christmas Carol!" shouted Mum from the kitchen as she started to defrost the Mince Pies made in a hurry one Sunday morning. "Put us in the mood!"

Dad took the book of Dickens into the kitchen and read one of the family's many favourite chapters. Everyone became quiet and a little melancholic. Mum brushed away a tear.

"Shall we have a party tea?" shouted Mum to the twins.

"Yes please!" they cried in apparent unison.

Laura liked party teas. You could pick at what you wanted when you wanted. More importantly it looked so good to eat when all the food was laid out on the table. Kit loved them too. He loved to choose one thing from each dish and return time and again.

Mum made little cocktail sausages, slivers of smoked salmon on the tiniest slices of brown bread, ham rolled into tubes stuffed with potato salad, cubes of Red Belgrave and Gouda cheese, silverskin onions, gherkins and lots and lots of Walkers crisps of different flavours. To wash it all down there was lemonade in fluted champagne glasses.

In the meantime Dad poured gin and Tonics for Mum and himself in the kitchen. They immediately began to wind down. When someone once asked Dad what was the meaning of life he answered "A gin and Tonic". According to Dad there is something about that first drink which cannot be recaptured with subsequent drinks. It relaxes the brain and puts life into perspective. The purpose of our existence becomes clear. To achieve this insight Dad said the drink had to be poured in the right way and it could only be Gordons and Schweppes.

He became quite distressed if he had to drink something else. Wherever Dad travelled in the world he promoted the healing benefits of gin and Tonic. It made him very popular.

Everyone enjoyed themselves that evening, even little Adam, who made as much noise as he could. There was a great deal of silliness and exuberance inevitable after the release from the institution of hospital. The Christmas tree was pretty pathetic everyone agreed, but they all enjoyed the joke. Mum and Dad felt a little tiddly by the time the children had gone to bed. They had not been used to relaxing. The alcohol went to their heads and they were glad of it. The pain went away. Dad had opened a bottle of Chinon and on top of the gin it succeeded in temporarily wiping their minds clean. They could have been staying at home forever. They slept well. The alcohol let them do that. It recovered them. When they awoke they were in the mood for the preparations of the day, for this was Christmas Eve.

Kit was a little perplexed as to why Christmas had come a little earlier this year.

"Nobody knows when the first Christmas occurred. It's an ancient festival. It is not only about Jesus, but also about Saxon legends of the forest, about winter gods and trees decorated with lights. It's a time of great mystery."

Dad went on to talk of the forests of Germany and the ancient gods. Kit imagined those ancestors decorating trees in the dark forests and was fascinated. Dad talked about the first Christmas, about Herod slaying the children and Kit was sad. He became happy when Dad told him of the newborn infant full of hope for the world.

Whilst Dad was talking, Laura lay in her room listening. She imagined the baby Jesus as best she could. It was difficult. He only came to see her as an adult person. She could not picture him as a child. She thought of the child in the crib as something different. Not a real child, but a conjecture of the grown up world, an image of the world's perception of a messianic child. He had to have a special birth being a very special person, she understood that. Humankind had given him one. Laura did not care how or where he had been born. She loved him and needed him regardless.

She hoped Jesus would be with her over Christmas. They would probably go to church. She would see his picture there. She wanted to go out if she could, to see some ordinary people who were not sick.

Unfortunately Laura still had a low white cell count. She could not mix for fear of infection. Nevertheless Dad took her and Kit for a walk in the village the following day, 'Christmas Eve'. She had a go on her favourite swing but quickly grew cold. Then he took her to see the sheep in the field, set against a backcloth of mist and frost that clung to the trees. She felt the cold terribly so Dad took them back home. At least she had been out. She was glad of that.

She was excited about Christmas Day. She knew she was getting a special present and wondered what it might be. I hope it is something that I can play pretend with, like the little mobile home in my hospital. I like to play with that toy with Dad and Kit because it makes me feel happy. It is so real. It makes me forget the pain and the hospital. I can pretend to be with my family for as long as I want and no one can interfere. Perhaps Father Christmas will bring me a mobile home, she hoped. The anticipation made her excited. The fear that she might not get it made her frightened and sad.

The night of 'Christmas Eve' arrived and after yet another party tea (Mum did not want to cook, she would have enough tomorrow 'Christmas day') the twins were made ready for bed. Laura was dressed in her favourite long blue nightie, Kit in his pyjamas. Adam was already sleeping, full of milk and biscuits and dreaming of the cosiness of his Mum's lap where he had fallen asleep.

They placed their stocking by the fireside. They were big stockings that Mum and Dad would have difficulty filling. A glass of wine, a mince pie and a carrot for the reindeers were placed on the hearth.

"I hope those reindeer don't make a mess again!" piped up Kit with a grown up look of annoyance. "They knocked down the bells on the mantle-piece and left bits of carrot, and Father Christmas didn't eat his mince pie!" The words tumbled out.

"I bet Father Christmas has a big tummy eating all those mince pies!" Laura joined in. "He should not eat so much!"

Kit was more concerned with the reindeer. He wondered how they got through the small fireplace but assumed it was all down to magic. Some children did not have fireplaces. One of these had told him that Father Christmas came through a keyhole. Another said he came through the central heating system. Kit pondered this and thought it unlikely. The truth was they did not know. They had not got a fireplace so had to say something. He was glad he had a fireplace.

"What are you thinking about Kit?" asked Dad.

"I'm glad we have a fireplace for Father Christmas to come down."

"So am I," replied Dad. "So am I."

Chapter 22

One of the best Christmas presents

They did not wake up early. Dad had to wake them.

He gently nudged Laura. He woke her first because he knew it would take her a little longer than Kit to get started. Her body was slower to react. Her limbs were still stiff and tired.

"Laura." Her eyes stirred. " Laura. Do you want to see if Father Christmas 's been?" Her eyelashes flickered.

She woke up, gently and with a smile.

"Is it Christmas?"

"Yes. You go downstairs and I'll wake Kit."

No sooner had Dad nudged Kit than he was on his way downstairs, Dad following with his dressing gown.

Laura could not believe her eyes when she arrived downstairs. It was there in the centre of the room. She stopped to appraise it. Then she slowly approached and encircled it, examining every detail but not touching it. Eventually she sat down in front of it and reached out.

"A doll's house! Dad! Look. See. Father Christmas brought me a dolls house and there's a real Mum and Dad and Kit and Laura and Adam in it." She pointed inside the doll's house. "Look Dad's still lying in his bed. You are lazy! Get up Dad!"

She laughed with a throaty chuckle, pleased with her own joke and even more pleased that her expectations had been exceeded. Dad was pleased. Grandad had built the house himself over many painstaking hours. It was the best of presents. Dad wished that Grandad could see Laura's face now.

In the meantime Kit had attacked his presents with gusto. Within minutes he had tried everything and of course demonstrated them all for Dad. Mum came in the room carrying little Adam. She plonked him down in front of his toys and he too was soon pre-occupied. They were all happy and it would be a long time before Laura would move from the doll's house.

Christmas dinner was a grand affair even though Mum had to tax her skills of improvisation. There was pheasant, for Laura preferred stronger meat, lots of vegetables and trimmings, with smoked salmon to start. Laura would eat smoked salmon on it's own. It was now her favourite delicacy although she did not treat it like a delicacy. Everyone had a glass of champagne before the meal. There were small glasses for the children. Adam was presented with a tiny glass so that he could enjoy the bubbles. He was not impressed and returned to his milky drink.

In the afternoon they played and played and played until everyone was very tired. When the children had gone to bed Mum and Dad made preparations for the next day. It was time to think about going back to the hospital.

This time the whole family travelled with Laura to Belgrave. Dad had more or less finished work for Christmas, the real Christmas that is.

They were put in a cubicle they had used once before. It had a view. It had been specially chosen for them. They knew they were potentially here for a long time. It could be months if things went well, less if they didn't. The family walked down the passage of the ward accompanied by Kit playing the Snowman on Laura's portable tape recorder.

"I thought it must be you," said one of the nurses. "I recognised the theme tune."

They were quickly settled in and treatment began immediately. Laura changed in an instance from being happy with her afterthoughts of Christmas to a state of total despair.

"We will have another Christmas in hospital," offered Dad when he saw her desperate unhappiness.

"I don't want another Christmas."

"It's going to be hard," said the health visitor.

Within days she went down. She stopped eating. The senior registrar came round and looked worried.

"She must keep up her strength," he said. "She will need every ounce if she is to get through the Maze."

It was almost as if she had given up. Her disposition was grim. It was black. There was no light, no hope, only darkness. Have they not taken all the hope or happiness from me, she thought? I was happy at home. Now I am here being injected with those horrible liquids that burn me inside and make me sick. I just want to escape, but there is no escape. They are doing it to me. They say it makes me better. It doesn't. It makes me ill.

The ward was emptied at Christmas. Radella was still there. Dear Radella fighting her own battle in parallel with Laura. She came to see Laura regularly. Laura smiled when she popped her little baldhead round the cubicle door. Then Dad would put Laura on the mat and she would play contentedly for a half hour or so with Radella until she got too tired.

Laura and Radella never talked about their illnesses. Laura often talked about her dolls house.

"And it has a little Mum and Dad. There is furniture and a pretend shower. Dad has a shower because he's very dirty," she laughed. It was a joke she made often when Dad played the dolls house. She continued "He sits on a poof and reads a book whilst Mum fetches him a gin and Tonic. Then he goes to bed and I come to wake him up. He doesn't like that."

So she went on. Radella listened and then told of her toys at Christmas. Poor Kit did not get much of a look in. As Dad listened to Laura he resolved to do one thing, even though the hospital might not like it. He would bring the doll's house in. They would pretend to have meals in it and then perhaps Laura could relate to that when presented with her own food. They could continue the game.

So it was that Dad made a special trip and brought in the dolls house. He expected her to be pleased.

She looked up from the pillow when he stumbled through the cubicle doors with his burden. She smiled.

"My dolls house!" she exclaimed with delight. Then the same black look came over her face and she curled up in a ball sucking her thumb.

Dad was distraught.

"But Laura. It's your dolls house. You can play with Radella now."

Laura heard him and certainly the thought of playing with Radella was a pleasurable one. But why has he brought my dolls house here? Am I to be here so long? I was looking forward to going home to play with it. It cannot be the same here in this crowded hospital cubicle.

She went to sleep thinking of her dolls house and the games she played with Dad. Next day they played and she was a little happier. However the house took up an awful lot of room and Dad was frightened it would get damaged. He was nervous of telling Laura now that she was playing with it, but he knew he had to discuss it with her.

"I think we can only keep the dolls house here for your second Christmas Laura. Otherwise it might get broken. Perhaps then we can take it back home to wait for you, and then you can play with it in your own home. What do you think?"

"I want my dolls house to go home."

So it did and there it was to be a great source of pleasure and comfort. The finest Christmas present of all.

Chapter 23

Surreal celebration

Christmas on the ward was a strange and unreal time. There were no nurses dressed in red and black capes singing carols on Christmas Eve. There was just the television set flickering in the corner and other smaller sets blinking away in the cubicles. Laura's cubicle was no exception. Everyone sat looking at the little portable set except for Laura who continued not to eat and just lay curled up in a ball sucking her thumb. The room was silent save for the television. It was warm and everyone felt lethargic. Laura's uneaten food lay on her bed table along with the syringes of medication that she refused to take. Mum looked at them with despair and a nagging sickness. At some point she would have to tackle Laura with them. She knew she would fight.

Amidst the debris was a syringe filled with a food substitute liquid. They had tried to force feed Laura. Mum felt nauseous when she thought of the struggle and how she and Dad had to forcefully hold her under the encouragement of the nurse. Never again she thought. I cannot do this to my daughter.

Suddenly Dad stood up. "I know," he said, and walked out.

He came back half an hour later with some smoked salmon, brown bread and cucumber he had bought earlier at Marks and Spencer.

"What a good idea!" said Mum.

Dad started to slice it up in front of Laura. She looked up. Mum dipped into the Marks and Spencer bag she had stuffed by the bedside cabinet and pulled out some packets of party food. They laid everything out but said nothing to Laura. She lifted her head and leaned on her elbow watching what was happening.

"What's that for?" she asked in a mumble, her thumb still in her mouth.

"It's the hospital Christmas Eve. We shall have a little party. Perhaps invite Radella and her Mum and Dad for a few minutes."

"Is Father Christmas coming again?" asked Kit hardly being able to believe his good fortune that there were two Christmases. He would rather be at home with one Christmas of course, but he was here so might as well make the most of it.

"Yes he is, with lots more presents."

Laura's eyes began to sparkle a little. They contrasted with her dull and grey complexion. Dad noticed her cheeks had begun to draw in giving her a slightly gaunt look. Her teeth were turning yellow. She hated cleaning them as it caused her pain.

She looked at the smoked salmon. Mum had cut it into very small slices set in a circle of cucumber. It looked tempting, but she did not ask for any. Dad knew that if it was offered she would refuse. He knew the game he had to play and perhaps Laura knew it too. He turned to Mum.

"Thank you for making me some smoked salmon. It's my favourite"

Laura looked at him. The sparkle in her eyes turned to a twinkle. She wanted to say that she liked smoked salmon the best but could not bring herself to say it. She knew the game as well.

"I am going to leave this here, so nobody touch it, especially you Laura," he said placing the plate near to Laura and taking a piece for himself. "That's my smoked salmon. Tee dee dee dee dee tee dee dee," he sang.

Laura knew the song and knew just what to do. It was a game they had played many times at home to make both Kit and Laura eat. She pinched a piece and popped it in her mouth with a large smile and a small giggle. She was surprised. It did not taste as good as she expected. In fact it did not taste of anything at all. She had completely lost her sense of taste.

Dad continued to coax a few more slices down her and a little drink. Mum knew the salmon and cucumber and a bit of bread would do her good. Keep her going until the next battle over food.

Dad dipped into a bag he had brought in with the salmon and pulled out a bottle of gin and some tonic water. Mum laughed.

"I think we need this," he said.

"You're wonderful!"

"You are not so bad yourself"

"Ah, but you haven't got any ice," she laughed.

"Want a bet. I've got some in the freezer compartment in the ward kitchen, and I saved a lemon from the fish this lunchtime."

So they had a gin and tonic and felt better.

"What are you going to do with the rest of the salmon? It won't keep that long and we can't eat it all. You realise you bought a full pound?"

"I thought it was expensive. I thought I'd been ripped off again like the Christmas tree."

"We can give it to the other children on the ward," suggested Mum.

Just then the ward sister walked in to check on Laura. Mum and Dad were responsible for taking her temperature and filling in the chart, so all she had to do was read it and then quickly look at Laura. She saw Mum and Dad, Kit and Laura eating the smoked salmon.

"This family never ceases to amaze me. You'll be drinking champagne next."

"That's for tomorrow," responded Dad and promptly pulled out a bottle from his bag. "Can I put it in the fridge in your office until then."

Mum choked on her drink.

The ward sister laughed in disbelief then said, "Give it to me....in the bag! I don't want the ward to see me wandering around with a bottle of champagne."

"Can we give this surplus smoked salmon to the rest of the children?" asked Mum.

"Yes! I suppose so. It is good for them. Nothing finer. It's especially good for Laura."

That night the children of The ward had smoked salmon with brown bread and cucumber rings for supper instead of fish fingers. Some of the parents came into Laura's cubicle and were given a small gin and tonic in a plastic glass, which they took back to their own child's bed. One of the visiting relatives from out of town, sipping a gin and tonic and picking up a sliver of smoked salmon commented on the quality of health care at the Belgrave Royal Infirmary and was pleased to see a special treat for the children on Christmas Eve.

The cubicle was very crowded with Laura, Kit, Adam and two grown ups, but they all managed to fit in. Laura did not like such a crowd. She felt compressed. She also liked space. That's why she liked her very own countryside. The open fields and hedgerow were her special joy. She liked to see the rolling hills, the beasts grazing in the field and the birds floating on the skyline. She thought of this scene as she went to sleep and felt content. The food had made her comfortable and sleepy.

She expected to dream of her countryside or even Father Christmas. Instead she dreamt of food. She saw tables of it, waiting for her. Behind the tables were nurses with large spoons begging and screaming at her to eat. She saw Mum and Dad crying in a corner when she refused the food. She did not know what to do. Should she eat even if she was not hungry and the food hurt the ulcers in her mouth? She tried but it made her feel sick. She tossed and turned in her sleep. In the remoteness of her mind she felt Dad's hand stroke her brow, gently and comfortingly. She heard him murmur soothingly until the food and the nurses faded away to reveal an open window. Beyond the window were fields and hedges. She walked to the window, looked beyond it and felt peace. Here was freedom and tranquillity away from the glare of hospitalisation. A deep sleep overcame her.

The presents came in the night. There were three huge pillowcases full of toys. Mum and Dad were surprised at how many toys there were. Being donated they were not of a high quality. Nevertheless the twins and Adam enjoyed playing with them. There was a doll with a pink dress that Laura particularly liked. Father Christmas visited the ward in the morning and there was a small Silver Band in the central corridor playing carols. Dad carried Laura out of her cubicle to meet Father Christmas. She tried to show some interest but he knew that she felt far too sick. Father Christmas talked to her but she ignored him, pointing back to her room for Dad to take her there. They went back and played with the dolls. They absorbed themselves in another world for a good hour. It made Laura tired and she went back to bed.

Lunchtime came and a table was laid in the cubicle. The other families were eating together in the playroom but Laura was too sick for that. There was turkey with all the usual festive trimmings and Mum and Dad drank the champagne but did not enjoy it. It was a bizarre Christmas dinner. Laura ate a little potato then went down again. This time she had decided not to eat any more. It was pointless, she thought. It only made her sicker. Better not to eat at all.

She ate nothing for a week. She drank a little.

They came to weigh her. They took off all her clothes and stood her on the scales. Dad looked at her. Her rib cage protruded and the skin hung loosely off her hip joints. Her legs were like sticks of loose flesh and her face was placid and gaunt.

Oh my poor dear child, thought Dad. What have we done to you? She stood quietly and sucked her thumb. What are you thinking of? Dad wondered. What are you doing? Is this your way of fighting?

"She must eat something otherwise she goes on a nasal gastric tube," said the senior registrar.

"I know she has to eat, but she won't," said Dad angrily. He looked at her again. She was living off chemicals. The medicine, the drugs were poured into her by mouth and through her Hickman line with regularity. She opened her mouth and heart and took it all. Chemicals were her only consumption, yet she refused any food. Why?

The world was at a loss to understand her. She was a child. They thought of her as a child. She looked and talked like a child. She was a child. It was her sickness, but they could not communicate with her about it. She would not understand. They spoke to her parents. She lived each day on the results of their discussion and deliverance.

She continued to refuse food for another week. She got some form of infection that made her cough incessantly. The senior registrar came back. He checked her body fat.

"I am using a technique normally associated with tests on children suffering from malnutrition and starvation in third world countries," he proudly announced, placing his fingers around her upper arm.

"Surprisingly she still has enough body fat to support her. Nevertheless she has lost about a third of her body weight. Try to feed her over the next two days, otherwise the drip."

"What about the infection?" asked Mum.

"We'll give a broad spectrum of antibiotics. It could be anything."

He left the room.

Mum and Dad told Laura of the food options but she did not answer. She sat up and pointed to the folic acid, a reminder to Dad that it was due to be taken.

She could see that Mum and Dad were upset. Is this not my body, she thought? Do they think I have given up? Am I not haunted nightly by this white phantom that has invaded me. I cannot eat the food, it makes me sick, but I know the drugs will kill him so I take them. Yet, he is still there. So what is the point? I see no future, no hope, only pain, and the only way through it is to try and sleep.

Radella's Dad said "There is no purpose in life. There is no point. It's a game of chance. We are all animals. We just happen to be top of the pile. At the front end of the food chain."

"If that were true we might as well behave like animals," said Dad.

"Ah but we do. But like very sophisticated animals. We think we have order when all we have is managed chaos. Life is a game of random selection. Some do well. Others don't, and there is no logic to it. Life is a game."

"It might be a game, but, surely, it's a game we can influence. We can plan and anticipate."

"You might as well throw a dice as plan your life. Yes, you might be successful but then something like what has happened to Radella and Laura crops up and then where are you."

"You are in a position to cope and manage the situation"

"You can do that without planning"

Dad took a sip of his beer. They had popped round to the City Arms for a drink and left Mum and Radella's Mum with the children. The bar was quite full of locals. Dad wondered what it was like to live in the shadow of a hospital. Perhaps they never noticed.

"You are a psychologist by profession aren't you," he said turning to the man.

"Professor of Philosophy, actually. Philosophy is about playing with words, psychology is trying to understand what makes us tick. Neither gives us any real answers. I have more questions than answers. Philosophers always do. You probably have more answers than I do. Then again I'm a cynic."

"I have no answers, only questions. The first question is 'why'?' why us? I do not believe in fate or destiny but surely there must be some purpose behind all this?" Again he waved his hand in the general direction of the hospital.

"There is a purpose but it is not predestined. Humankind has determined so-called 'purpose in life'. It is based on a rational view of life because we expect life to have a purpose. Most modern thinkers know that life has no other purpose than to sustain itself. At the end of the day we take potluck. Life is a gamble. Whether we want to play or not makes no difference. We are forced into participation. Control is beyond us. It belongs to statistical projections and good fortune. Our future depends upon statistics."

"I'll explain. Why are there so many Leukaemia cases in Corby?" he continued. "I'll tell you. It's a statistical cluster. Let me give you an example. If you pick up a handful of sand and then cast it out it will not fall evenly. There will be clusters that contain more grain. This is the hidden secret of statistics. Nothing is certain. Good statisticians should know that. Psychologists certainly do. What I am saying is that we are here because of the statistics of genetics, environment or accident. It depends upon where you live, to whom you were born. It's all pot luck."

"I agree that life is a bit of a lottery. Having said that I believe there must be some purpose to our lives, otherwise we would grab what we could with little regard to hers. We don't because we believe or want to believe in an overall purpose to our lives. As individuals we are microcosms of the world in which we live. We want to achieve something, leave something behind. Animals don't. They are concerned with eating and breeding and the perpetuation of their species and nothing else. Likewise we want something more than perpetuation. We want to make things better. For example; why art? Why literature? Why music and science? We are searching for the truth. We have not yet found it. Perhaps we never will. Still we search. I believe the search for the truth is our purpose."

Dad felt tired. He knew that the man could maintain his argument far longer. They both became quiet, took a sip of their beer and glanced around the room. A young couple in the corner by the jukebox were arguing over whether his stepmother should be invited to the christening. The windows had long turned black with the advance of the evening. night was here. Eventually someone would draw the curtains.

The man knew that he was not here to win an argument. He was a friend of Dad. The trouble was that they were both perplexed by the way of things. They were both looking for an answer. Perhaps they might find it by exploring each other's minds, perhaps not.

The walked out of the pub into the cold air and noise of the night traffic and across to the hospital. They arrived back on the ward to find Radella's Mum and Mum in deep conversation.

"We have to do something about the conditions on this ward," said Mum the minute Dad walked into the cubicle.

"What do you mean?"

"I mean the fact that Radella and Laura are Neutropeanic and there are kids with coughs and colds out on the main ward. As well as that, half this ward is a general medical ward. Tonight we had a case of Pneumonia on the general medical bay. We are in serious risk of cross infection, not from this case in particular but potentially from others. The same nurses are used on both bays. We need a dedicated oncology ward."

"The nurses must be traipsing germs in and out of our cubicle. It's no wonder Laura keeps getting colds," said Dad with a cold realisation of what was going on.

"We are going to find someone famous from the county and write to them and ask them to give us the money to build one," said Radella's Mum.

"Well you have been busy whilst we have been philosophising. But before you ask anyone for money we first need to know what we mean by a dedicated unit, we have to design one and we then have to persuade the hospital to create it."

"Exactly!" said Mum. "So lets do it!"

So it started.

Chapter 24

She thinks he is the king

Dad was sitting by Laura on her bed. He was talking to her. She listened and smiled and looked into his face and occasionally touched his hand. Mum watched them. They are captivated with each other, she thought. Sometimes they have eyes and ears for only each other. She thinks he is a King. Everything he does is right, whether it is right or not. It's a captive sort of love, this father daughter relationship. It's not the same as the dependant love a son has for his mother.

Their total absorption with each other intrigued her although she understood it and somewhat encouraged it. She knew that it was a different relationship to the one she had with Laura. She knew that Laura would still come to Mum when she was hurt. Mum soothed all her ills. She continued to watch them.

She smiles for him. He tells her she is the world, the end, and the whole. How much does she know? She surrenders her innocence thinking she is the light and dark, the being and the end because he has told her so. She is like the wind, clear, crisp and invisible. His eyes sparkle as he leans to kiss her. She hugs him and whispers her happiness. They look at me and smile.

I watch her grow, day by day and wonder at her future. Will she be a woman, know a man like I do? Will she have children or has the radiation destroyed that possibility? She has love now in different ways from each of us in her family.

Love will survive in any circumstance. Like the wind it will return and never go away. Love will overcome all for love is all and all. It matters nothing that today they only have time for each other, are lost in each other.

They fitted a nasal gastric tube. Forcing the tube down her nose and throat made her sick. The bile that she vomited was medicine, which had been her only food. Despite the tube Mum

217

and Dad still had to feed her. They had to connect bottles to it and pour the contents down her reluctant throat, half choking her. It was force-feeding in which Laura was defenceless. She gave up and accepted it.

They let the family home for a short weekend when there was a break in the treatment. One of Laura's friends came to see her. He could not come in the house. Instead he looked through the window. He saw her pale, gaunt figure, and the drip in her nose and was afraid. The experience made Laura sad and feel different to other children.

Her weight stabilised at two thirds of her normal weight in the middle of February but she would not eat solid food at all despite all the trying. Until she did they could not be confident of going ahead. Mum and Dad began to despair. Depression set in.

Dad read her stories most nights. Her favourite was Great Expectations. Dad told the story the way he knew it not necessarily straight from the book, although he sat with the book on his lap. Laura identified with Kip. She too was looking for a way and a purpose in life. They waited until all the medication had been completed, the drugs trolley had gone away and the nurses left them uninterrupted. Then Dad took Great Expectations out of the drawer and began the story. Laura curled up, sucked her thumb and gazed into Dad's eyes and listened. He read in a gentle quiet voice. Her mind absorbed the world of Kip and she slowly drifted into a half world of sleep and wake until the sleep overtook her. Then she slept deeply and satisfactorily and Dad was happy. He telephoned Mum and said she was asleep.

The days seemed interminable. There was no change in her condition. Mum and Dad became convinced that they and Laura were losing the battle. She had become totally lethargic, but so had Dad. He lost his enthusiasm for the fight. Laura noticed and became frightened. He saw her fear and knew he had to do something. There had to be change. He called a team meeting. The consultant, senior registrar, health visitor, ward sister and child psychiatrist were to attend. Dad wanted to work out a plan to recover the situation. He knew the meeting would take place in an atmosphere of hostility. He should not be calling such meetings. Nevertheless he knew this meeting would determine whether Laura had a future or not.

The day of the meeting Dad had to go to Birmingham. He took Kit with him. He first called at his office to complete some reports and Kit was given a lot of attention. Then he went to a small engineering company and made Kit wait in the locked up car for half an hour. He knew it was wrong but what do you do? After the meeting Dad drove back toward Belgrave for the meeting. He was late setting out but hoped to catch up by exceeding the speed limit. He did and the Police caught him doing it.

"You realise that you were doing well over 90 miles an hour," said the policeman. "We are having a purge on speeding on the motorway in the West Midlands. You people are all the same. You set off too late and then try and make up the time by speeding. You have a child in the car. Think of him. Is it worth risking his life?" He paused expecting a response but gone none. "What's your hurry anyway?"

Dad told him.

"It's no excuse. You were driving well but too fast. We caught you on video. I'll let you off on this occasion. Please take care in the future, if not for your own sake, for your children."

Dad thanked him and got back in the car. When he got into Belgrave he had only minutes to spare when he hit the traffic turning off Yarborough Road into Bisford Road. He forced his way through on the inside and annoyed a number of drivers. He thought of the policeman and knew that he would not be pleased with him.

He parked the car on double yellow lines in the hospital grounds and dashed up onto the ward for the meeting, five minutes late. He saw the consultant leaving the ward. He dashed through the double doors to the ward Office where the meeting was due to take place. The other people were there. Mum was there.

"Where have you been? You are late and now he has gone. Is your job more important than this meeting?"

She was annoyed.

"The consultant is very busy," said the senior registrar.

Dad became angry. "Well so am I!" he exclaimed. "I am five minutes late. I don't believe the consultant's time is so damned precious that he cannot wait five minutes. It's my child," he looked at Mum, "our child. We are the clients, the customers, it's about time some people realised that."

"Calm down," said the health visitor. "We'll get another meeting sorted, today if we can. I'm afraid that we are not used to dealing with people like you two. You've upset one or two conventions. We have to get used to that. But please remember we all want the same thing, the best for Laura. You must believe that."

"We do, we do," said Mum.

Dad was quietly very annoyed.

They had the meeting later that day and it was agreed that advice would be sought from the paediatric oncology specialists at Great Ormond Street hospital in London regarding the next stages.

The two nurses who had moved from Great Ormond Street were still working on the ward. They were very well trained, professional and confident. The nurse who had helped overcome previous difficulties with the consultant was also very concerned over the downward spiral in Laura's morale and recognised that something had to change.

It was a bright sunny morning. Dad woke early. For some reason he felt full of energy. Perhaps he had a good night's sleep. Perhaps it was something else, intangible and unfathomable. He still wanted to do something. Implement change, influence things.

Laura was in her usual mood, quiet and reflective. She was still going nowhere.

"Today, Laura is when things change. We have to break the mould. We have to get better." He knew he was talking to himself. She listened but did not hear.

The nurse from Great Ormond Street walked in. Dad told her of his plan.

"We'll completely change the layout of the room. We'll create a separate area for play and one for reading and painting. We can't stimulate her body so we'll stimulate her mind. We'll make her mentally active. That might stimulate something in her body. It's worth a try. What do you think?"

"Great! Lets try it," said the nurse from Great Ormond Street.

They worked industriously for a good two hours. They moved the furniture, including the bed, and dusted, cleaned and polished. They brought in a desk, a blackboard and a new chair from the playroom. They pushed the curtains right back and tied them to create more light. The floor was scrubbed and all surfaces were washed clean. A couple of posters were put on the walls.

Laura began to take note of all this industry. The place was lighter and brighter. She was interested in the desk and all the painting things neatly laid out. What are they doing, she thought. Something must have happened to stimulate this change. I want to be a part of it. I want to paint but my body does not want to leave this bed.

She sat up and watched.

"Carry me!" she said.

Dad and the nurse from Great Ormond Street stopped what they were doing.

"Would you like to sit at your new desk, Laura?" Dad asked.

She nodded and stretched out her arms.

"Carry me!"

Dad picked her up and carried her over to the desk. The nurse completed the tidying up then quietly left.

Dad and Laura created many paintings of country walks, beasts in the field, tractors and hedgerows. They built a world into which they could quietly slip and be at peace. A world of ridge and furrow, meadows, rabbits in the hedges and chattering bird song. It was a world Laura longed for. She looked at the picture she had created. It was almost entirely green. I belong to the country, she thought, and the country belongs to me. It seems a long time since I was there walking in the meadow and down the long lane to the stream by the mill. Surely, if I was there in my countryside I would get better. Why don't they let me go home?

Laura liked her new room. Kit liked it too. Adam hardly noticed. He had now become totally integrated into the ward. When he arrived each day he was taken away by nurses and fed and played with. He was quite often to be found in the bath alongside other children. Sometimes he lost his identity and was treated like a patient. One day a new nurse arrived on the ward and demanded to see his drug chart. The nurses changed his nappy and played with him. However, because they were very busy they could not always find time to feed him. At such times they gave him a bottle of milk to drink with a straw. He was perhaps the only baby to be drinking through a straw at six months old. He grew to be independent and free spirited.

Despite Laura's recuperation in the new room layout she once again began a decline into body loss and despondency. She ate no food and was starving herself to death. Grandad came to see her and was appalled and upset. There seemed to be no future for her now. Surely this was the end?

Laura needed a blood transfer. Dad waited all night. Eventually it came at one o'clock in the morning. Normally the injection of new haemoglobin revives the spirit. It helps generate oxygen to feed and stimulate the brain. It made little difference. It simply kept her alive. She was very lethargic and seemed to have no wish to go on. The new room layout had temporarily revived her spirits. Something else needed to be done. Her body had become a chemical depository. She needed food.

It was a dull day. Mum arrived a little late with Kit. Adam had once again stayed at the hospital. Nevertheless she felt tired after an evening of washing and ironing, telephone calls and caring for Kit. She had not slept with worry of Laura. Could she sleep again?

She passed a few words with Dad. He was not pleased that she was late and she was not in the mood to argue with him. What was there to say? Is she eating yet? No.

The cubicle became quiet as the checks and injections were completed. Mum tried to work up some energy to read or attempts to play with Laura. She could not. Lethargy overtook her. She sat by her bedside. She noticed the room become a little lighter and glanced outside to see the sun struggling to filter through the mistiness of the morning. A single beam made it to her window and fell on Laura's bed, lighting up her face a little.

You are still beautiful, Mum thought. Without your hair, even with your pale gaunt complexion you are still beautiful. Surely Laura you have the strength to win. I know you have. I know it is within you. Dear God let her have whatever strength is left to finish what must be done. I am your mother Laura. I know you better than anyone. You came from my body. I know you still have strength.

She laid her head on the pillow next to Laura. Laura looked at her from behind her clenched hands and thumb sucking. Mum smiled gently. Laura did not. She simply stared, fixedly and with great concentration. So they lay together sharing a bond that is as old as life on earth, the bond of mother and child.

Mum's song

Have you any life left in you Laura?
You must have something left?
A little
I know you have some life in you yet
You do want to live
Don't you
Don't you
Want to live?
You do
Don't you?

I stand by my motherhood
You are my child
My pain
I know you want to live
I know that I can give
Don't you
Don't you
Want to live
You do
Don't you?

My darling we are the same
Same body, some soul of
Woman
You have strength in you yet
Strength to fight and persevere
Don't you
Don't you
Want to live
You do don't you?

Dad came back at lunchtime and he and Mum and Kit went downstairs to the staff canteen for lunch. They weren't supposed to, without a pass, but there was nowhere else for parents to eat. They were not allowed to eat with their children or bring in food. They had to use the drinks machine in the Lift area, but for how long can you live off hot chocolate? Mum and Dad ignored these rules and no one complained. When Dad was questioned in the canteen he said he was a visiting consultant, which was not entirely untrue.

They sat in a state of melancholy before their meal, not really eating but moving the food around on the plate. Adam was on the ward in his pram. Kit sat beside them and tried to keep them cheerful by continually chattering.

"Give it a rest Kit!" said Dad with irritation. "Just get on with your meal"

"I'm not hungry," said Mum pushing away the plate. "I can't eat when I know she is starving herself to death. We can't feed her intravenously forever. She needs building up; otherwise I just can't see how she is going to cope with a transplant. It's gong to be far worse than this."

One of the nurses off the ward came and sat down at the next table. She gave Kit a friendly wave. He waved back and smiled.

Dad watched this then turned to Mum. "We are going to take a look at the Transplant unit this afternoon aren't we?"

"Yes! They are going to explain to us what is involved. We are having another team meeting afterwards. Remember? You asked for it. The child psychiatrist will be there. What the hell for I don't know. She needs medical treatment not psychiatry."

"Well, perhaps it's to do with how Laura will cope in isolation. Come on. Lets get back to it."

They got up to go. Kit waved to the nurse. "See you later!" she called.

Still in a state of depression they stood by the lift door. It seemed to take forever to arrive. Eventually the doors opened. The Hospital chaplain stepped out on his way to the canteen. He smiled as they brushed past him then stopped to speak.

"Ah! I'm glad I've seen you. I popped in to see you in the cubicle." His voice turned to a whisper as if he had a secret from the other passengers in the lift. "I have some news. Laura has started to eat. I've just seen her consume a bowl of cornflakes. A small one I'll admit but nevertheless she finished it. That's good news isn't it?"

Mum and Dad hardly had time to agree. They pressed the button to take them to the fourth floor and walked quickly down the corridor, dragging Kit along with them, through the double doors of The ward and into Laura. She was talking to one of the nurses.

When they entered she looked across and gave them both a great big smile. They rushed to her, laughed and hugged her.

"I am sending you all home," the senior registrar stated with boldness and determination as he paced into the cubicle surrounded by an entourage of nurses. "I'm taking a chance I know, but I'm prepared to take if you are. I think the only place she will eat is at home. What do you think."?

Dad thought he saw a look of satisfaction on the senior registrar's face. He is rather enjoying this role, he thought.

"But her treatment hasn't finished!" said Mum. She glanced at the chart she had been keeping. "She has another two weeks of Donaroubacin."

"You can bring her in for injections. Any other medication I am happy for you to give her. You have been doing it anyway in the hospital. You both know how to clean and maintain her Hickman Line. Any problems, just call the health visitor or us. She needs building up for the Transplant and we must get her in remission before we go ahead. Technically she is there, but there are still Leukaemia cells. We must destroy them. Make her clean. Give her the best of chances."

Laura listened to this dialogue with increasing interest. Can I believe what I am hearing, she thought. Home? Am I really to go home after these weeks, these months? Has this been brought about because I ate a little? I ate because I feel a change inside me. A change for good. My body feels a little cleaner. The pain is less and the dreams have gone. I still hurt and feel sick in my tummy but there is a feeling of optimism in my heart, which I do not fully understand. That is why I ate. Can I really be going home at last?

"Before you go we have our meeting and you are due to visit the Transplant unit. You realise that Laura is the first child in the hospital to undergo this treatment in the new unit. They normally have to go away. She is certainly the first twin. Quite an event really. You are making history."

225

The thought that Laura was the first frightened Dad. Would they get it right? Did these people know what they were doing? This was the smallest oncology department in Britain with only one paediatric Oncologist. Did they really have a chance here? Should they have tried for Great Ormond Street or even Birmingham?

Mum and Dad were very impressed with the Transplant unit. A man whose grown up son had died of Leukaemia had created it. They were shown the procedures of showering up before you enter, the sterilisation of food, and the need to keep the place germ free. This was accomplished through an extraction system that literally sucked the bugs away. Mum was very impressed with the quality of training of the nursing staff. They knew their oncology and Haematology. They were specialists, not general nurses like most of those on The ward. They spent some time inside one of the two units and felt very comfortable about Laura going in there. It was agreed that Dad would take a few weeks off work and stay with her in isolation for the duration of the treatment. This was estimated to be something like four to six weeks.

Feeling buoyant and hopeful they returned to the ward, checked that Laura was all right and then went straight to the meeting.

The senior registrar and consultant were both there. So were the ward sister, the health visitor, the nurse from Great Ormond Street and the child psychiatrist.

Everyone supported the decision for Laura to go home. They discussed the medication to be given at home and these had been prepared and placed in a special pack. Lots of needles, swabs and syringes.

"Don't put the syringes in the dustbin," said the health visitor. "They might get into the wrong hands. Bring them back. We count them."

They went through the routine of the Hickman line.

"Clean it every other day and flush it out," the ward sister said. "Don't use the same syringe twice. I've written it down. The Prednisilone is better before breakfast. It's more effective. The other drugs can be toxic. Stick strictly to the instructions. I have included plenty of gloves. Also don't forget to swab her before an injection."

"You are the first parents we have tried with treatment at home," said the senior registrar. " Live up to our trust."

They talked about the bone marrow Transplant. Dad noticed that the child psychiatrist had said nothing, confirming his suspicions about the need for her presence.

"Do you think Laura is prepared for the Transplant unit?" asked the senior registrar.

"You should know," said Dad. "You have been treating her."

"I don't mean physically. I mean emotionally and mentally."

The child psychiatrist leaned over.

"Laura must feel comfortable about going in the unit. I suggest she goes to see it first. That way she will not be afraid of the unexpected. It's good that one of you will stay with her all the time, but I think it is very important that she sees both parents and her brothers too. Treat it like a special hotel, her hotel. Ask her to approve it."

"And what about Kit. Does he understand what he has to do? What have you told him?" she continued in a gentler voice. Dad noticed that her spectacles were slightly smeared. She must have her mind on higher things, he thought, and no time to clean them. He was glad she was there. She was broaching a subject he knew had not been addressed.

"He knows he has to make a sacrifice," said Mum.

"Does he know he is giving a part of his body?"

"Yes."

"I understand from the file that the twins like to play soldiers. I suggest you tell him that he is donating his good soldiers to fight the bad soldiers in Laura. Good soldiers always win."

Indeed they do. Good soldiers always win. Mum and Dad knew that. But first they must prepare for battle. The family went home to do just that.

Chapter 25

Egg and bacon

Egg and bacon! Glorious egg and bacon!

Laura ate a little food on her first night at home. A few crisps, then a little cereal. In the morning she awoke feeling properly hungry. The sort of normal hunger she used to feel before the medicine made her sick. She had often thought about egg and bacon, one of her favourite meals. She actually referred to bacon as chicken bacon. This was a throw back to when she was very little. She liked chicken. It was easily palatable. So Mum and Dad called everything chicken. She knew it was a trick but the suggestion was enough to make eating other meats much more acceptable.

Dad could cook the most wonderful egg and bacon. Such a meal they had that morning. He carried her downstairs, for she still had some difficulty walking and had not seen stairs for a long time. He served her tea in her yellow cat cup. She sat at the kitchen table sipping it. The morning light was coming through the kitchen window. A bird sang. A cock crowed. There was the occasional sound of traffic in the distance. A tractor was working in the field and next door's horse was being shod. The familiar sounds of a morning at home. The light became stronger and turned into a watery spring sunshine that cast rays across the kitchen floor. She sipped her tea.

The smell of the bacon grilling was glorious. The crack of the eggs was a sound of the greatest comfort and expectation. They sputtered in the frying pan. The toast went under the grill with the bacon and its aroma was warm and reassuring. At last the dish was put before her. Bacon. An egg cooked both sides. Little squares of toast freshly covered in butter. Just looking at it almost satisfied her hunger. Dad sat down with her and they began to eat. He looked up and smiled. She smiled back. This was living. The hospital seemed a long way away. So far away she did not think of it.

Days of springtime, blossom and hedgerows full of budding shoots and sticky buds. Frisking lambs jumping off their back legs pursued by calves with eyes so beautiful they made you weep. The buck hare in the meadow played with its young so nonchalantly it must have known the hunting season was over. The fox, the indefatigable rabbit, the vole, mole and field mouse took ownership of the field; it was their time to rule the land.

In the sky the lark ventured, the yellow-headed wagtail skipped the hedges and wrens began to nest. The thrush sang in competition with the blackbird, and not many knew the difference in the tune. The sky became alive with song.

The earth joined in chorus. The winter wheat and oats and barley shimmered green across the meadow. Soon they would turn gold. Theirs was the soil, the lifeblood of the county. They made it come to life. Its sustenance supported all life across these rolling hills of Belgraveshire, the heart and essence of England, a county whose history spelt the lifeblood of the country. Ridge and furrow are its mark, the very symbol of medieval days. Rolling hills and three hundred acre fields are the characteristics that make it good for the hunt, a hunt that requires a horse and mount with the perseverance to endeavour three hours in mud and meadow on wet misty mornings. But the hunt and shoot were over. Now was a time for replenishment and growth. The county was filled with optimism. If it had music it would sing to the soul of Vaughan Williams. It was a time to sow seeds, to plant for the future, to make families. It was a time to look forward. The land was full of hope and joy.

Life became normal once again. Breakfast with Dad, walks to the swing park and across the meadow, what else was there to life?

She missed her friends from playschool and the village. Dad organised for her to play in the village with the other children. He organised races with bikes and pedal cars. There was a great deal of noise and exuberant enthusiasm that ended with some tears and bruised knees. Otherwise everyone enjoyed such physical activity, especially Laura, who wanted so much to be treated like an equal in terms of ability.

They threw all their energy into living. So much so that Laura soon began to let the hospital become a memory.

Her appetite had returned immediately. She ate with great enthusiasm. However she no longer had a taste for childish foods. Now she only wanted food with 'flavour'. Smoked salmon became her favourite. She ate it unaccompanied by accoutrements. She ate well. No fatty indigestible food, only good wholesome dishes. It was almost as if she knew that she had to eat well. Yet, she ate because she was hungry. Her days of starvation had refined her taste. Now she wanted to taste the food and enjoy it for its own sake.

It must have only been two weeks that they were at home but it felt like many months. Laura had completely recovered her body weight and looked well. She felt well.

The best part of being at home was to sleep in her own bed. Mum and Dad never fully appreciated how much that meant to her. She felt secure and content. It was a joy to go to bed at night, for Dad to read a story whilst she snuggled down to a hot water bottle and Horlicks. This was life.

Dad told amazing stories. He would start with a book but before long she knew he was not reading it. He took her into a world of mystery and enchantment, of peace and contentment and a place full of humour and irony, which she now began to understand. His stories were about her and the people and places she knew. The village, woods and meadow all featured along with the mysterious creatures that inhabited them.

Such peace and contentment made her strong. The senior registrar was right. In the end he took no risk. He knew she would come through. Or did he?

They drove back to hospital. She was not going to stay. It was a check up. Was the treatment working or not. She looked well but was she yet in remission?

"There are no signs of Leukaemia cells. She is fully in remission. In fact she is in remarkable condition, much better than I could ever expect. We can go forward with every confidence of success. Well done!"

The Registrar was very pleased. He had not expected so much so soon. He was pleased not only for the family but for the fact that he now had a fighting chance of success. It was his job, his life to succeed, to secure life and make whole those who were sick.

So it was they named the day when she would come back. Another break, then the Transplant unit. Now it was Kit's turn.

Dad had never really dealt with the media before apart from the odd newspaper interview. He was apprehensive about meeting the broadcaster. One day the broadcaster turned up at the clinic. The health visitor told Dad to go over and talk to him about the need for more cash for the hospital. He did and found the broadcaster to be quite normal. The broadcaster told Dad to come to a special day at the Home from Home for children with malignant disease that was due to be opened. Dad agreed.

"Bring the twins," said the broadcaster. "It will make a nice story, how you have coped."

The whole family travelled into Belgrave for that special day. It was a Sunday. The new Home from Home had just been refurbished. It was an open day. In the basement the Professional Fundraiser was serving glasses of Riesling wine which had few takers, nevertheless he continued to persuade people to take it. Elsewhere dishes of food, comprising mainly sandwiches and sausage rolls, were being served. The children hunted for the occasional bowl of crisps.

"Laura has Leukaemia. How do you find it, having to cope with a situation like this? It must be difficult," asked the broadcaster. He passed the microphone to Dad, who sat beside him on an old settee.

"It's not easy. Laura has already relapsed on treatment," responded a nervous Dad.

"Oh! I'm sorry."

"That's all right. She has now gone into remission once again and we are looking to secure her future through a bone marrow transplant."

The broadcaster became vividly interested.

"Really! Who is the donor?"

"Her twin brother, Kit."

"And what exactly is involved. Will Kit have to have an operation."

"Yes, it is an operation. They extract a sample from his marrow whilst he is under anaesthetic. I believe the operation involves injections with a lot of needles, not just one. It takes a couple of days. He will be a little sore afterwards. Nevertheless it's a big thing for a four year old."

"How is Laura given the marrow? Does she have an operation alongside Kit?" The broadcaster had a mental picture of the twins lying side by side in the operating theatre with the marrow being pumped from one to the other.

"No. She receives the marrow through her blood stream, an injection in one of the veins in her arm we are told. It amazingly finds its own way to the marrow. Before that she has to have total body irradiation to make sure the leukaemia cells have all been killed."

"I understand this is the first time for children so young in the transplant."

"Yes. It is."

"What about Kit? How does he feel about it? If he's around perhaps we can ask him."

Kit was playing nearby. Dad called him over. The broadcaster introduced him on the radio then leaned over toward him so that they shared the microphone.

"I believe you are going to do something special for your sister, aren't you Kit? What exactly are you going to do? Would you like to tell us about it?"

"I'm going to give her my good soldiers to kill her bad soldiers and make her better."

"That's marvellous! Perhaps you would like to say that again for all the people out there listening. " He moved the microphone closer to Kit.

"I'm giving her my good soldiers."

"And your soldiers are going save her? Eh... Kit?"

"Yes."

Kit lost interest and walked away to play with Laura who had found a new young friend. They played with a toy pram that someone had donated to the house.

The broadcaster turned to Dad.

"Is this a story you have told Kit to let him understand what is happening?"

"Yes," replied Dad thinking of the child psychiatrist. "It was suggested to us at the hospital as Kit and Laura often used to play soldiers together."

You assume that what is often important in your own life is not always of any significance to others. You travel through this circus of living engrossed in your own problems. You resolve them as best you can without recourse to others. You expect this to be the normal course of events. Your problems are of no consequence outside yourself. But occasionally others do take an interest. It may be an accumulation of circumstance or the fact of being in the right or wrong place at the right or wrong time. It may simply be that what you thought was uninteresting was in fact interesting. Others may see more in your life and your story than you could ever see. It may be that the package has been put together in such a way that the world cannot fail to take an interest and would be moved by it.

Eventually someone reaches down and picks up a thread of your life. It becomes woven into something that you did not realise was there. It is passed on. Once the interest has been aroused this small garment of a story will grow and grow. People, particularly journalists, get to hear of these things. It comes at a time that is appropriate and opportune. There may be general interest in the subject, a need to fill a gap in the news bulletin, or simply the availability of a good story.

So it was that a few days later a photographer and reporter came to Laura's home. They were from the main newspaper in the city and county. They chatted and took photographs and notes. Two days later the front page of this paper ran a story. Large headlines. 'The love of a brother'. It was the story of Kit's donation of good soldiers. Probably half the population of Belgraveshire have sight of this particular newspaper. The community adopted the twins and Laura's fight became a community fight. National newspapers made contact and featured the story. Radio and television did the same. Now Mum and Dad knew that the outside world was watching their progress.

"It must help," Dad said to Mum. "The hospital has to do its best. This publicity might help focus them."

Laura's progress was monitored by more than her family. The community watched and waited. When they next walked into the hospital accompanied by Kit and his cassette player with the 'Snowman' tune things were different. They felt different. They were more confident. Now they had some support in their battle to improve, not only their own situation, but also, perhaps, the longer term prospects of other children with cancer. Could they use it effectively? Only time would tell. They had moved up one more rung of the ladder. There could be no looking back. The story had now become public property.

Chapter 26

For the love of Laura

Kit's first song

Love lies bleeding alongside my heart
There is nothing else I can give
My heart, my soul, my love, my blood
Laid out front
For you
And you alone
For the love of Laura.

I have not much to give outside my heart
This little heart of mine
What I have, my body, soul, my very marrow
Laid out front
For you
And you alone
For the love of Laura

My love of Laura, she's my heart
She is my being and apart
I have nothing to bear except this soul
Laid out for you
For you
And you alone
For the love of Laura,
Kindred Laura, second heart.

The Transplant unit was a strange place. It was situated
through a doorway halfway down one of the oldest Florence
Nightingale style wards to exist in the hospital. This part of the
building dated back to 1771 when the Infirmary was founded.
The structure had not changed at all, although the culture had.
In those days the patients had to wash their own linen, if they

could walk, and generally help out with the non-medical duties. The ward mainly dealt with infectious diseases. The survival rate was not high but it offered a better chance than had previously been available. Belgrave was one of the first provincial general hospitals to be founded. Its directors, consultants, Nurses and staff are proud of their heritage. Having said that they do not look back very often.

Their eyes are on the future and the continued growth and success of this, one of the largest and most reputable of hospitals outside London.

All this is of no consequence to a child potentially dying from Leukaemia, who does not fully understand history or its significance to life today. Yet, Laura could not entirely eliminate the history of this place from her mind. She knew it as something that crept though the brickwork and woodwork. Those souls who had suffered and died or, alternatively, suffered and survived whispered to her through time. It cannot be possible that so much emotion could pass through such a confined space without something being left behind. You have life, they said. Keep it. Honour it and respect it. Remember it has limitations. It is not the end in itself.

Laura very quickly settled into the unit. Mum and Dad noticed an immediate difference in the knowledge and quality of the members of the care team. They were confronted with nursing staff that were thoroughly trained in haematology. They knew what was happening to Laura's body. They were strict in the application of the regime of drugs. Very strict. They were professionals in their subject and expected to be successful.

The unit was like a carbuncle to the ward. It protruded out toward the Gallstone Road, one of the main arteries of the city, as if it were trying to demonstrate its existence to the passing motorists and pedestrians. It was not successful in this endeavour. Most people driving into the city did not even glance at it, intent as they were on getting to their place of work on time.

The unit contained two independent rooms for patients and a smaller observation room for the care team, as well as shower facilities for the nursing staff and parents. Laura took the right hand room, which had a window overlooking the road. Her bed was central under a special air extraction system, which would take away all the bugs in the air, or so everyone hoped. Dad had a bed adjacent to hers, but near the window. She was pleased that he was going to be there to share this experience.

They started her on a course of treatment, which included some chemotherapy to keep her in remission. Before they could take Kit's marrow and transplant it into Laura they had to make absolutely sure that Laura's marrow was free from the Leukaemia. The chemotherapy would help but there was only one way of making absolutely certain. She had to be given total body irradiation. A most daunting assignation for a four-year-old child. Three hours of non-stop radiation would clear her marrow, veins, pores and brain of these evil Leukaemia cells. Of that the consultants were confident. But first she had to survive it.

A meticulous timetable had been worked out. The sequence was important. First the total body irradiation and then the operation on Kit and the bone marrow Transplant. Preparations began and the morning arrived for Laura to go for radiation.

She had been to the radiation department in the early part of her treatment. She also went there in preparation for this day. Then they had sized her up. They fitted electrodes all over her body and head and made indelible marks on her skin. She was thus decorated like a Sioux warrior, ready to do battle. She only had a few whispers of hair left. Soon these would also disappear along with the eyebrows and some eyelashes.

They had to work out a route to the radiation room, which involved minimum risk of infection. She also had to wear special shoes, along with a gown, skullcap and facemask to further protect her. They planned to take her on a stretcher but Dad said he wanted to carry her and she wanted him to.

"I'm afraid you can't carry her and walk," they said. "But what we can do is to push you both in a wheel chair. She can sit on your knee. The porter will push you."

Dad said he wanted to look the same as Laura so they dressed them in identical garments, including a facemask. The Wheelchair had been especially cleaned. It waited for them in the nurse's station. It glistened and shone. The porter stood by it dressed in cap and mask. The nurses who were to care for Laura stood there also. Dad walked out of the Transplant unit first and took his place rather sedately in the chariot that was to take them into battle. Mum walked out with Laura. She lifted her on to Dad's knee. Laura looked down on him and gave him a very large smile. It was as if she was trying to reassure him.

"What are you doing?" She said with a grin. "You look silly!" She looked at Mum. "Dad looks silly doesn't he Mum?"

"He does. He wants to be like you I think"

She snuggled down into his lap and he held her tightly. The porter wheeled the chariot out of the unit into the ward followed by a train made up of nurses, Mum and the health visitor. The elderly tenants of this cancer ward for women must have been made aware of Laura's journey for they shouted encouragement.

"Good luck little girl!"

"We're thinking about you Laura!"

One old lady tried to reach out to touch her but the black nurse gently deflected her outstretched hand.

Laura felt very important. She knew she was the centre of attraction. This knowledge gave her strength and determination. She knew she was going to something unpleasant but least people were rallying round her. It must be something very special that I am doing to attract all this interest from grown ups. They will carry me through, she thought, and I have my Dad and Mum with me.

They glided through the corridors toward the lift. People stopped to look and Laura became aloof to their stares.

Down the lift. Laura and Dad in the middle surrounded by the entourage. Out of the lift and down the last corridor toward the Radiation department. They arrived at the door and turned left to enter. A reception awaited them.

There was a corridor of people. On the floor they had laid a carpet to minimise the transfer of germs. As she was wheeled through, people began to offer support. There was the occasional clapping and cry of 'Good luck Laura!' from nurses and patients. She felt like a Princess and a spasm of pride overwhelmed her small body.

Dad and her favourite nurse went into the treatment room to settle her. A large tube like machine coupled with by a computer and all sorts of control panels confronted her. A table lay in front of the machine. Wires hung from its sides. It was upon this machine that Laura had to lie. She looked and was afraid.

"Stay with me Dad!"

"I'll stay as long as I can. I shall be just outside and will be able to talk to you all the way through. I've brought some stories to read to you. It will soon be over."

"I don't want to stay here by myself. I don't like it here. I'm frightened. Please stay with me."

Dad became distressed. How could she cope with what has yet to come. Three hours of intensive radiation.

"Take your time settling her down," a voice echoed over the loudspeaker. "I suggest you come outside and start talking to Laura whilst the nurses fix everything up."

Dad went outside the treatment area into the control room. Through a large window he could see everything inside the treatment room. He spoke to Laura through the microphone.

Dad's voice sounds distant and tinny, Laura thought. Why can't he just stay here by my side whilst they give me this special medicine? They have told me that I have to lie very still for a long time to let the magic rays from this machine work. I heard them say to Mum and Dad that I will vomit frequently during the treatment and that they will have to stop the machine. The more I vomit the longer it will take, they said. I know what vomit means. They use words they think I can't understand. They treat me like a person without eyes, ears and the capacity to understand. I am only four years of age but they have made me older than my years. I do understand. I probably understand better than they. Is it not my body, which has been invaded by this awful beast that destroys my lifeblood? Do they really know how I feel?

The voice spoke again. It spoke to the nurses. It ignored Laura. It sounded unreal, like that of one of the robots she had seen on children's television.

"Come outside please. We are ready to go."

The nurses obeyed mechanically and walked away. They closed the inner and outer doors. They sealed her in this tomb of radiation. There was complete silence. It was a silence and a loneliness that Laura had never experienced. She was in utter isolation. She felt desolate. Would she come out alive? Some did not. She had heard that. Her despair deepened.

"Would you like a Jimmy story, Laura?"

It was Dad's voice! Metallic, distant, it was still Dad's voice. He was there. The despair began to ease a little.

"Yes please!"

"I can hear you Laura. Are you lying comfortably? Then I shall begin."

He always said this before a bedtime story.

The machine made a gentle hum and moved over her. She expected to feel something penetrate her body but felt nothing except isolation. The humming noise was overtaken by the gentle sound of Dad's voice.

In the control room things began to happen. Dials showed the radiation level to increase. When they reached the right level the process began. It would come in waves of 15 minutes. Pulsating through her body, it aggressively attacked the leukaemia cells as well as any other matter, organ or healthy cell that fell in its path. Respiration and heartbeat were monitored throughout. After the first 15 minutes the nurses went in to check on Laura. She was comfortable if a little sleepy.

The second 15 minutes began. The fingers on the clock on the overhead panel moved slowly round the dial face. Mum and Dad kept one eye on the clock and one on Laura. Dad had brought a tape recorder and now began to play her some of her favourite music over the microphone system.

Laura began to feel dizzy. The music and Dad's voice became very distant. The dizziness turned in to nausea. The second 15 minutes had just finished when she sat up and was sick. Her head began to swim. She felt hot and cold, as if her body was no longer her own. The nurses masked up and went in again to clean up.

"She's doing very well," the radiology consultant said. "She is keeping very still."

Mum and Dad felt helpless. They saw their daughter locked in this room beyond their reach being attacked by the most intensive radiation. Furthermore it was making her very sick.

The machine continued to hum and dispense its awesome dosage of rays.

Mum and Dad watched the dials closely. They did not fully understand their functions but wanted to participate, wanted to understand. Looking through the glass window they could hardly see Laura's face. Only her prostrate shape could be seen.

Once again Laura leaned over and vomited. The nurses reset her. The machine started up again and the rays fell upon her, eating into every tissue of her still young body. Poor child. She lay as still as she could. That is what she had been instructed to do. She kept faith with these instructions, trusting in the ones who gave them.

Suddenly the fingers on the dials flickered and fell to zero. The machine had stopped.

"What has happened?" Mum asked anxiously

There was silence whilst the oncology consultant and the Technician looked at the controls.

"What has happened?" Mum repeated in a near scream. "What's going on?" She went pale.

The Technician looked at the oncology consultant, turned to Mum and, in a cold and meticulous voice said, "It's broken. The damned machine has packed up."

Chapter 27

To defeat the Phantom

"There must be a back up," said Dad.

"At half a million pounds a time we cannot afford a back up," said the oncology consultant.

"What happens now?" asked Mum.

"We repair it. This has happened before," said the Technician. He was already on the telephone.

"But surely, this interruption must affect Laura's treatment," asked Dad.

"It won't if we get the machine going quite soon," the Technician responded as he waited for an answer on the telephone. At last it came. He garbled some message and put down the receiver. Shortly a man arrived and began to tinker with the controls. Mum and Dad looked at Laura anxiously. The nurses gave Dad permission to go and see her, which he did.

"Are we finished Dad?" she asked.

"No. Not yet. We are having a short break. You are doing very well."

There was a wave from the window. The machine was going again. Dad hugged Laura then went back into the Control Room. Mum was quizzing the medical team about the after affects of the interruption. They said there would be none. Mum felt uncertain. So did Dad. But who were they to disagree.

So Laura persevered a further three hours of radiation and vomiting. When she emerged she was different. She looked different. Her skin was tanned. Her face was particularly brown. From a distance she looked healthy. Look close up and you realised she had been burned. Not only had her skin been burned but she had suffered third degree burns internally. The skin was blotchy and peeling in parts. Any sign of body or facial hair had totally disappeared. She had no eyelashes.

If these rays were so destructive surely they must destroy the leukaemia cells, thought Dad. He wondered about the state of her body and her long-term prospects. It was unlikely she would have children they had told him. What else?

They wheeled her out of the radiation room, subdued and defeated.

It was a quiet journey back to the Transplant unit. A sad journey compared to their outward trip. The old people on the ward were pleased to see them. Laura hid her face. She was exhausted and not in the mood for communication. These dear old people riddled with cancer understood that. Were they not fighting the same battle? They smiled and offered their comfort. One old lady gave a meek wave from weak hand.

They wheeled Laura back into the unit.

"What happens now?" asked Mum.

"We have to monitor her very carefully this evening," replied the tall black nurse. "She will have a very high blood pressure. We must make sure it comes down. It could take all night. I am on duty tonight with Laura," She smiled "It could be a long night but I am sure everything will be all right."

"So, it's not all over yet then?" asked Mum.

"No. But there should be nothing to worry about. Everybody has a reaction to the radiation. We just have to monitor it. Who is staying with Laura tonight?"

"I am," said Dad. " I'm here for the duration."

The tall black nurse was right. Laura did have a very high blood pressure. Mum left for the evening with Kit and Adam. Dad sat by Laura's bedside watching her and the tall black nurse who continually monitored her blood pressure, temperature and respiration. Occasionally the nurse would go off to report to the consultant over the telephone.

Laura's blood pressure began to rise. It was early evening. Dad realised that he had not eaten since breakfast. He had hunger pains. He felt guilty and was glad of it.

The nurse took another reading. It continued to rise. Her pulse rate increased and with it so did her temperature. The nurse looked worried. She went out of the cubicle to telephone again.

"What's happening'" asked Dad rather anxiously.

"I thought her blood pressure and pulse rate might have settled by now, but they're still going up," She looked at Dad and saw that he was worried. "The consultant said it was all right. She is young. He said to ring in an hour if it did not start to go down."

The tall black nurse and Dad sat on opposite sides of Laura's bed. Dad held Laura's hand and talked to her. She was not very talkative but was pleased to hear Dad comforting her. She was hot. He looked at the nurse. She looked at him and smiled.

"It will be alright you know!"

Laura listened to this conversation. Do they know how I feel? I feel dizzy, she thought, such a strange sensation. My brain and body are burning. They are alive with a flaming heat of such intensity that it burns my tummy and dries my mouth. The blood running through my veins is hot. I can feel a beating and pulsating inside me. It is a repetitious beat that thumps inside my head but comes from my body, from my blood. It is out of my control. I lie here quietly and yet this pulsation increases. Soon it will rise to such a crescendo that it will not be able to contain itself in my little body. It will burst out, ripping me apart, spilling my blood upon the floor and destroy me forever.

What have they done to me? Is it them or is it the Phantom returned yet again to hurt me. I feel as if my body has been taken over. Surely only one person can take me over. It must be the Phantom again. I am lost. Lost in a seething heat of desolation. My mind is sinking into oblivion. I am lost.

She fell asleep. Rather strange considering how uncomfortable she must feel, the tall black nurse thought, but, nevertheless, she fell asleep.

Her mind and thoughts drifted and soared away from this place of dilemma. She sailed to the sun, to a place of heat, but also a place of light. The heat and light were so great that she could not comprehend them. She fell into a spinning, dizzy descent that landed her in a place of quiet desolation. It was a place that had little life. No trees. No grass. There was only sand and above her the sun. Around was emptiness.

She stood and waited. She was here for a purpose that she knew. She waited such a long time that she thought she could not be dreaming, for dreams have no delays. Eventually the sand and sun became one and she only saw a blur, a hot, hazy blur. Her body burned and she gasped for something to cool her down. A drink! A dip in a cool lake! But there was no hope, no way out, for she was lost. She collapsed into the pulsating and consuming warmth of the hot sand. She decided to let it overcome and overwhelm her. It might give her peace from the intense heat within her. As she did the light turned to dark. Trees of such dense foliage surrounded her and consumed all the earthbound light before it struck upon receptive souls. They cast long shadows of black tree trunk and foliage green.

She heard a gentle comforting voice. It was not Dad, but she did recognise it. She looked up from her collapsed state. At last! He had returned. Jesus stood before her. He was calm, cool and serene, yet he seemed a part of this place. He must have been here for many days. He spoke.

"I am the light. Let me take you from the shadows of this place."

She took his hand and left the sand, sun and shadows.

Dad smiled when the tall black nurse told him that Laura's temperature and blood pressure had started to go down. It was early morning. The nurse was right. It had been a long night. She went to phone the consultant. Dad telephoned Mum. Then he went to sleep in his bed beside Laura. He slept deeply and dreamt little.

Eventually he awoke. The tall black nurse brought him a cup of tea and opened the curtain. He awoke with a half smile. The nurse smiled and said good morning. His half smile became full. He remembered where and why he was. He said good morning and began to drink his tea. He turned to Laura's bed and saw her looking out of the window. He had not realised that she was awake. As he was closest to the window she had to look past him. Her eyes went beyond him and ignored him. He knew she was thinking.

The early morning traffic drifted into the city. She woke up disturbed. Her sleep had not been good. The dreams had been vivid and severe. In contrast the room was peaceful. Despite her dreams she also felt a strange and unexpected peace as if she had overcome some great obstacle or reached the peak of a mountain. She looked over to him. Still encapsulated in blanket and sleep and clutching a cup of tea he sat still. He looked like a lost and helpless child. She thought of better times and also became conscious of how she looked.

244

Laura's second song

Lying on my bed, looking at you
Freshly woken from my dream
Flashback to when we were together forever
When life was spring and willow winds

Sometimes I picture me
As only you want me to be

After my picture fades
And spring turns to dark
When dreams and confusion take over
I look out my window and wonder if I'll be okay

Sometimes I picture me
As only you want me to be.

Confusion is not new to me
Sleep is only darkness, I'm still here
I have no fear, tomorrow's page
Holds no worse fear than has already been.

Sometimes I picture me
As only you want me to be.

You think I will not get there
Yet I know, I can keep up
I know more than you, lived more than you
Haunting wind through leafy lane
Whistles my tune
I'm here, at your side.
Here, don't go away.
Hear me.

Sometimes I picture me
As only you want me to be.

Today was Kit's day. He was being prepared on the ward.
Dad left the bone marrow unit to meet him and Mum on the
ward. He accompanied Kit downstairs to the operating Theatre.
Kit was unafraid. He wanted to be here, doing this for Laura.

He wanted to be nowhere else. This was his duty and his love; after all he loved and knew her more than anyone else. She was his twin sister. She was a part of him. They put him to sleep.

Having extracted the marrow they spun it in a large bowl. The centrifugal force separated the white and red cells. They span and span. The colours were vivid. The red and white spread the spectrum. The red cells they gave back to Kit. The white cells were injected into Laura's blood stream one hour later. It was a complete anticlimax. A non-event. It took just a few minutes. All they had to do now was wait.

In the early evening of the day Dad changed places with Mum. He went to see Kit lying in the Intensive Care unit. When he saw the size of the plaster and realised that Kit had received the equivalent of 76 needles in his back he realised how brave the little boy had been. More than that he could see that Kit was very proud. Now he could really say that he had shared in Laura's suffering.

He was on a drip. He showed Dad.

"Look Dad! A drip just like Laura's!"

"Yes Kit. What you have done is a wonderful thing. You can feel very proud."

"Can I go on the ward to see the children?"

"Of course!"

Dad checked that it was okay with the nurses then picked him up. Kit pushed the drip on its mobile stand whilst Dad carried him and a sick bowl for Kit was still coming out of the anaesthetic. When they arrived on the ward all the children were delighted to see him. He rewarded them by being sick in his bowl and was proud to do so, for now he was surely a member of their club.

Dad sat in the large armchair by her bed. He had managed to bring in a bottle of Gordon's gin and some Schweppes tonic water. The nurses had put them through the microwave oven in order to sterilise them. They also did this with his daily copy of The Independent.

He had made himself a large gin and Tonic. Laura was asleep. Everything was going well. Now he could sit and read for half an hour. His mind could not settle. It drifted. He thought of life after the Transplant. He thought of how different life had been here in the unit and how much easier it was than on the ward. He thought of the many things that Mum had said to him about the need for a dedicated paediatric oncology unit where there was no fear of cross infection. He took up a paper and pencil that he had been using with Laura and began to design the outline of how such a unit might look from the simple perspective of a parent.

One of the strange things about a bone marrow transplant is that the clinicians actually want the host body to partially reject the graft. They call it graft versus host disease, abbreviated to GVH. When this happens they know that the marrow has arrived and is doing its job. It took a long time for GVH to appear in Laura, but eventually it did. In the meantime Dad had to keep her occupied.

Each day there would be aerobic classes, which involved one of the nurses, art lessons, reading and dance. Notice of these lessons was posted on the window of the Transplant unit for the edification of passers by. There would also be hours of playing with the toy house that had been donated. This was the favourite game. Dad and Laura would pretend they were at home and would go through the routine of a normal day. They found it therapeutic. When they played this game they would be lost in time and space for a good hour or so.

Four weeks after the Transplant, in record time according to the hospital, Laura's blood count returned to normal. It was time to go home. It had been a long stay, but had gone well. Before they left one of the consultants took a photograph of Kit and Laura. Strangely there was a tinge of sadness as they left the unit and said goodbye to the many friends they had made. Outside the hospital Mum's mother waited in the car. It was now a time for happiness. The battle was over. Now they could concentrate on building a future for Laura and the family could resume normality.

Chapter 28

The ride home is the best

A few days after their release they walked across the meadow. Spring was becoming summer. The black finger trees were turning into green bouquets, though the May blossom still filled the hedgerow. Laura felt overwhelmed by the bursting greenery. The air was full of bird song that was permanently in crescendo.

Kit ran ahead. He had a stick, which had become a spear. He was a Zulu warrior hunting his prey. He was Umbopa tracking down the Masai. He was a long, long way from the hills and hedgerows of South Belgraveshire.

"Look at Kit!" giggled Laura "What's he doing?"

"He's pretending," said Dad, looking down at Laura as she half ran alongside in an effort to keep up.

"Carry me"

Dad picked her up and put her in her usual slot.

"Why is he pretending?" she asked curling her arm around his neck.

"Well, doesn't everyone like to pretend sometime? Don't you pretend when you play with your dolls?"

Laura stayed silent.

"Even grown ups pretend sometime. Some grown ups pretend a lot."

"You mean they tell fibs!"

"No. Sometimes they pretend things are not what they really are. I remember when I was quite young. I always wanted to drive an MG car. I could not afford such a car. Instead I bought a Ford Anglia."

Laura did not appreciate the subtleties of automotive marques. She wondered what Dad was trying to say. Dad knew her thought process and went on.

"An MG is a very fast and very beautiful sports car. It has no roof and is, or was, the sort of car every young man would want to drive. The Ford Anglia was a cheap and ordinary car. Anyway, I could not afford the MG. I bought the Anglia. But to me it was an MG. When I drove it I used to imagine I was driving an MG. The bonnet was that of an MG. The steering wheel was from an MG. I imagined the speed was that of an MG."

Laura tried to picture a young Dad driving this car with a name she did not know and of a like she did not know.

"I was very happy with that car and happy to pretend it was something else. So, you see, it is sometimes nice to pretend. If it makes us happy and doesn't make anyone else unhappy."

Laura laid her head on his shoulder and thought about what he had said. Kit was still playing. The bird song had changed. She stirred herself from inward thought. Above her a bird floated. It had a sound that was new. It thrilled and excited her. It hovered then ascended to a great and glorious position in the heaven where its song reached a crescendo. It hung and hovered there and sang. It looked like a thrush but was not a thrush. It was bigger. She wished she could be like that bird. To rise into the sky and sing must be a beautiful thing.

> *He rises and begins to round*
> *He drops the silver chain of sound*
> *Of many links without a break*
> *In chirrup, whistle, slur and shake,*
> *All intervolved and spreading wide,*
> *Like water dimples down a tide*
> *Where ripple ripple overcurls*
> *And eddy into eddy whirls.................*

A lark was ascending. He was aloof and he was high. He raised the spirit of their life. He lifted the level of their hope and erased their anxieties. He was life, yet he was above it. He hovered in the sky and sang. His song and the way he sang it lifted them spiritually to the same height. They were carried by his song to a plateau that left them basking in an excitable but prolonged peace of mind, of days gone by, of tranquillity and continuity, yet also of exhilaration.

"Who is this bird, Dad?" asked Laura.

"Who?"

"Yes! Who is he?"

"Do you not know him? He is the lark ascending. The great mystery of the meadow. Soon he will be no more. Every year his brothers and sisters die and are not replaced. It's all part of the changing countryside. Like we do not see as many Swallows on the telegraph line each year and we never see the Swift. Thank goodness for the Yellow Headed Wagtail. He keeps coming back."

"But who is he? He sings as if he knows us. What is his name?"

"He sings for you. He has no name save 'the lark ascending'; that is enough"

"Will he come back to sing for me again?"

"He will. For you and me both"

That evening when they settled down after dinner Dad became melancholy. He played some of his favourite music. Laura recognised the piece he was playing. She had heard it in the meadow. It was the lark and it was ascending, ascending most spectacularly, and as it ascended she ascended with it and was happy.

She squeezed Dad tightly. He stopped his playing. She felt such love for him. She reached out to touch his face. He responded by looking at her with a smile.

"Dad?"

"Yes, little poppet?"

"Can I pretend that I am not poorly any more?"

Dad looked at her with a great understanding. He felt the perplexity and confusion of her mind.

"But Laura," he said, "you are better now."

"I know Dad, I know."

Spring finally became early summer and the trees were suddenly and wholly green. The last white tissues of May blossom were consumed by the ground on which they lay. The lambs ceased to spring and jump and the first signs of life appeared in the blackbird's nest. A deeper blue now crowned the tree tops and the sun cast down rays that were warm on the skin.

Their days were filled with walks in the meadow and the simple pleasures of a country garden. One weekend they went on the river. Cygnets still drifted over the green brown ripples near the bulrushes beside the old Mill. The sun shone the whole time from the moment they left the Marina.

They drifted slowly and leisurely downstream to Crick. Here they moored for the night. Ducks and drakes caressed their boat as they sat in the outside berth whilst Mum prepared dinner and Kit fished. Laura fed the ducks. Dad drank a gin and Tonic.

They sat inside for their meal of Chicken in lemon and green salad. The ducks still waited, quacking their presence. Across the water two hares sparred amongst a field of sheep and cattle too consumed with the rich grass.

There were only four berths in their small boat, which meant that Adam had to sleep on Dad's chest. But Adam was used to sleeping in strange places. The next day at Crick they had lunch at the pub. Laura enjoyed the Pate and French bread and ate it all up. She felt as if she were abroad. In reality she was only a fifteen minutes drive from home. Such is the power of the river. It is like looking at the countryside from the inside. It truly is another world.

On their last night near Yelvertoft, as they yet again sat outside in the evening some men came past in a small boat obviously out for some kind of evening's entertainment on the river. Dad did not like the look of them and sat up all night with the mooring pole until they had returned.

One day, it must have been about six weeks after their release from hospital Dad asked Laura if she wanted to go swimming.

"How can she?" asked Mum. "She is still a little Neutropenic and very susceptible to cross infection. The consultants said don't let her mix with other children outside the family for about three months."

"But I want to go swimming," said Laura.

"And so you shall," said Dad.

"What are you going to do? Hire the whole swimming pool?" asked Mum unbelievingly.

"Yes," said Dad, and that's what he tried to do. He telephoned the Leisure Centre and they said they could not hire out the children's pool on a regular basis. Dad explained why they wanted the pool. The man on the phone said 'wait a minute' whilst he went to speak to the manager. He came back to the phone and said that if they came in at eight o'clock each Saturday morning they could have the entire pool and all the changing rooms to themselves free of charge for an hour. Laura was delighted.

So it became a regular event. Dad, Kit and Laura would go swimming each Saturday morning. Accordingly, Laura's legs grew stronger and her little lungs expanded to accommodate her new fitness. Both Kit and Laura still swam with water wings but how they swam. Their little legs traversed them across the pool. Dad would follow and sometimes swim beneath them, pretending to be a shark or a whale.

Each week Laura would go to the clinic as before. Each week the tests showed that she was making progress. Eventually her blood count was such that Mum and Dad were told that she could start mixing with other children.

"Just be careful, that's all," said one the Senior Registrars.

They were. Very careful. It was not worth the risk. She played in the Close as before. They had trips to Wicksteed Park and the cinema. Life was normal and full of happiness.

Dad was very busy at work and in negotiation with hospital authorities concerning his and Mum's plans for a new children's cancer unit. Each evening they would sit around the kitchen table until very late discussing the plans for this unit. Sometimes they would argue about it. Laura would lie in her bed and listen. Down the corridor Kit was doing the same. Sometimes they would go to fetes to raise money. Kit, Laura and Adam would go along. They quite enjoyed these trips because they could have a go on various roundabouts and swings.

Sometimes Dad would return from a meeting at the hospital very disappointed. A lot of parents were hoping that he would complete a successful negotiation to build a special unit for children with cancer. He was conscious of this and wanted to do his best. However the hospital management were dogmatic in terms of the provision of care for children with cancer. They were restrained by budgets and National Health Service guidelines. They had to comply. They also had to make a surplus on their budget. Unfortunately they had committed themselves fairly heavily to the creation of a new wing to the hospital. There were some who thought the timing of the building of this new phase was inappropriate. Its viability was in the balance according to some. Dad arrived with his projects and his funds at the right time. Perhaps he tipped the balance in favour of the new wing. Some say he did. All Dad knew was that the new cancer unit would be built in the new wing.

They decided to go to Devon for a holiday in August. They rented a cottage. It was actually a terraced cottage on a farm. Pero the dog came too. She liked the farm and the farmer liked her. She was good with the sheep and cattle and the other farm dogs. She would run out with the farmer and his dogs each morning when Dad was cooking egg and bacon for breakfast.

Each day they would go to the beach and every day was sunny. Laura loved the seaside. Whenever she arrived on the beach she would think of her Rupert Bear stories and recall the happy pictures of his adventures at the seaside. It was a magical world that seemed far away from her normal life in Belgraveshire. She had travelled abroad but there was still nothing like the seaside, in whichever country that might be.

Here in Devon the sun was kind to her. It warmed her and made her body feel good. She could feel its goodness permeate her body. The sun warmed her whilst the gentle sea breeze stroked her face and rippled her hair in tantalising exhilaration. The sea played its part. The sound of its foaming crests falling on the sand was soothing enough to settle her mind and offer comfort and peace. When she paddled in its fall the water tickled and washed her feet. As the afternoon deepened she rested on a blanket on the sand and felt its sunburnt warmth encapsulate her. She fell asleep, shaded by Dad's body.

Her dream was as gentle as the day in which she dreamt it. She stood by the side of the desert, looking back as if at the end of a long journey. Jesus was by her side once again.

"I am the way," he said, looking out over the desert. "Remember that."

She looked across the sand. She could see footprints. Had she really been on a journey?

"I am the truth," he said in a hushed tone bending over her. "The truth is hard to find, but you will find it."

"I am the light." He looked very sad. A tear gently made its way down his cheek and fell in the sand. The place on which it fell rippled and swayed then turned to water. Laura watched it in perplexity. "I have to be the light of the world," he said, turning to look out across the sand. "I have no choice."

With that he walked back into the desert, his head bowed. As he did the horizon became dark and faded into black. Laura heard the sound of the sea and felt the cold evening breeze on her cheeks. She awoke and knew that the torment was over.

Dad watched over her while she dreamed. He knew she was at peace and was happy. He also felt the most sublime peace. He looked at her face and gently stoked her newly grown hair. He wanted to hug her he was so much full of love for her. She is my whole life, he thought, and he knew it was a selfish thought, for he really loved his two sons equally. But the love of a man for his daughter is a strange thing. It is like no other love. It is a love of possession and obsession. It is a love that is only satisfied day by day through touch, look and tenderness. It is the deepest of all loves. That of the love of a girl for her father only exceeds its depth.

The next day on the beach Dad began to build a castle. At first everyone watched him. Eventually their curiosity overwhelmed them and they began to join in. Mum went to the Beach Cafe to buy some toy flags. Dad delegated tasks to Kit and Laura. Adam was too young to help. Instead he drank the remnants of discarded canned drinks and ate sand. Kit dug a moat. Laura built a pathway to the castle from pebbles she had found and called it Pebble Path. Dad did the main construction work. By mid afternoon the castle was complete. It was huge. People stopped to look and comment favourably. They named it Stone Castle. Having built it they began to play with it. Thus began their adventure.

Laura lay captive in the castle. Her hero, Captain Kit, came to her rescue supported by Eagle Eye Dad. They slowly made their way over the battlements as showers of pebbles fell about them. When they arrived in the centre of the Castle and found Laura (who could be seen in the form of a lollipop stick) they prepared to take her away.

"But I have rid myself of my captors, gallant sirs. Rescue me no more. Just stay and protect me."

So they stayed in the castle and played until its sides became eroded as the sand dried and the wind whipped it away. Its turrets began to collapse and it was finally washed away in the evening tide along with their adventure.

It was the last evening of the holiday. They arrived back at the cottage after another full day on the beach. As they were unpacking and shaking the sand from towels and shoes, the farmer's wife came to call.

"We traditionally take the children on a tractor ride on the last day. Would your children like to come?"

"Yes. I am sure they would love to go," said Mum.

"Parents can come too," said the Farmer's wife. "Seven o'clock outside the barn."

Dad took the three children round to the barn at seven. Other parents and children were there. The children were very excited. Within a few minutes the tractor arrived towing a large trailer with bales of hay laid out in two rows to form seats, which was enough to accommodate everyone.

The farmer brought a box for everyone to use as a mount, and very quickly and noisily the trailer filled up. When it was full the tractor slowly pulled away, bumping the trailer over the rough terrain of the farmyard. Everyone laughed as they were jostled and bumped about. When it arrived in the main street of the village the tractor stopped. The farmer turned round from his position in the tractor cab.

"Who wants to come and sit in the cab? Two at a time and you can all have a turn."

All the children put their hands up and the first two were selected. Kit and Laura missed out. They were sat at the back with Dad.

The tractor and trailer, full of happy bouncing people, left the village and trailed up a bridleway toward the arable fields and meadows. The hedges on either side were thick with blackberries. The trees were rich in colour as they approached their autumnal clothing. Berries had begun to appear on many trees and the whole countryside lay in preparation for autumn. The sky was a deep purple flecked with cream billows of clouds. The sun glowed corpulent and orange as it began to settle in the west. Its rays cast long shadows of trees, sheep and hedgerow.

The farmer pointed to the beasts settling in the field, to the hundred acres of golden corn and the hay gathered in bales across the skyline.

"Who else wants a turn in the cab?" he shouted looking over his shoulder and stopping the tractor. Two volunteers quickly made their way to the front. Dad noticed Laura edge her way forward and noticed her look of disappointment when she was not noticed. Kit made his position more obvious to the driver. Laura assumed that she would not be chosen and resigned herself to snuggling up to Dad and watching the scenery as it passed by.

As they descended into the valley, two more volunteers were requested. Unspeaking, Kit pushed himself forward and was very soon sitting in the cab. Laura looked even more disappointed. Dad felt for her. He leaned over to the farmer and asked if there would be more opportunity for children to ride in the front. "Yes!" came the reply.

Rising out of the vale and reaching the crest of a hill they could almost see the whole of Devon. This was a view the farmer was particularly proud of. This was his land and it was his view. They heard him sigh. They stayed here for a good few minutes watching the sun set.

Once again the children in the cab were changed. Kit came out looking quite upset. It had been a much shorter turn than the other children. The next two children went in.

"Do you want to go in the cab Laura?" asked Dad.

She shook her head.

"Soon be home!" shouted the farmer.

They continued along the crest of the hill. The sun was turning a deep red and the sky had become a pale blue. The shadows of trees were long and black. The grass looked a deep green. The sound of homeward birds could be heard right across the valley. It was the last hour of the evening. They arrived at a junction in the bridle path. To the left was the way down to the village and the farm. Ahead lay the longer route along the bridle path on the ridge, which would bring them in at the far end of the village.

The farmer dismissed the two children from the cab. The remaining youngsters clamoured to have another turn.

"My turn!"

"Please let me have a go!"

"I only had a short ride last time!"

Laura looked over her shoulder toward the distant hills. The dying sun brought out clarity in the landscape that she had not noticed before. The air was cool and a little damp as the evening settled. She felt very close to the landscape sitting on this bale of hay on the tractor's trailer as it trundled and bumped along this ancient bridleway. She was surrounded by the countryside and she was happy. She felt at one with it. Peacefulness overcame her that she did not want to let go. It was nice here in the trailer but it would also have been nice to go in the cab.

The farmer turned round. His face was kind. It was round, red and hardened by the all year round weather. It was a face that knew a diversity of weather conditions that cared little for itself, more for the animals and crops in its care. He looked toward Laura. He did not even glance at another child. He knew that this child was special like he knew the sick lambs from the healthy ones, the grieving cow from the one with twins and the tree that would best flower. He was a man consumed with earth and life, the wisest of men. For did not the earth give birth to life and does not life regenerate the earth.

She caught his glance and her heart raced in anticipation. Their eyes spoke to each other.

"I think now it is your turn, m'dear," he said with a smile especially for her. He turned to Kit. "And you too."

Dad lifted Laura into the cab. The other children became silent. This was the best bit. The ride home.

The farmer started up the tractor again. He did not turn left. He went straight ahead, the long way back. It was a glorious ride. The longest of rides. Laura frequently looked over her shoulder to Dad and smiled. He knew she was very happy and that all was well.

Chapter 29

Do not believe what you see

Summer quickly descended into the bronze of autumn. There was a damp coolness in the air. It was time for Kit and Laura to go to school. Mum and Dad had chosen their school with some care. They found a place in a village close to Belgrave. When they visited it they were impressed. It had an ambience of stimulation and achievement. In addition the children looked happy, although hard at work.

The morning of the new term finally arrived. Kit and Laura dressed in smartly pressed school uniforms. They stood outside the house for photographs before being loaded into the car.

Laura was excited, but nervous. The uniform felt strange. It was crisp and new. She was frightened of moving in it in case she spoilt its appearance. She looked out of the car window at the passing trees and hedgerows. Many times she had travelled this road on both sad and happy journeys. Today she had mixed feelings.

No matter how I feel the trees and hedgerows are always there, she thought. They empathise with my moods. When I had to return to hospital on those damp November days they would be rich in berries and misty cobwebs and a tranquil nostalgic mystery that took me back to that Spinney opposite the railway station in Picardy. They reflected my sadness, which was sadness not of despair or hopelessness but of contemplation. When I left the hospital after Kit gave me his good soldiers they were full of blossom and budding buds, leaves unfurling into life like my new life. I am a part of these hedgerows and these fields. They are a part of me. I am truly a girl of the fields and meadows; a country girl.

Dad slowed down for a passing horse and rider. The rider waved to them. Laura waved back and looked out of the rear window as the horse and its passenger disappeared from site.

They arrived at school to bustle and turmoil. There was a roll call. All the children were allocated pegs for their coats. The parents rushed off to sort them out. Then the parents were asked to leave, to allow the teachers to teach.

"A kiss, a love and a smile please," asked Dad looking down on two nervous little faces.

A little boy with mousey hair and a pale face began to cry.

Dad leaned down to Kit, kissed him on the lips, hugged him and retracted to give him a big smile. Kit smiled back.

"You do the same Laura," Dad said, turning to her.

"A kiss."

"A love."

"And a smile."

She smiled. Dad had inaugurated a daily ritual. It was ritual that was a necessary part of the day as all rituals are. It was a ritual that was to endure.

"Play hard and work hard, but not too hard," said Dad as he walked away laughing and waving. He did not want to leave and was to worry about them both throughout the day. They both looked sheepish as he left.

He had a quiet day at the office. Mum was to collect the twins. He was hoping she would call to say that she could not make it and could he collect, but she did not.

Laura's arrival at school epitomised her arrival in life. She knew that she was different to the other children, but she wanted to be the same. Her hair was short. She was stiff and lacked natural childish agility. She was contemplative and at times moody. Fortunately she had a teacher who loved her for herself regardless of her frailties. She was normalised by the school process. The hospitalisation, institutionalisation and sterile world she had become so accustomed to shrank before the crayon, desk and assembly hall.

School days. They filled her with stimulation, wellbeing and friendship. The past was the past and well done with. She contrasted her current autumn with those past and the nostalgia of these months was filled with hope and not reflective sadness.

Her birthday soon arrived. She and Kit were five! Such long lives in so few short years. Mum and Dad arranged for a magician to come. Kit invited his friends from Prep school. Laura invited hers. What an evening! Dad and Mum collected everyone from school. First there was a buffet of crisps, sausage rolls and sandwiches. Then the magic show. Such fun! The magician transfixed Kit and Laura.

At the end of the show the magician got them up to paint a picture using Laura's tongue for water and Kit's sweater for colours. They really believed that they had painted a picture from such materials.

After the party Dad took the children back home. It was very foggy and he had to drive slowly. Laura did not like the fog. In its mistiness she saw strange unwelcome shapes reminding her of the misty days when she used to travel to and from the hospital.

Laura still went to the clinic and the hospital on a weekly basis. One day she went on a different mission. Mum and Dad had arranged a special event where they were to launch an appeal to build a new children's cancer unit. Dad had created the original designs and was hoping to raise a lot of money to build it. Laura did not want him to be concerned with the building of a new unit. She wanted to forget all about cancer and leukaemia but Mum and Dad could not forget about it. They would spend many hours discussing the subject over the kitchen table. Laura could hear them as she lay in bed.

This time she went to a different part of the hospital. It was close to her bone marrow unit and the old ladies but it was not like a hospital room. In fact it was an office, very special office. It was old and contained pictures of black clothed men with severe faces. Despite their severity Laura liked them. You see, they were paintings and the artist had caught the humanity of their eyes on the canvas even though the sitters had probably tried to look as serious and important as possible.

"They are the people who used to be in charge of the hospital," said Dad when he caught her looking at the pictures. "They used to work for nothing. This hospital was paid for by the people of Belgraveshire," he turned to Mum, "until after the war, which is one of the longest periods of public subscription to a hospital on record."

"You know," he went on, "the people of this city and county have a long history of supporting local causes."

"Yes. I know," said Mum. "I just hope they support us in building a new oncology unit."

"We'll soon find out. It will be interesting to see if this thing takes off. Our life has already been changed by the events in Laura's life. Is this another step change?"

There was warmth in this room, which Laura liked. Dad said it was old. It was part of the original building in 1771 he said. She knew it was old because she had feelings of belonging to a long train of succession, like she had stepped into the last few links of a human chain. It was a feeling of comforting sadness that left her melancholic but not depressed. She was reminded of her lark ascending in the meadow in the late spring. Families of larks had ascended over the same nesting ground, probably for centuries. Now there were less of them. Perhaps they were the last few. Was she one of the last few of the great chain of humanity that lingered between these historic walls? Were Mum and Dad inspired to do what they were doing because of her or because of a tradition that had overwhelmed them when they became a part of this great and historic hospital. These questions confronted her as Dad began to make his speech and Mum squeezed her hand.

So it began. Mum and Dad were busy most evenings, making plans, telephoning people and going to meetings. Kit and Laura were busy at school. They enjoyed it.

Sometimes Laura would feel a slight stiffness in her legs and feel a tremble in her tummy. She knew this was all part of getting over the bone marrow Transplant. Nevertheless it reminded her of her long time in hospital. Then she became quiet and reflective. The teacher did not understand this and would ask Laura what was wrong. How could she possibly explain? She would be expected to explain in the language of a child. How could she when her thoughts were too mature for her to articulate? That was Laura's dilemma. Her personal battle had matured her mind but not her vocabulary.

The story of the good soldiers and bad soldiers continued to grow. Many avenues of the media including radio, TV, newspapers and magazines picked it up. Mum was contacted by a woman's magazine. They arranged a Children of Courage Award each year at Westminster Abbey. They wanted to put Kit forward for his donation of bone marrow to Laura. Mum agreed. The whole family were to travel up to London for December for the event in December. Everyone was excited and proud for both Kit and Laura. It would be a suitable reward for the whole family and, surely, the final accolade at the end of a long journey.

In the meantime life was for living.

She liked to dance. She loved to feel the movement of her body in synchronisation to music. She had lessons, which told her about movement and the interpretation of it. She enjoyed them but best of all she liked to feel free to express yourself to the music. Inevitably because she had taken ballet lessons one of her favourite pieces of music was Swan Lake.

Dad often played this music. Then she would dress in her blue ballet costume and dance for him. She found the music of Tchaikovsky both poignant and exhilarating.

The days became shorter and the nights misty and dark. December came and with it Advent. It was the first weekend in December. Dad put up the lights on the trees in front of the house. They softly twinkled in the cold night as the wind whispered and danced around them. The first Sunday afternoon in Advent was the day they always went to see the Christmas reindeer.

In the north of Belgraveshire is a large wooded area of several square miles. In the centre stands a hill with a beacon that keeps a motherly watch to the perimeters of the whole county and beyond. The air is white and dry. It fills your lungs and spins the mind into dizziness. There is purity and stillness on the lips. Below the hill deer graze wild and free. Dad always says that these are the deer that Father Christmas will use to pull his sleigh. It is a tradition that the family see them before they fly off to the North Pole.

They parked the car in the village and walked by the side of the river that rippled, roamed and danced over rocks and stones through the light brown fern. They were to take the long way round and make it a full day. Dad carried a pack with sandwiches and drinks. The river was full and flowing. Leaves lay musty and damp by the forest pathway. They left the trees and came into the tumbling space of fern and deer rising to the summit and the beacon.

A redbrick ruin lay before them. Rooks sailed over the roofless monument.

"Does no one live here Dad?" asked Laura.

"No. It has been empty for a long time."

"Well, who lived here?"

They left the pathway and stepped over clumps of rough grass to come close to the ruined house. Laura touched the red brick wall. Despite the cold air it felt warm from the filtering winter sun. Her heart was filled with a quiet but beautiful sadness that gave her peace.

Dad was looking away from the house toward the river.

"Dad. Tell me. Who lived here? Tell me. Do you know?"

He turned to her.

"It was a girl who had your name."

263

"Laura?"

"No, your second name, Jane. She believed in something. She had faith and beauty but she was only a child. A cruel man tried to make her a queen and she did not want to be."

"What happened to her?"

He thought of Lady Jane Grey, a child, fumbling her blindfolded way to find the block that would receive the axe. He was overcome with sadness.

Laura looked at the greyness of his eyes.

"Did she die?"

"Yes, she did, but she died in grace and what she believed in came true."

Laura looked at the ruins of the house, the forest beyond and the river behind and her heart rested in tranquillity. She felt truth and beauty nearby and was happy.

It was time for the Christmas Show at school.

Before the Christmas Show Kit and Laura went to Christingle at church. She had been before but not for three years. It was a festival of light around the world. She thought of the light of the world. Was it really Jesus?

One night in November on her way home from hospital Dad had diverted through Stilton Road in Belgrave to show her the lights of Diwali. She liked them. He told her that the people who lived there had a festival of light. He stopped at a Restaurant and bought some food to take home for Mum and the rest of the family. Whilst he and Laura waited for the food he talked to the man who owned the Restaurant. They talked of many things. Eventually they settled on the Festival of Light and things spiritual. They talked of David and Moses, of Solomon and his great wisdom and how it was needed today. They talked of Jesus and his disciples and of Jerusalem and Babylon and Mecca and The Koran and Allah and his prophets and Hinduism and the great river Ganges in which float the souls of all those looking for the purpose of life. They talked for longer than it took for the meal to be prepared.

Laura listened although she did not fully understand.

They talk about the purpose of life, she thought. Many times I have heard Dad talk about this. I know what he means, but does life need to have a purpose? He talks about tomorrow and the future. Surely we are to be together forever? I have my Mum and Dad. They have me. What else is there? Life will go on forever. What else can there be? Perhaps I ought to ask Jesus. He will know. Grown up conversations still confused her. Sometimes they confused the grown ups.

The twins came home each night full of music from the Christmas Show. On Sunday after dinner Mum would make them rehearse their parts. They would sing and dance acting out the part of chickens in the barn or angels in the heavens. Kit and Laura were given the parts of Joseph and Mary. It was a central role but there was not much dialogue. Nevertheless they were very proud and enjoyed joining in the chorus.

The afternoon of the Show arrived. Dad had been to collect a video camera and was only just on time. He parked in the long tree lined driveway up to the school a good distance from the hall.

The hall was very full. People were standing but there was still space amongst the seats. Mum had saved him a place. She sat with Adam on her knee talking to other parents and grandparents. The narrator introduced the story and before long the hall was filled with the disjointed out of key singing of children.   They sang with feeling and enthusiasm if not tone. Their tiny dry voices filled the hollow hall with warmth and simplicity.

Laura frequently looked out from the stage toward Mum and Dad. She knew she dared not wave yet she wanted to. She was proud to be here, yes, but more than that the whole thing amused her. She found it entertaining and rather strange to be on this stage dressed up. Many times they had rehearsed at home and at school. Now she was finally here. The irony of it made her smile.

Laura's third song

My Dad
He's my Dad
When he is here I can smile
And when I smile I will beguile
My very whim
He will begin
To understand, comply.

Love transcends
Encompasses
The world
The soul
Of life.

My Mum
She's my saviour
I cannot live without her
I shall never be without her
Let her be
Here close by me
And never go or stray away.

Love transcends
Encompasses
The world
The soul
Of life.

That night Laura dreamt of the play. She re-lived every moment of it over and over again. She particularly remembered the proud look on Mum's and Dad's faces. She knew that with Kit she was the centrepiece of the whole play. The poignancy and significance of the moment did not escape her or the audience. Most of them knew the story of Laura, and were pleased to see such a full recovery and a happy ending. Laura slept well, in peace and contentment.

It was another cold and grey weekend approaching Christmas. It was the Christmas party at the hospital. They decided to go.

Everyone was pleased to see them. They had games and songs sung by the hospital teacher. Kit and Laura joined in them all. Dad looked across from his conversations with other parents and noted with pleasure the way that Laura had become a normal child again.

After the games they went into another room for tea. The children sat at trestle tables whilst the grown ups picked at the food and chatted. Two of the consultants were also there. Mum congratulated them on the success of Laura's treatment. They nodded and asked how she was.

"She's doing really well. It seems a long time since we were in the Transplant unit."

Dad walked across. He had been attending to Kit and Laura.

"How is the Appeal going?" one of the consultants asked.

"It has got off to a good start."

"Hm," the consultant reflected. "It's a lot of money to raise."

"I'm less worried about raising the money than getting agreement on the design of the new oncology unit" replied Dad.

"I'm sure you can use your business negotiating skills to achieve that," the other consultant said with a wry smile.

"But it's not just about the right facilities," Mum interrupted. "Surely we have to improve the quality and calibre of nursing staff. We also have to make sure we are applying the most appropriate regimes and to do that we have to improve the diagnosis and prognosis on presentation."

The consultants looked at each other.

"We are doing those things. What we need is more money so we can provide the most up to date facilities," one of them said.

Eventually the party broke up. As everyone left the other consultant took Dad to one side.

"Your wife is right. There is a lot more to it than facilities. There is a lot that needs to be done to bring us toward the best practice in the country. But you know there are politics in the health profession as any other and at the end of the day it all comes down to unit cost, to money."

Most of their free time was now spent in working to raise the money to build the new children's oncology unit. Straight after the children's party they left for the village of Allesby to collect a cheque from a Fish and Chip shop. They were looking forward to this. It was a well-known Fish 'n' Chip shop of high quality. Hopefully they would be able to sample some of the food.

The watery autumnal sun was beginning to set in a grey sky as they drove out of the city. Allesby was to the north. After the party everyone was full of high spirits and looking forward to supper.

Dad parked up and they tumbled into the Fish and Chip Shop. It was quiet this being early evening. They were expected and sure enough were given a treat of Fish and chips in the small room behind the counter. Such a treat! They were the best fish and chips ever. Fresh out of the pan. Fish so big you wondered how you could possibly eat it. The batter on the fish was golden crisp and crunched in your mouth as you bit into it to reveal the pure white Haddock. The chips were large, dry and crisp.

After their supper the Greek proprietor gave Mum and Dad a cheque for their new oncology unit. He also presented Laura with a beautiful doll. She loved it immediately; possibly because it was unexpected. She held it close to her and would not let go of it all night. When they got home she took it to bed with her. That night everyone went to sleep happy and content with life. It had been a wonderful day.

In the early hours of the next morning Laura walked into Mum's and Dad's bedroom and woke them.

"My legs hurt," she said.

Mum looked at her and wept inwardly. She reached out and touched her forehead.

"I feel hot," said Laura.

Dad felt nauseous. This was unreal. A nightmare.

Mum turned to Dad "Yes!" she screamed.

Dad looked devastated with disbelief.

"It could be anything," he said.

"Hardly! I'll ring the hospital."

Dad could hear Mum talking on the phone. He played with Laura on the bed and pretended everything was all right.

Mum came back into the room.

"We have to take her in the morning. They said it might be an infection. Do they have any idea? Of course it's not an infection. They always say that. Do they think we are stupid? It's not another one of their bloody infections!"

"What are you saying?"

"I'm saying it's come back. Oh my God! It's come back again. Where do we go now? Tell me! Where do we go now?"

Laura limped back to her bed. She understood. There was nowhere to go, only back to hospital, and trust that Jesus would be there too. Dad went downstairs to play some music. She fell asleep with the sound of Dad's music filtering through the walls.

> Oh taste and see
> How gracious the Lord is
> How blessed is the man that trusteth in thee
> Oh taste and see
> How gracious the Lord is
> How blessed is the man that trusteth in thee
> Blessed is the man that trusteth in thee
> Blessed is the man that trusteth in thee
> The man that trusteth in thee.

Chapter 30

No more treatment

"We are only going in for a short visit," Dad said to Laura as he fastened her seat belt. It was a chilly morning so he had left the engine running for a few minutes to warm the car.

On their way to hospital they stopped at the twins' school in Great Glen to drop Kit off. Mum told the teacher that Laura would not be in today. "I hope she's all right!" called the teacher as Mum left.

She spent three days on the ward whilst they checked out her infection. On the fourth day she was due to accompany her twin brother Kit to Westminster Abbey where he was to receive the Children of Courage Award. They gave her a bone marrow aspiration, they tested her blood, and they checked everything. On the third day they confirmed Mum's and Dad's suspicions. Dad was invited into the office of the consultant. She answered his questions. No more treatment.

"It's come back"

"There is no more treatment"

"Nothing else we can do. It's the end of the road, everything else is experimental."

"About six weeks"

"Quality of life is the most important thing. The alternative is that she dies on a laboratory table"

"You might as well take her home. There is nothing more we can do here. I'll make sure the health visitor takes care of you."

Mum came into the room. She knew. No words were spoken or necessary. There was silence. Finally and in desperation Mum said "Is there no hope?"

"None," said the consultant. "It's the end."

The health visitor walked in. She was crying. The consultant looked upon the display of unprofessional behaviour with disdain.

Mum looked up at the health visitor.

"Six weeks! That's all we have! Six weeks of life."

"It could be longer. Some children go as long as ten weeks," the consultant offered.

"It's academic," said Mum. "Six or ten weeks. It's not a lifetime which is what she should have."

The consultant observed the scene. What could be done? Had not everything been tried? Were there not moments and hours of anguish about the prospects for the future? This was not the first relapse. There were many more and more to come. Do I not lie sleepless at night thinking of the children? Could I make them live? Do I have so much power? These parents do not understand. I have to think of the cause, of the vast majority of children, of the clinical trials. In the end we believe in the same thing except that I want mankind to live without the fear of disease. They only think of their child, which is as it should be, I suppose.

"Can we make a telephone call?" Dad asked, expecting the consultant to say no.

"Yes. Of course. I'll leave you."

Mum and Dad rang Grandma and Grandad. They said all the right things over the phone but were very quiet about it.

They went back onto the ward. Everyone looked at them as if they knew. Mum and Dad identified with the other parents. They knew they would understand. They felt a bond with them, a bond that was unfettered by unreal sympathy. It was a bond of true compassion. They told them what had happened.

The health visitor came to see them.

"We should have been going to the Children of Courage Award tonight," Mum said sadly. "They reserved a suite for us in a hotel in London. The service is tomorrow. Laura would so much have liked it."

"Go!" said the health visitor. "Just go! Laura still has the rest of her life in front of her. Live it! It may be short but...live it!"

They drove home in quiet reflection, thinking of the words of the health visitor. The moon was bright and lit up the fields which were barren of beasts at this time of year. It was a clear sky. Probably a frost tonight, Dad thought.

The lights of the village appeared in front of them as they left the Northampton Road to go to North Peveril their home. Its lights were incandescent and unreal. It was hard to believe that people in this place were still living normal lives. As they passed the White Lion and The Swan pubs they thought of the people inside, many of whom they knew, laughing and having a good time. Could it be? Does not the whole world know of our circumstance?

Kit, Laura and Adam were all tired when they arrived at their home. They were taken straight to bed and fell asleep almost immediately and only half undressed. Dad telephoned the hotel in London and asked to speak to a journalist from The Woman's Own magazine.

"Oh, I am so sorry!" she said. What else could she say? "I suppose you want to be at home now with Laura. We wondered where you were."

"No," said Dad." "We are coming. We shall come down on the early train. We shall be there."

"Are you sure?"

"Of course I am sure. Laura still has the rest of her life in front of her. We are going to live it."

It's strange. When you only have weeks to live you think of life not of death. Laura's death was Mum's and Dad's death. A part of them would go. It was a shared death except that Laura had the burden and the pain. Mum and Dad held each other close in the calm of the night. They listened to the sound of owls in the woods, the wind gently skipping through the trees and the rumble of distant traffic. They stared at the ceiling and did not speak. Dad had held Mum many times. Times ranging from great passion to blissful peace. This was the power of a woman. To be the solace of comfort and strength. Her body, her aroma were a comfort to him now. He felt the gentleness of her breath alongside him and the pulsation of her heart. He did not feel sad or distressed. He felt a peaceful acceptance of what was to be. He hoped she felt the same.

The morning took a long time to arrive. Dad had set his alarm and was awake early. Mum was curled in a ball fast asleep. He squeezed her shoulder and got up. He walked to the window as was his routine and looked out across the Spinney and the Close. As he was confronted by the morning light and life, the peace and acceptance of last night were dramatically replaced by feelings of anger.

Why the hell should she die? This five-year-old girl! It was not right! God! Who believes in God! What sort of God is it that allows this to happen? What is the point in praying and going to church if it only comes to this? Where is God when you need him anyway?

Dad's bitterness was unbounding and unending.

There must be an answer, he thought.

With a feeling of nausea he thought of the many mistakes he had made during Laura's treatment.

The time when he gave too much medicine on one day instead of the prescribed dose. It must have killed her!

He recoiled when he remembered that they had agreed to clinical trials. Surely Laura's count was high? She should have been on a more severe regime.

Why did they stay at the Belgrave Royal Infirmary when the only paediatric Oncologist was sick? Why did they not go to Great Ormond Street? Why did I not insist on the best for my daughter, Dad reflected with increasing anxiety?

He thought of the treatment at the hospital and the sloppiness of some of it. The way Mum and Dad had to fight to make sure things were done on time.

He turned to Mum.

"When are you going to get up?" he demanded and went downstairs. Mum awoke in perplexity at what he had said. She was set to embark upon the same emotional journey as Dad.

They enjoyed the train journey. London is a wonderful place even when you are dying. Laura did not know that she was dying. Mum and Dad decided not to tell her on the basis that they thought she was too young to cope with it or control it. Anyway, now was not the time. One has to make these judgments or decisions as life's crisis occur. They decided she would go back to school until Christmas. Life was to be normal until her condition dictated otherwise. Happiness for sick children is in the family, in normality and the everyday things of our life. Not in sudden trips to Disneyworld or special presents.

Laura had a bacon sandwich on the train. Dad went to the buffet bar to buy it and took Kit with him. He met a man there whose child went to the same Prep school as Kit and Laura.

"Having a day off?"

"We're going up to London for a special service at Westminster Abbey," Dad replied quietly.

"Well, have a nice time!"

The man took his coffee and croissant and walked away.

Kit looked up at Dad.

"Will we have a nice time do you think, Dad?"

"I am sure we will Kit, excuse me," he said turning to the Buffet Bar Steward. "Three bacon rolls, a croissant, three cups of tea and a cup of coffee." He returned to Kit. "Laura is poorly once again. I trust you not to say anything to her. We want her to be happy for the next few weeks. I shall tell you more later, but for now we must concentrate on making her happy. Will you help us do that?"

"Yes, of course I will Dad."

Kit stood by Dad and stared up at the counter of the buffet bar. He swayed slightly as the train negotiated a slight bend. He enjoyed travelling by train. However on this occasion his feelings were mixed. On the one hand he was glad to be going up to London but he also knew, long before Dad told him, that Laura was sick once again. He also knew that this time was different; that this thing could not go on forever. He could not articulate his feelings but he knew that there had to be an end to Laura's perpetual suffering.

Dad paid for the breakfast and they began to walk back to Mum, Laura and Adam. As they walked through the corridors of the train Kit observed all the faces that looked and smiled at him.

Do they know that I am special? He thought. Or do they have the same problems in their families? Is what we are going through quite normal? I know she is sick. Am I not the closest person to her? Do Mum and Dad not realise that she talks to me about it. Do they think we keep silent about this subject? Our minds might be small and immature but they are also uncluttered with grown up emotions. We have discussed Laura's disease many times. We also know about death, in that we know it exists as a frailty of human endeavour.

They travelled across town in a black cab. The streets were busy and they only just arrived on time at Westminster. They were escorted into an oak panelled room. Other families were there. The photographers and reporters were busy with them. The journalist showed them to a quiet corner. The five of them sat in a row behind a long oak table.

"You will be all right here. We will be going through to the service shortly."

Eventually one of the photographers paused from his picture taking. As he adjusted his equipment he glanced across at the five behind the table. He turned to his colleagues.

"Look! That must be the bone marrow kid. The Good Soldiers story. They have arrived at last."

His colleagues, having exhausted their current subject eagerly turned toward a new one.

The journalist saw the advancing army and hurried over to deflect their charge.

"I think this family needs to be left alone."

"Well, why are they here if they want to be left alone?"

The five of them sat blinking in front of a barrage of light as the flashes of the cameras of all the national daily newspapers exploded before them. After the flashes came questions, lots of them.

"What was it like?"

"Was it a big operation? Did it hurt?"

"Is Laura all right now?"

"What did he say after the operation?"

Laura was perplexed by the array of flashing lights before her. She knew they were taking photographs for newspapers. Had she not seen her picture in many newspapers already? This was something different. Something bigger, more important.

Before they went across to the Abbey the Duchess met them. She was dressed in something reminiscent of the middle ages. It was boyish. She was talking to the actor and his wife. Dad remembered to call her "Mam" and introduced Kit and Laura. She was friendly but seemed more interested in the grown ups than the children.

The actor's wife asked about Kit and Laura. Mum liked her.

Very soon they were in the Abbey. Before the children went up to the chancel steps to collect their award from the Duchess the choir sang The Coventry Carol.

"And Herod in his wisdom
All children he did slay"

Dad was moved to tears when he heard it and thought of his poor dear Laura. He hugged Adam who was sat on his knee and squeezed Laura's hand tightly. She did not get an award. Her reward for her pain and battle with Leukaemia was a destiny with death. But she would not begrudge Kit his award; after all he did it for her and he deserved it for his bravery. Such is the irony of life.

Laura looked across to the tapestry windows. Jesus was still on his cross.

Jesus, when will you come down from your cross? She cried inwardly. When will you come to rescue me? They think I know nothing of what is going on. I know that I am sick again and I know that this time it is different. After all, it is my body. I know best how it feels. I just can't speak these feelings.

Now is the time, Jesus, now is the time to be with me.

Dad looked down at Laura. He saw that she was looking at the stained glass window.

"Jesus is still there Laura," he said.

"I know, Dad, but why is he always on his cross?"

"His cross is the pain he has to bear for all humankind. He carries it for you, so that he can take your pain away. He carries it so that you don't have to carry it."

Laura thought carefully about this. She felt that Dad was telling her things to make her peaceful. He was condescending and patronising. It was not like him.

"Sometimes, Dad, he should get down from that cross and be with us if he really loves us. I think it would be nice to see Jesus."

"It must be very nice to see Jesus, and I am sure we will all see him. But before that we have to die, because Jesus is in his heaven. That is where he waits to see us."

"But if I die I won't see you and Mum and Kit and Adam and Pero the dog any more will I?"

"Of course you will! When you die you just go to sleep and when you wake up we are all together again. Death is nothing to be afraid of. Death is nothing at all. It is like moving to another room" He was recalling some words he had read by Frederick Scott Holland, but he was not sure that he could believe in them. Death was for older people, not for children.

"Will I die Dad?"

"We all have to die sometime, little poppet. It comes to us all someday."

"Will you die first Dad?"

"It is usually older people who die first so perhaps I shall. I hope I shall then I can wait for you. Anyway we should not be talking about dying when we have so much living to do."

The Coventry Carol ended and the children made their way up to the Chancel steps. Before each child went forward the actor read a citation of what the child had done to win the award. Some had rescued others, one had saved her mother's life, and others had suffered pain or hardship and borne it bravely. They all deserved the award. As Kit proudly but modestly took his award from the Duchess Laura thought of those children slain by Herod. The atmosphere in this place was oppressive and reeked of age and death. She did not like it. The service too was sombre and melancholic.

On their way out she stopped before a crypt newly made for the Christmas season. She looked at Baby Jesus in his manger. You were a child, she thought. You have been where I have been and know where I am going. Be a child again and be with me. Come down from your cross.

After the service they spoke with the Dean. They told him of their situation. He took them to his private chapel and said prayers for Laura and for the family. He promised to help in any way. He was a kindly saintly man who was as close to God as any man can be and they were glad of his prayers.

After leaving the Dean in his Abbey they all went downstairs for more photographs. They sat on stone steps and Kit sat on the Duchess's knee. He was proud. Mum and Dad were proud for him but would have preferred it if Laura had sat there with him. Things were beyond their control. The Duchess was only here for the morning. She was only briefly sharing in their lives. They were just passing images that might be remembered later in some conversation with an interested mind over yet another dinner table.

They walked across the busy road into the house of Lords. A special lunch awaited them. There were many film stars and famous actors and actresses and other personalities. Mum egged Dad on to speak to them about support for their little project in Belgrave. They were not interested.

Dad got some food for everyone. He spoke to the Treasure Hunt lady who was expecting a baby. She smiled and turned to talk to a colleague. Many years later she would help them and not recall this meeting. Dad brought the food over. Mum and Dad each had a glass of wine that went straight to their heads but they felt better for it. They ignored the people around them and concentrated on each other.

"Do you mind if I join you."

It was the actor. He stood before them dressed in a blue suit and white shirt with a cut away collar. He was very smart and elegant. Mum liked him immediately.

"Yes of course!" said Dad and made space for him. Dad also liked him. He was human. He was not really an actor. Acting was his job.

Kit began to chatter to him. Laura looked at him with quiet charming eyes. She liked him. He was a bit like Dad and she noticed that he and Dad were talking in the fashion of friends. After the endurance of the day both Mum and Dad were relieved to be able to talk to someone outside of their world of hospital and leukaemia. It was less than twenty-four hours since they had been told that Laura was terminally ill. To be thrown into this world of media superficiality from an environment of sick children in institutionalised care and the news that they were to soon be without Laura was unreal.

"Tell him," whispered Mum to Dad.

"Tell him what?"

"About Laura!"

He did. The actor listened, quietly and with great attention.

"I will help you with your charity. I am not sure what I can do, but I will help."

And he did.

Chapter 31

Lady in red

After lunch they were invited on a tour of London. Instead they went back to their hotel suite. They had enjoyed many trips to London and preferred to see the city in their own way.

In the reception of the Hotel was the biggest Christmas tree the twins had ever seen. Laura stood before it in astonishment. It was very big but simple. It was covered in red ribbons and twinkling white lights. It was not confused by a variety of decorations. By her side little Adam sat in his buggy blinking in time with the lights. He was confused by the size of the tree. He could not see the top and assumed it must go straight through the roof of the hotel into the clouds.

In the evening there was a party for all the families. Lots of presents, Father Christmas , food and drink were all there. Everyone was celebrating. Everyone was filled with hope and optimism, everyone except Mum and Dad. They cried inwardly. They could not tell anyone of their predicament. Laura was too close.

The next morning they took breakfast in their room. Mum made some telephone calls to the Great Ormond Street and Royal Marsden hospitals. No hope. Not now. Not after a relapse after a bone marrow transplant. But they would see her. There were some new experimental treatments being tested in Cambridgeshire. They might suit Laura. Mum and Dad did not want her to die in a laboratory. Quality of life was important.

On the last night they spoke with the parents of a child with a more severe form of leukaemia. He was well on the way to recovery. He had been to Great Ormond Street. Should they have gone there? It was too late now. They were filled with despair as they left the hotel and clambered into a black cab.

Back home Mum and Dad spent hours on the telephone exploring opportunities. There were none. They wanted Laura to be at home; to live a life; to leave this world from home not from a remote hospital ward. They worried unnecessarily about Laura having a place to rest when she died. They telephoned the Rector. Of course, he said. There is space, plenty of space. Choose your own spot, but do not worry about it now. Next day he came to see them and said prayers with Laura. He acted normally and played with the twins and Adam. The children adored him. He was a man of compassion. He thought of his young colleagues in the Royal Air force and the sacrifices they had made in the Second World War. He never talked about it. It was a long time ago.

The next day a parcel arrived from London. It contained a doll. It was from the actor. He had gone to America. He could not forget Laura. Whatever help you want with your appeal I will try to be there. I admire you all, he said. Mum and Dad shed a tear at his words but were glad of them.

The Saturday before Christmas Laura was invited to her friend Anne's birthday party. It was to be held at the village hall in Reynard, a little village close to the famous Locks and the Canal. Mum dressed Laura in her best red velvet dress, with white stockings and pretty black patent leather shoes. Her hair was washed and Mum did the best she could to make it look longer than it was. She looked a very grown up five year old. Laura was excited about the party and was looking forward to seeing her friends from school.

As Dad drove her in the car he imagined he was taking her to her first teenage dance, something she would never experience. He turned off the main Horbury Town road and headed toward the hills of Morley. The sky was the colour of brass as the sun gave out it its last burst of life before the comforting cloak of darkness crept over the countryside. Sheep and cattle grazed in the twilight and the fluttering and chirruping of birds echoed from coppice and wood.

"What is the matter Dad?" Laura asked from the back seat.

"Nothing. I was just thinking how nice it is to go to a party. Perhaps you will have a dance with me?"

"Dad! This is a party for children!"

When they arrived the Village Hall was full of noisy mobile children. Eventually some grown-ups appeared and began to organise things.

After playing Pass the Parcel a dance was organised. Dad was very nervous of Laura dancing on the shiny mahogany floor. He was afraid she might slip and fall. If she fell she would bruise so easily because of her lack of platelets. He knew the bruises would stay until her last days and he would bury her with them. He could not bear the thought of her being marked in any way. As a consequence he held her hands and danced with her. He was the only grown-up dancing with the children. Other parents looked at him strangely and whispered to each other. They are probably saying I spoil her and dote on her, he thought. If only they knew. But they will not know. Better their stares than Laura falls and is marked. She danced slowly and tenderly. The music was "Lady in Red". Dad told her that the music was especially for her as she was wearing a red dress. She smiled and was happy.

As Dad looked at her she was no longer a child but a mature young woman, slim and petite with long auburn hair and a gentle round face. He and she were transformed through time and space to her first teenage dance. He took her in his arms and danced round the room with her. She looked into his eyes and smiled. She had come of age. She was a woman. She was a lady in red. She looked up at him and smiled. He heard a mature and mellow voice.

"You can have this first dance Dad. I promised you that, but only this first dance. Then I have to dance with my friends."

They continued to circle the room.

She looked happy in his arms as he danced her round the room. She threw her head back with a smile then moved away from him dancing for a moment by herself, then slowly coming back to him. They were momentarily transfixed by each other's eyes. The smile faded from her face. A hint of realisation and fear glanced across her brown eyes.

The moment passed and she was a little girl again; a little dying girl.

It was time to play a game once again. One of the mothers beckoned the children to the centre of the room, whilst giving Dad a curious look. Laura ran away from him and sat on the floor amidst her friends. In the midst of her play she looked over her shoulder toward him and smiled.

She is reassuring me, he thought, of what?

Through the blackness of an English countryside in winter he drove her home. She fell asleep on the back seat. He carried her into the house and laid her on the settee where she recovered her strength before telling Mum all about her party and the news that Anne was to stay with them during the Christmas holiday. But first she had to go swimming.

The project that Mum and Dad had created to build a children's cancer unit was now growing and they had to attend many fund raising events. One of these events was at the Health Centre in Allestone. Mum and Dad were not very keen on going. They knew there would be a lot of parents from the hospital. They may or may not have heard of Laura's condition. Whichever way they would ask about her. Mum and Dad had resolved to tell no one unless it was appropriate or necessary. What do you say when someone tells you that their child has only a few weeks to live? How do you treat them?

Dad took the twins in the changing rooms with him. Mum took care of Adam. As Dad undressed Laura he examined her body. He looked for platelet spots and bruises. There were none. Her body looked beautiful, smooth and clean; a normal child. He put on her swimming costume and water wings, did the same for Kit and took them into the children's pool.

They swam with freedom and safety. Mum came out with Adam.

"Oh no!" she said looking at Laura.

"What?" asked Dad, seeing no danger.

"You shouldn't have done that. Her water wings! The pressure will bruise her arms"

"But I didn't blow them up too much."

"Well. It's too late now. Let her enjoy herself."

And she did. But Dad did not. All the time he watched her and hoped she was not too badly marked due to his stupidity. Eventually he relaxed and slid into the water with the two of them; gaily throwing Kit into the water and gently floating Laura round the pool on his tummy.

When they got back to the changing rooms Dad very carefully removed the water wings. Mum was right. There were two small bruises. Dad swallowed and felt sick. He knew they would not go for several weeks. In other words they would be with her to the end of her life.

After the pool they went upstairs to dance and eat some party food. Dad held Laura in her special slot and danced with her whilst Kit ran around the room. Mum took a photograph of them for a keepsake.

Today I am happy, thought Laura, but why do Mum and Dad look so worried. They think I do not notice. When I look at them they smile. When I look away Dad twiddles his hair and Mum bites her nails. I really am happy. They should be happy too. Perhaps grown ups cannot be happy all the time. Mum says they have to think about other things than being happy. That is all part of being a grown up she says.

So Laura danced again. This time it was Laura the child.

They visited Grandma and Grandad before Christmas. After a short stay they drove back over the Pennine hills. It was a blustery, rainy day interspersed with bouts of intermittent dazzling sunshine. The car gently made its way from the moor down to the stone terraces and walls of Holmfirth. The car occupants looked out of the side windows to say farewell to the hills. In the vale there was the most complete and clear rainbow they had ever seen. Laura's eyes sparkled.

"Look. A rainbow!" she exclaimed, drawing out the 'bow'.

She continued to stare at it until it disappeared from their view.

If her happiness could be achieved through something as elementary as a rainbow, thought Dad, then surely the pathway to eternal happiness must be the simple yet transcendent spectrum of the acceptance of nature. Both Mum and Dad knew that henceforth whenever they saw a rainbow they would think of Laura.

Christmas came again. Strangely, this was the best Christmas the family had ever had. Laura seemed as fit and healthy as ever. A little more tired. As if she had a bit of a cold, that is all. They bought lots of toys and went to see Father Christmas in Lewis's as usual.

She had a toy typewriter and special diary that said 'Top Secret' on the outside. She wrote in it straight away. She also had a ballet dress and shoes. She had taken lessons at school. Her favourite music was from Swan Lake by Tchaikovsky. Dad came into the Living Room one day and found her dancing. She was fully dressed in her ballet dress and shoes and gracefully recalled all the movements she had been taught. The music of the dying Swan she enacted with grace and feeling. Dad sat transfixed by her tender portrayal.

The days went by very slowly. They did something every day. They told no one they met of their situation. They took no advantages.

For a few days in the middle of January they went to Center Parcs, a holiday resort in the Sherwood Forest. Here they were free from care. But here Laura began to feel ill. She would not swim. She found it too cold on the back of Dad's bicycle, yet she had to walk around their holiday chalet naked because she was too hot. Mum and Dad knew that things were moving to a conclusion. One lunchtime they went into the village of the Parc for lunch. They ate well and Dad had a large glass of beer. Two old ladies sat adjacent to them. They continually looked at Laura and smiled to each other, obviously enjoying her beauty. They got up to leave.

"You have a such a beautiful daughter. I'm sure she will grow up to be a beautiful woman," one of them said.

Mum and Dad looked at them and smiled.

"Thank you. Who knows what tomorrow might bring."

The ladies walked out of the restaurant. As they passed the main window they looked back for one last glimpse of Laura. Everyone smiled at them. Dad was inclined to pursue them and tell them the truth but it would have been for his own satisfaction and he knew that. Why spoil these ladies their moment of happiness?

The following weekend they all went to Warwick Castle. Laura had to be taken in the Twin buggy she used to use as a toddler because she was tired and disinclined to walk. After the castle they went to Stratford for tea. They found a place near the town centre that looked very nice. They sat at a table near the window. Dad ordered Darjeeling tea for him and Mum and special drinks for the children. Laura had tea. He ordered the children some cakes. Only the boys ate them. Laura picked at her slice and moved it around the plate.

Dad excused himself to go to the toilet, which was upstairs. On his way back he stood at the top of the stairs and looked down at Laura and his family. As he looked he was looking at the world; at life. He did not know why he did this. Perhaps he wanted to spy on them; look at them from the outside. She was staring into the Restaurant; at nothing in particular. Her face was completely white. Her eyes were dark and hollow. Mum was looking out of the window. The boys sat quietly with their unfinished meal in front of them. Dad knew. The time had come. This was the beginning of the end. Now it was days and hours. He went down and picked her up. She snuggled into her usual slot. Mum offered the buggy in silence.

"I'll carry her," he said.

Laura stared into his eyes as if to speak but said nothing, nor did anyone else.

I'm so tired, she thought. So tired. When can I go to sleep?

Kit's second song

By my side but not for long
Together once and all
Together, ever, so we thought
Playing, running, laughing.
Now prostrate she lies
Beside me, but alone.

What can I do?
Too young am I
To do anything.

No longer twin I walk alone
And carry her inside my head
I take her mind
I take this heart
She gave me when
In the womb
We were as one, and, ever one
We will return to be as one
And make the greatest sacrifice
Our blood, our life, holy alliance
We'll rise together
Together be
Forever in the tomb.

Chapter 32

A lark ascends

I woke that morning full of pain, an unbearable pain that was lost amidst the confusion reigning in my mind. I had the most vivid dreams through the night. I was unsure as to where I really was. At one point my pushchair appeared upon my bed top. I know it was there, but I don't know why. I knew this thing could go on no longer. I knew it had to end. My mind was becoming totally confused. It was not because of the morphine, because they had given me little. I heard them saying that I was hallucinating because my body had no water.

I didn't dress that day until late. The water, as they washed me, felt sharp and abrasive on my skin, the clothes felt unfamiliar, and the perfume of the soap on my hands was alien to me. My teeth felt dry, but to clean was an intrusion in my mouth I could not bear. The bristle of the toothbrush grazed my gums, my very flesh. Every touch of these other human hands was intrusive, offensive and of no comfort to me. I only wanted to lie where I should always have lain; in my Dad's arms; but he was not here. He was upstairs and time was running out.

I thought about my life. It was short, that I knew, but there was perplexity and confusion in its brevity. I thought of all those extremities of happiness and unhappiness. The many things I had done. The laughter of joy and silliness when I played with Kit and Dad and Adam. The comfort of Mum's breast and the soft smell of her flesh near mine. The tears of pain when I fell or was without love. Worst of all the sustained and sad depth of the pain of those days when I dreamed of the White Phantom. Those days in hospital. These were not the memories I wanted to take with me, but these were the experiences that helped mould me and others like me.

287

I heard her. Mum's and Dad's friend that is. She said, "The time has come". Don't you think I know? I felt like screaming but my mind was not mature enough to articulate these feelings into their language. I just shouted loud and with great resonance "Dad! Dad!"

He came. He always did. Now I had them both by me, Mum and Dad, but still I did not want to go. I saw the tree through the window. A bird softly landed on a branch. I tried to see it more closely but the picture became hazy. Kit was there. I felt him. It was like the beginning. Dear, dear Kit. My dearest brother. How I shall miss you. I could breathe his breath. I wanted him to come with me, oh how I wanted him.

I became frightened. Now I could hardly see the bird. The sky itself was blurred yet I knew the bird was there. I began to descend and sink into a sleep that I knew would never end. I felt very, very frightened. My head was dizzy. It span.

"Mummy, don't let me go to sleep!"

They both talked to me. There was confusion. I could not fully hear them. I was lying in my Dad's arms. My head was nestled in his arm. I felt safe yet afraid that I was falling into a great chasm and beyond his control. They kept talking. Voices. Noise. Distant murmurings. A whisper. A leaf falling on my face that closed my eyes. A swimming dizzy descent that sent me whirling into a black oblivion. I floated and as I did grasped at the faint voices that surrounded me in this black world. Radella called me. I heard her small voice reach out above the others to reassure me. The Phantom that had pursued me was now finally beaten, yet he had also beaten me. As I descended and hit the base of cold emptiness that had swallowed me up I finally knew what had happened. I was dead. I had no life. It had ended. My mind was in paralysis. I was in limbo, a void, an emptiness. I was in nothing.

****

The Bird had landed gracefully on one of the lower branches of the tree outside the window. It paused, looked around, then with a hop and a flutter ascended to the next branch, where the food basket hung. It leisurely investigated the contents. The basket was empty.

The health visitor said that in her experience the best thing was not to move the body for at least half an hour, as this would allow the soul to depart.

Kit walked outside. He had to breathe. The world had changed; dramatically. He saw the lady from across the Close. She asked how things were.

"Laura's dead," he said, his mind confused and dizzy.

She ran indoors sobbing.

The Bird sat on the branch. Its head moved to and fro as if it observed the goings on around it. It stood witness to these events; to Kit's outburst in the Close and to the tapestry inside the window. It inquisitively cocked its head to one side and continued to watch.

Dad saw the bird and was about to tell Laura when he remembered with a jolt that she could no longer hear him. He couldn't make out what sort of bird it was. It was new. It was not of a species that he could recognise; yet it did not look unfamiliar. Suddenly its whole appearance changed as it dramatically began to flap its wings. The branch vibrated slightly and it began to ascend.

Mum and Dad took Laura upstairs to her bedroom. They lay her on top of her own bed. They attended to her. As they did so the sun filtered through the watery wintry clouds that hovered about the place and sprinkled its way through the bedroom window onto her bed covering. The same sun flickered on her young dead body as they bowed over her and tied a scarf under her chin and over her head to avoid rigor mortis leaving her with an open mouth. They placed moist cotton wool over her eyes and dressed her in a fashion to save her dignity in her final days in the house. They laid her out professionally and adequately, supervised by her mother's mother.

The health visitor and the doctor said she must go to the "Chapel of Rest". Mum and Dad said no. They turned off all the heating in the house. They made it cool for her. The doctor and the health visitor still debated between themselves as to whether Laura should go to the Chapel of Rest. Mum and Dad ignored them and carried on with their business of ensuring Laura's dignity.

The Bird sailed gracefully across the tiles of the roofs bordering the Close. Its ascent had been very slow, almost as if the weight of Dad's gaze and the burden of what it had seen had slowed it down. Eventually it gained speed but not so much that it lost the dignity of graceful flight. The village below was still and calm reflecting the normal inactivity of Saturday lunchtime.

The Bird skimmed the Poplar trees near the Green, glided over the Village Hall and landed gently amidst the branches of an old pine tree in the south east perimeter of the church Yard.

Laura stayed with her family. The undertaker had said keep the room cool. He knew. He was an old fashioned undertaker. To him death was a part of everyday life. He worried about the practicalities first, of getting the job right. The emotions came second. That was his job. Having said that he was always upset at the thought of burying a child. Who wouldn't be? Keep her cool, he said, you know why. They switched off the heating, and would you believe there was a frost that night which lasted a whole week. No danger of flies or other things, the undertaker said.

****

I said goodnight to her every night. I held her hand. It became warm and the rigidity of her rigor mortis disappeared and she was alive again. I kissed her poor dead lips and they also lived. She only slept. Her closed eyes gave testament to that. Sometimes I thought I caught her breathing but realised it was only the peaceful settling of her body. I read her a story. I lay next to her. I hugged her. I talked to her. I went crazy through the love and lack of her.

In this nursery where we used to lay her nightly in her cradle of life she now came to rest in the cradle of the after-life. Now we knew she was to be taken from us. We laid her in it with her favourite toys. We were frightened of this wooden box at first, but eventually saw it as just another stage in the journey. At least it kept her safe. It enclosed her. It did her no harm. It could not hurt her. She had been hurt too much already. Now she knew no pain. She could rest and sleep the great sleep of those who live on earth.

I organised the funeral with a precision that was unlike me. I spent the early morning of the funeral day at the church making sure the arrangements were in place. I was acting robotically, oblivious to the absurd reality of the situation. As I drove back from the church a lorry ploughed into the back of me sending my car spinning across the road. I got out and the emotion of the past years burst out of me with a scream and a flood as I wept, embarrassing the lorry driver. The proprietor of the village garage came running across and took me away.

I walked back to the house as if in a dream. If this was reality it was a kick when I was already down. Then as the moments flew by until the time of the funeral I realised how unimportant yet significant this accident was in relation to the matter of living and dying, and if this was unimportant then how trivial were the other crisis in a person's life. Laura had put my whole life into proportion and that could never ever change. My approach to living henceforth had to be different. Had to be or she had lived in vain, I thought.

The church was packed. I carried Laura and wore her favourite pink tie as well as a pink carnation. I wrote the prayers myself as I felt only I could do justice to her in words. I wanted it to be a "good" service. My years serving at the altar had given me the experience that finally was of use. As I walked toward the Chancel steps with Laura on my shoulder to the strains of "The Snowman" I felt proud. Proud that I was carrying her, that she was my daughter.

Mum walked behind totally unsupported, with a dignity and strength that startled all around her. No tear was shed by her or Kit whilst all around descended into a watery sadness. They did not understand. They did not realise that this was just another step, another forward move in the great game of life. They did not realise that life itself is a living microcosm of our own lives. Everything is a circle. They did not realise that as they saw Laura carried to the altar they were seeing the answer to that nagging question about the end of the universe and the existence of God. This was it! If children could die before their parents then anything could happen. If they could not understand this they would not, could not, understand the meaning of the world.

The Priest was a friend. He had come down from Manchester to conduct the service. He was a Priest of great ability and northern intuition on the matters of life and death. He said her death was a tragedy but not a waste. So it was. He said in her short life she, perhaps unknowingly, had done far more and influenced far more than those who lived for seventy years. He said she had not died in vain.

It was frosty cold when they took her outside. The mist hung low over the hedgerows. The stark black fingers of trees protruded through the mist. The ground was hard and white. The hole was black and deep surrounded by a beige green that was unreal. Words were said. Otherwise the air was silent. No bird sang, no wind whistled. The distant traffic was no more. They lifted her for the last time. The ground consumed her and she was gone. The mourners left. They covered her with earth. We lingered and wondered. It was over.

****

Dad took Pero for a walk every morning. He walked over the field toward the church, through the meadow where cows and sheep grazed. He climbed the fence into the churchyard whilst Pero sat patiently waiting for him in the field. He knelt by Laura's grave. He talked to her still. Every day he waited for a sign. He looked to the clouds as if she were there watching him and he hoped and yearned to hear from her. He saw flights of birds in the shape of a letter V that he assumed and hoped to be the letter L for Laura. He wanted a sign. He heard tell of people that dreamed of their dead children every night. He had never dreamed of Laura and many days had passed since she had passed on. He remembered when he was a young boy and prayed to God to talk to him. He looked for a sign that God had spoken, in his mind, in the words of the priest, or in the formation of clouds in the sky and in the way he felt. He never received such a sign and concluded that God did not want to communicate with him, was perhaps not there any more. It was a disappointment but one that he expected. Perhaps it was because he did not pray hard enough or even use the right words in his praying.

As he knelt that morning by Laura's grave and talked to her he noticed snowflakes falling all around him. The sky became light and bright. There was vibrancy in the air that he had never noticed before. He thought he heard the sound of a mature and mellow female voice.

I am here.

I am beyond your reach.

I am alone, not quite alone, but alone, surrounded by a mist so dense it suffocates me.

Beyond the mist there is a great light. Sometimes I see it. I know that I must go there someday, but only with you.

Do you think I am at my journey's end? This is only a small part of the journey; this great journey of life, for death is a part of life and living only a time before death, for death is longer than life and far more enduring. It comforts me. I feel safe. Where else can I go? Only into the light and then what?

I have learned this great truth. I know you have searched and never found it nor understood that it was there around you all the time. I also did not understand the reason for my living, but I did not search for this secret of life. I was never given the time for such an exploration. You had the time but never found it. Now I can reveal it to you.

First know that when you can comprehend infinity you will know everything, even the truth and the purpose of life. Space and time are the basis of your life. They go on forever. So must life. That is the truth. But these are not the only dimensions in earth. There are some that are beyond your understanding. The scale of sounds goes beyond your hearing. Animals hear songs that you cannot. Likewise the spectrum of colours in the Rainbow goes beyond your seeing. There are colours you cannot see. They reach to infinity. The truth is not here on your earthly floor. Look out into space and the cosmic past. There you will find it.

What is truth? Pontius Pilate asked of Jesus, but he did not answer. Perhaps it was a rhetorical question. Perhaps it was not. The answer was in his silence.

You will also come to know that the way to truth is beyond death. Our short lives are contained between birth and death. Is there nothing either side? The Venerable Bede said that when a sparrow flies through a hall no one knows from whence it came or where it goes. So it is with life. If there were no death where would our living end? It is death that gives our life a focus. We all have the same destiny; some reach it earlier. Look around you. Death is everywhere. It is not a barrier, an end or culmination. It is a state and a step forward.

We grow in the world to seek truth, beauty and wisdom. In our wanderings we find faith, hope and love. Love never dies. Who will kill it?

So, what is after death? Death is the apple tree. You once told me that matter could neither be created nor destroyed. If living matter cannot be destroyed do you think the human soul and memory are different? They also cannot be destroyed and likewise cannot be recreated. Once the soul has been created it stays created. Your soul and mine are there forever. It is a part of your body not separate to it. It lives in perpetuity in the world and out of it. It continues beyond death. It is not reborn. That would be an injustice to the purpose of earthbound life. It just continues.

Your soul is not just a jumble of dreams in your head. Dogs dream in the night, but they do not paint pictures or write music. Your soul is your inspiration, your charity and your faith.

Travel in a craft to the ends of the universe and you will travel until you and all your descendants die. The truth is there but cannot be reached by earthly means. It can only be reached through the dimension of our soul. It is a spiritual journey not an earthly one.

Extinction is only a route to heaven. This is not the extinction of the mind. This is not oblivion. It is peace in perfection of a vacuum of the like that you will not understand. It is a vacuum surrounded by a light and permeated by peace. A peace you call paradise.

People want to live forever or at least for longer than their so-called allotted time on earth. If you lived forever what would be your impression upon the world. It would diminish as time went by, like the great empires of the ancient world that now give way to newer stars on the imperial horizon. If the measure of our lives is the impression we make we could not live forever. Longevity of life is not immortality. It is the memories you leave behind that count. They are immortal.

Our lives are just a microcosm of the Great Life; a step in the pathway to infinity and the truth. We are like the grains of sand that paved the way from fish to fowl.

I am already perplexed by the complexity of my personality in this place, for my personality is a fountain of souls.

I know of these things. For now I am wise. I know many things, not all, for some are beyond all comprehension, even yours. There are things I know that frighten me, not for my sake but for yours and those close to you who are yet to come here.

Someday the puzzling thoughts that keep you awake will be clear like the clarity of a new day and you will know that much more, as I now know. But, despite all this knowledge, my mind is still unclear on some things. Most unclear of all is the reason for my being in this place so soon. Only you, with time, can lift this fog of mystery that surrounds me still. You have much to do in my name. Please do it and remember where I am.

This is the place where dreams become reality and reality is a dream. I am surrounded by a cosmic emptiness that has no beginning or end, where time is as short or as long as your last memory but means nothing, for here we have no scale, no perception, and no relativity. I am without being or form but know that I exist, even though I do not see my own body. I exist as I existed with you for without you I am nothing. I see you all. I watch. I wait. I am with you everywhere. I am in you all. Do not be afraid. I am not a ghost. I am I. I am Laura. I am here beside you, standing by the tree. Look. See me. Touch me. I want you and love you and will always wait as you waited with me. You are my father. But, please remember, I am alone. I wait for you. Let us come together soon, someway, somehow. I can't bear to be without you. Please, please..........I wait...and long...to be with you all again.

The voice faded. He stood up and looked around as if he had awoken from a dream. Things looked normal. Perhaps he had imagined this moment. Grief does strange things with the mind he had been told. All around him there was nothing but silence save the approaching song of a bird. He recognised the bird as an early lark. It rose from the ground in chirrup and song. He watched its progress carefully. Pero whined beside him to tell him to come home but he stood and watched until the lark had finally ascended.

The End

Three years later on Monday the 23rd November 1992, the day and the month when Laura should have been born, Mum gave birth to a beautiful golden haired girl. She grew up to be extremely attached to her father and would not leave his side, nor he hers. She had perception and sensitivity. She would sit on his lap and look into his eyes with an understanding smile. They named her Georgina; the Greek name for a girl of the country.

The Moores went on to build a children's cancer unit, introduce children's community nurses and fund research. They created The Laura Centre; a bereavement counselling service for those affected by the death of a child and finally built and funded, Rainbows, a children's hospice and haven of peace in the forest of Charnwood.

Many of the people who knew Laura became instrumental in the success of these projects. Some of the care team at the hospital staffed the new COPE Cancer unit, and eventually joined the care team at Rainbows.

Laura was named after the girl in her father's favourite book, Lark Rise to Candleford. It is an autobiography of Flora Thompson (Laura) as a girl, set in the Oxfordshire countryside. In the book Laura and her mother meet a gypsy who says that Laura is going to be loved by people she's never seen and never will see.

As you walk in lonely grief
You are not alone
Feel my hand upon your heart
Your eyelids flutter is my breath
The wind that whispers is my voice
Walk slowly
I am near

Look into the distance
The dim and distant over the hill
To the light that shows the way and truth
To the place of peace
Where we will walk together
On another shore
And in a greater light

Love conquers all.